2018 IBC® SEAOC STRUCTURAL/SEISMIC DESIGN MANUAL

VOLUME 2
EXAMPLES FOR LIGHT-FRAME, TILT-UP, AND MASONRY BUILDINGS

National Council of Structural Engineers Associations

INTERNATIONAL CODE COUNCIL®

Copyright

Publisher

Structural Engineers Association of California (SEAOC)
921 11th Street, Suite 1100
Sacramento, California 95814
Telephone: (916) 447-1198; Fax: (916) 444-1501
E-mail: seaoc@seaoc.org; Web address: www.seaoc.org

The Structural Engineers Association of California (SEAOC) is a professional association of four regional member organizations (Southern California, Northern California, San Diego, and Central California). SEAOC represents the structural engineering community in California. This document is published in keeping with SEAOC's stated mission:

> To advance the structural engineering profession; to provide the public with structures of dependable performance through the application of state-of-the-art structural engineering principles; to assist the public in obtaining professional structural engineering services; to promote natural hazard mitigation; to provide continuing education and encourage research; to provide structural engineers with the most current information and tools to improve their practice; and to maintain the honor and dignity of the profession.

Editor

International Code Council

Disclaimer

First Printing: July 2020

ISBN: 978-1-60983-997-0

T025182

Suggestions for Improvement

Comments and suggestions for improvements are welcome and should be sent to the following:

Structural Engineers Association of California (SEAOC)
Don Schinske, Executive Director
921 11th Street, Suite 1100
Sacramento, California 95814
Telephone: (916) 447-1198; Fax: (916) 444-1501
E-mail: dschinske@seaoc.org

Errata Notification

SEAOC has made a substantial effort to ensure that the information in this document is accurate. In the event that corrections or clarifications are needed, these will be posted on the SEAOC website at **www.seaoc.org** and on the ICC website at **www.iccsafe.org**.

SEAOC, at its sole discretion, may issue written errata.

Table of Contents

Preface to the 2018 *IBC SEAOC Seismic/Structural Design Manual*

The *IBC SEAOC Seismic/Structural Design Manual*, throughout its many editions, has served the purpose of illustrating good seismic design and the correct application of building-code provisions. The *Manual* has bridged the gap between the discursive treatment of topics in the *SEAOC Blue Book* (*Recommended Lateral Force Requirements and Commentary*) and real-world decisions that designers face in their practice.

The examples illustrate code-compliant designs engineered to achieve good performance under severe seismic loading. In some cases simply complying with building-code requirements does not ensure good seismic response. This *Manual* takes the approach of exceeding the minimum code requirements in such cases, with discussion of the reasons for doing so.

This manual comprises four volumes:

- Volume 1: Code Application Examples
- Volume 2: Examples for Light-Frame, Tilt-Up, and Masonry Buildings
- Volume 3: Examples for Concrete Buildings
- Volume 4: Examples for Steel-Framed Buildings

In general, the provisions for developing the design base shear, distributing the base-shear-forces vertically and horizontally, checking for irregularities, etc., are illustrated in Volume 1. The other volumes contain more extensive design examples that address the requirements of the material standards (for example, ACI 318 and AISC 341) that are adopted by the IBC. Building design examples do not illustrate many of the items addressed in Volume 1 in order to permit the inclusion of less-redundant content.

Each volume has been produced by a small group of authors under the direction of a manager. The managers have assembled reviewers to ensure coordination with other SEAOC work and publications, most notably the *Blue Book*, as well as numerical accuracy.

This manual can serve as valuable tool for engineers seeking to design buildings and building components for good seismic response.

Rafael Sabelli and Katy Briggs
Project Managers

Preface to Volume 2

Volume 2 of the 2018 *IBC SEAOC Structural/Seismic Design Manual* addresses the design of light-frame, concrete tilt-up, and masonry shear wall building systems for seismic loading. These include the illustration of the design requirements for the shear walls and diaphragms, as were illustrated in previous editions, and also important interfaces with the rest of the structure.

The design examples in this volume represent a range of structural systems and seismic systems. The design of each of these systems is governed by standards developed by the American Concrete Institute (ACI) and the American Wood Council (AWC). The methods illustrated herein represent approaches consistent with the ductility expectations for each system and with the desired seismic response. In most cases there are several details or mechanisms that can be utilized to achieve the ductility and resistance required, and the author of each example has selected an appropriate option. In many cases alternatives are discussed. This *Manual* is not intended to serve as a building code or to be an exhaustive catalogue of all valid approaches and details.

This *Manual* is presented as a set of examples in which the engineer has considered the building-code requirements in conjunction with the optimal seismic response of the system. The examples follow the guidelines of the *SEAOC Blue Book* and other SEAOC recommendations. The examples are intended to aid conscientious designers in crafting designs that are likely to achieve good seismic performance consistent with expectations inherent in the requirements for the systems.

Douglas Thompson
Volume 2 Manager

Acknowledgments

Volume 2 of the 2018 *IBC SEAOC Seismic/Structural Design Manual* was written by a group of highly qualified structural engineers, chosen for their knowledge and experience with structural engineering practice and seismic design. The authors are:

Douglas S. Thompson, S.E., S.E.C.B—Volume Manager and Example 1
Doug Thompson has over 40 years of experience in designing of wood structures. He is the author of several publications in timber design including the WoodWorks publications: *Four-story Wood-frame Structure over Podium Slab and Five-story Wood-frame Structure over Podium Slab*. Doug has instructed license review classes in timber design for the PE and SE exams for 20 years. He is a past president of the Structural Engineers Association of Southern California and holds licenses in six states. www.stbse.com

John Lawson, S.E.—Examples 2 and 5
Professor John Lawson has provided structural engineering consulting services for over 30 years, including overseeing more than 100 million square feet of low-sloped roof and tilt-up concrete engineering. He now teaches in the Architectural Engineering department at California Polytechnic State University in San Luis Obispo. John is the recipient of the 2006 Tilt-Up Concrete Association's David L. Kelly Distinguished Engineer Award. www.arce.calpoly.edu

Michael Cochran, S.E., S.E.C.B.—Example 3
Michael Cochran is a Vice President with Thornton Tomasetti, Inc., in Los Angeles, California, with over 25 years of design experience. He has an extensive background in the design of multistory light-frame commercial and multifamily residential wood and cold-formed steel-stud buildings. He is a registered structural engineer in California, an active member of the AISC Connection Prequalification Review Panel, a past president of the Structural Engineers Association of Southern California (SEAOSC) and the Structural Engineers Association of California, and a SEAOC fellow.

Jeff Ellis, S.E., S.E.C.B.—Example 3
Jeff Ellis, Director of Codes and Compliance for Simpson Strong-Tie Company, Inc., has more than 28 years of experience as a professional engineer and manages the company code and compliance efforts. Additionally, he is involved in research and development and provides support for existing product lines, including technical guidance for connectors, fastening systems, and lateral-force-resisting systems. He was a practicing design engineer for commercial, residential, and forensic projects for more than nine years prior to joining Simpson at the end of 2000. He currently serves on the International Code Council Evaluation Service Board and has served as president of the Structural Engineers Association of Southern California (SEAOSC), SEAOC secretary, chairman of the AISI COFS Lateral Design Subcommittee, and president of the Cold-Formed Steel Engineers Institute (CFSEI).

Chukwuma G. Ekwueme, PhD, SE, LEED AP—Example 4
Dr. Ekwueme is a Principal with Thornton Tomasetti in Los Angeles, California. He has an extensive background in the design and analysis of a wide variety of structures, including concrete and masonry construction, steel and aluminum structures, and light-frame wood buildings. He is a registered structural engineer in California and Nevada and is an active member of the main committee, the seismic subcommittee, and the axial flexural loads and shear subcommittee of the Masonry Standards Joint Committee (MSJC).

Additionally, a number of SEAOC members and other structural engineers helped check the examples in this volume. During its development, drafts of the examples were sent to these individuals. Their help was sought in review of code interpretations as well as detailed checking of the numerical computations. The reviewers include:

James Lai, S.E.

Alan Robinson, S.E.

Tim Stafford, S.E.

Doug Thompson, S.E.

Tom VanDorpe, S.E.

Close collaboration with the SEAOC Seismology Committee was maintained during the development of this document. The Seismology Committee has reviewed the document and provided many helpful comments and suggestions. Their assistance is gratefully acknowledged.

Production and art was provided by the International Code Council.

References

Standards

ACI 318, 2014, *Building Code Requirements for Structural Concrete*, American Concrete Institute, Farmington Hills, Michigan.

AISI S100-16, 2016. *North American Specification for the Design of Cold-Formed Steel Structural Members*. American Iron and Steel Institute, Washington, DC.

AISI S240-15, 2015. *North American Standard for Cold-Formed Steel Structural Framing*. American Iron and Steel Institute, Washington, DC 20036.

AISI S400-15, 2015. *North American Standard for Seismic Design of Cold-Formed Steel Structural Systems*. American Iron and Steel Institute, Washington, DC 20036.

American Wood Council, 2018, *National Design Specification for Wood Construction Including Supplements, NDS-18*. American Wood Council, Washington, DC.

American Wood Council, 2015, AWC *Special Design Provisions for Wind and Seismic*, American Wood Council, Washington, DC.

ASCE/SEI 7, 2016, *Minimum Design Loads and Associated Criteria for Buildings and Other Structures*, American Society of Civil Engineers, Structural Engineering Institute, Reston, Virginia.

International Code Council, 2018, *International Building Code* (IBC). International Code Council, Washington, DC.

TMS 402-16, 2016. *Building Code Requirements for Masonry Structures*, The Masonry Society, Boulder, Colorado.

TMS 602-16, 2016. *Specification for Masonry Structures*, The Masonry Society, Boulder, Colorado.

Other References

ACI 551.2R-15, 2015. *Guide for the Design of Tilt-up Concrete Panels*. American Concrete Institute, Farmington Hills, Michigan.

ACI 551.1R-14, 2014. *Guide to Tilt-up Concrete Construction*. American Concrete Institute, Farmington Hills, Michigan.

AISI D100-08, *AISI Manual, Cold-Formed Steel Design*. American Iron and Steel Institute, Washington, DC.

AISI D110-07, *Cold-Formed Steel Framing Design Guide*, Second Edition. American Iron and Steel Institute, Washington, DC.

American Forest and Paper Association, 1996, *Wood Construction Manual.* American Forest and Paper Association, Washington, DC.

American Plywood Association, 1997, *Design/ Construction Guide—Diaphragms and Shear Walls.* From L350, Engineered Wood Association, Tacoma, Washington.

American Plywood Association, 2007, *Diaphragms and Shear Walls.* Engineered Wood Association, Tacoma, Washington.

American Plywood Association, 1993, revised, *Wood Structural Panel Shear Walls.* Report 154, Engineered Wood Association, Tacoma, Washington.

American Plywood Association, 1994, *Northridge, California Earthquake.* Report T-94-5. Engineered Wood Association, Tacoma, Washington.

American Plywood Association, *Performance Standard For Wood-Based Structural Use Panels.* PS2-04. National Institute of Standards and Technology, Washington, DC.

American Plywood Association, 1997, *Plywood Design Specifications*, From Y510, Engineered Wood Association, Tacoma, Washington.

American Plywood Association, 1988, *Plywood Diaphragms*, Research Report 138. American Plywood Association, Tacoma, Washington.

American Plywood Association, 2002. *Effect of Green Lumber Framing on Wood Structural Panel Shear Wall Performance.* APA Report T2002-53. American Plywood Association, Tacoma, Washington.

American Plywood Association, 2005, *Using Narrow Pieces of Wood Structural Panel Sheathing in Wood Shear Walls, APA T 2005–08*, The Engineered Wood Association, Tacoma, Washington.

APA, 2011, *Evaluation of Force Transfer around Openings—Experimental and Analytical Studies*, APA, Tacoma, Washington.

Applied Technology Council, 1995, *Cyclic Testing of Narrow Plywood Shear Walls ATC R-1.* Applied Technology Council, Redwood City, California.

Applied Technology Council, 1981, *Guidelines for Design of Horizontal Wood Diaphragms*, ATC-7. Applied Technology Council, Redwood City, California.

Applied Technology Council, 1980, *Proceedings of a Workshop on Design of Horizontal Wood Diaphragms*, ATC-7-1. Applied Technology Council, Redwood City, California.

Arevalo, Ricardo, 2012, *Tie-Down Systems for Multi-Story Wood Structures*, Wood Design Focus, Fall 2012, Forest Products Society, Madison, Wisconsin.

Bendsten, B.A. and W.L. Galligan, 1979, *Mean and Tolerance Limit Stresses and Stress Modeling for Compression Perpendicular to Grain in Hardwood and Softwood Species*, Research Paper FPL 337. US Department of Agriculture, Forest Service, Forest Products Laboratory, Madison, Wisconsin.

Bendsten, B.A. and W.L. Galligan, Vol. 29, No. 2: Pg. 42–48, 1979, *Modeling and Stress-Compression Relationships in Wood in Compression Perpendicular to Grain.* U.S. Department of Agriculture, Forest Products Research Society (Forest Products Society) Forest Products Journal, Madison, Wisconsin.

Brandow, Gregg E., Chukwuma G. Ekwueme and Gary C. Hart, 2009. *Design of Reinforced Masonry Structures,* Concrete Masonry Association of California and Nevada, Sacramento, California.

Breyer, Donald E., Kenneth J. Fridley, David G. Pollock, Jr. and Kelly E. Cobeen, 2007. *Design of Wood Structures ASD.* McGraw-Hill Book Co., New York, New York.

Bugni, David A., 1999, *"A Linear Elastic Dynamic Analysis of a Timber Framed Structure."* Building Standards, International Conference of Building Officials, Whittier, California.

Building Seismic Safety Council, 2003, *National Earthquake Hazard Reduction Program, Recommended Provisions for Seismic Regulations for New Buildings,* Parts 1 and 2. Building Seismic Safety Council, Washington, DC.

Cobeen, K.E., 1996, "Performance Based Design of Wood Structures." Proceedings: Annual SEAOC Convention. Structural Engineers Association of California, Sacramento, California.

Coil, J., 1999, "Seismic Retrofit of an Existing Multi-Story Wood Frame Structure," Proceedings: Annual SEAOC Convention. Structural Engineers Association of California, Sacramento, California.

Commins, A. and Gregg, R., 1996, *Effect of Hold Downs and Stud-Frame Systems on the Cyclic Behavior of Wood Shear Walls,* Simpson Strong-Tie Co., Pleasanton, California.

Commins, Alfred D., August 2008, *Rod Tie-Down Systems, Part 5-Inspection,* Structure Magazine, National Council of Structural Engineers Associations (NCSEA).

Cook, J., 2010, "Simplified Analysis of Wood Shear Walls with Multiple Openings" Proceedings: Annual SEAOC Convention. Structural Engineers Association of California, Sacramento, California.

Cook, R.A., 1999, "Strength Design of Anchorage to Concrete." Portland Cement Association, Skokie, Illinois.

Countryman, D., and Col Benson, 1954, *1954 Horizontal Plywood Diaphragm Tests.* Laboratory Report 63, Douglas Fir Plywood Association, Tacoma, Washington.

CUREe, 1999, *Proceedings of the Workshop on Seismic Testing, Analysis, and Design of Wood Frame Construction.* California University for Research in Earthquake Engineering.

Dolan, J.D., 1996, *Experimental Results from Cyclic Racking Tests of Wood Shear Walls with Openings.* Timber Engineering Report No. TE-1996-001. Virginia Polytechnic Institute and State University, Blacksburg, Virginia.

Dolan, J.D. and Heine, C.P., 1997a, *Monotonic Tests of Wood Frame Shear Walls with Various Openings and Base Restraint Configurations.* Timber Engineering Report No. TE-1997-001, Virginia Polytechnic Institute and State University, Blacksburg, Virginia.

Dolan, J.D. and Heine, C.P., 1997b, *Sequential Phased Displacement Cyclic Tests of Wood Frame Shear Walls with Various Openings and Base Restrain Configurations.* Timber Engineering Report No. TE-1997-002, Virginia Polytechnic Institute and State University, Blacksburg, Virginia.

Dolan, J.D., and Heine, C.P., 1997c, *Sequential Phased Displacement Test of Wood Frame Shear Walls with Corners.* Timber Engineering Report No. TE-1997-003, Virginia Polytechnic Institute and State University, Blacksburg, Virginia.

Earthquake Engineering Research Institute, 1996, "Northridge Earthquake of January 17, 1994," *Reconnaissance Report, Earthquake Spectra.* Vol. 11, Supplement C. Earthquake Engineering Research Institute, Oakland, California.

Ellis, Jeff, August 2012, "Designing Cold-Formed Steel Framed Lateral Force-Resisting Systems," *Structure* magazine. National Council of Structural Engineers Associations (NCSEA).

Faherty, Keith F., and Williamson, Thomas G., 1995, *Wood Engineering Construction Handbook.* McGraw-Hill, Washington, DC.

Federal Emergency Management Agency, 2003, *National Earthquake Hazard Reduction Program, Recommended Provisions for Seismic Regulations for New Buildings and Other Structures and Commentary.* Federal Emergency Management Agency, Washington, DC.

Ficcadenti, S.K., T.A. Castle, D.A. Sandercock, and R.K. Kazanjy, 1996, "Laboratory Testing to Investigate Pneumatically Driven Box Nails for the Edge Nailing of 3/8" Plywood Shear Walls," Proceedings: Annual SEAOC Convention. Structural Engineers Association of California, Sacramento, California.

Foliente, Greg C., 1994, *Analysis, Design and Testing of Timber Structures under Seismic Loads.* University of California Forest Products Laboratory, Richmond, California.

Foliente, Greg C., 1997, *Earthquake Performance and Safety of Timber Structures.* Forest Products Society, Madison, Wisconsin.

Forest Products Laboratory, 2010, *Wood Handbook Publication FPL—GTR—113.* Madison, Wisconsin.

Ghosh, A., S. Pryor, and R. Arevalo, June 2006, "Multistory Light-frame Construction: Understanding Tiedown Systems," *Structure* magazine. National Council of Structural Engineers Associations (NCSEA).

Goers R. and Associates, 1976, *A Methodology for Seismic Design and Construction of Single-Family Dwellings.* Applied Technology Council, Redwood City, California.

Gupta, R., H. Redler, and M. Clauson, 2007. "Cyclic Tests of Engineered Shear Walls with Different Bottom-plate and Anchor-bolt sizes (Phase II)." Department of Wood Science and Engineering, Oregon State University, Corvallis, Oregon.

Haygreen, J.G. and Bowyer, J.L., 1989, *Forest Products and Wood Science—An Introduction.* University of Iowa Press, Ames, Iowa.

Hess, R., 2008, "For What Planet Is This Code Written?," *Structure* magazine, November. National Council of Structural Engineers Associations (NCSEA).

Hohbach, D., S. Shiotani, 2012. *Improved Seismic Analysis of Wood Light-Framed Multi-Story Residential Buildings*, Wood Design Focus, Fall 2012, Forest Products Society, Madison, Wisconsin.

Ju, S. and Lin, M., 1999, "Comparison of Building Analysis Assuming Rigid or Flexible Floors," Journal of Structural Engineering. American Society of Civil Engineers, Washington, DC.

Knight, Brian, June 2006, *High-Rise Wood Frame Construction. Structure* magazine. NCSEA.

Kong, H, Eatherton, M, and Schafer, B, 2019. "Design of Fixed Base Hollow Structural Section Columns Subjected to Large Seismic Drift," Proceedings of the Annual Stability Conference, April 2019, Structural Stability Research Council, St. Louis, Missouri.

Lawson, J., 2019, "Improving the Accuracy of Wood Diaphragm Deflection Computations and Its Impact on ASCE 41 Pseudo-Lateral Force Estimates," SEAOC 2019 Convention Proceedings, Structural Engineers Association of California, Squaw Valley, California.

Lawson, John, 2007, "Deflection Limits for Tilt-up Wall Serviceability," *Concrete International*, American Concrete Institute. September.

Lawson, J, Koliou, M, Filiatrault, A, and Kelly, D, 2018. "The Evaluation of Current Wall-to-Roof Anchorage Force Provisions for Single-story Concrete and Masonry Buildings with Lightweight Flexible Diaphragms," SEAOC 2018 Convention Proceedings, Structural Engineers Association of California, Palm Desert, California.

Matteri, Dominic, 2009, *5 Over 1 High-Rise Podium Structures*, Wood Solutions Fair Presentation.

Matteson, Thor, 2004, *Wood-Framed Shear Wall Construction.* International Code Council, Country Club Hills, Illinois.

Mayo, John L., 2001, "Metal Roof Construction on Large Warehouses or Distribution Centers," Steel Tips. Structural Education Council, 141 Greenbriar, Moraga, CA 94556, June.

Mendes, S., 1987, "Rigid versus Flexible: Inappropriate Assumptions Can Cause Shear Wall Failures!" Proceedings: Annual SEAOC Convention. Structural Engineers Association of California, Sacramento, California.

Mendes, S., 1995, "Lessons Learned from Four Earthquake Damaged Multi-Story Type V Structures," Proceedings: Annual SEAOC Convention. Structural Engineers Association of California, Sacramento, California.

Murphy, Michael, 2012, *Shrinkage Challenges with Mid-Rise Construction*, Wood Design Focus, Fall 2012. Forest Products Society, Madison, Wisconsin.

Nelson, R.F. and S.T. Patel, 2003, "Continuous Tiedown Systems for Wood Panel Shear Walls in Multistory Structures," *Structure* Magazine, March. NCSEA.

Rose, J.D., 1998, *Preliminary Testing of Wood Structural Panel Shear Walls under Cyclic (Reversed) Loading*. Research Report 158, APA—Engineered Wood Association, Tacoma, Washington.

Rose, J.D., and E.L. Keith, P.E., 1996, *Wood Structural Panel Shear Walls with Gypsum Wallboard and Window [Sheathing Standard, Sec. 2.3.3]*. Research Report 158. APA—The Engineered Wood Association, Tacoma, Washington.

SCCACI/SEAOSC, 1982, *Report of the Task Committee on Slender Walls*, Southern California Chapter American Concrete Institute and Structural Engineers Association of Southern California, Los Angeles, California. September.

Schmid, Ben L. (1996), *Three-Story Wood Apartment Building—1994 Northridge Earthquake Buildings Case Studies Project*, Seismic Safety Commission, State of California. Sacramento, California.

SEAOC, 1999, *Acceptable Diaphragm-Rigidity Assumptions for Distribution of Horizontal Forces in Light-Frame Construction*. Structural Engineers Association of California, Sacramento, California.

SEAOC, 1997, *Seismic Detailing Examples for Engineered Light-Frame Timber Construction*. Structural Engineers Association of California, Sacramento, California.

SEAOC, 1999, *Guidelines for Diaphragms and Shear Walls*. Structural Engineers Association of California, Sacramento, California.

SEAOC, 1999, *Plan Review—Codes and Practice*. Structural Engineers Association of California, Sacramento, California.

SEAOC Blue Book, 1999, *Recommended Lateral Force Requirements and Commentary*, Structural Engineers Association of California, Seventh Edition, Sacramento, California.

SEAOC Seismology Committee, 2009, "Anchor Bolts in Light-frame Construction at Small Edge Distances," June, M5, M6, M7 in the *SEAOC Blue Book: Seismic Design Recommendations*, Structural Engineers Association of California, Sacramento, California. http://www.seaoc.org/bluebook/index.html

SEAOC Seismology Committee, 2008, "Light-frame Wall Hold-downs," August, in the *SEAOC Blue Book: Seismic Design Recommendations*, Structural Engineers Association of California, Sacramento, California. www.seaoc.org/bluebook/index.html

SEAOC Seismology Committee, 2008. "Tilt-up Buildings," The *SEAOC Blue Book: Seismic Design Recommendations*. Structural Engineers Association of California, Sacramento, California at: www.seaoc.org/bluebook/index.html

SEAOC Seismology Committee, 2007, "Wood-framed Shear Walls with Openings," May, in the *SEAOC Blue Book: Seismic Design Recommendations*, Structural Engineers Association of California, Sacramento, California. www.seaoc.org/bluebook/index.html

SEAOSC, 1979. *Recommended Tilt-up Wall Design*, Structural Engineers Association of Southern California, Los Angeles, California. June.

SEAOSC/COLA, 1994. *1994 Northridge Earthquake (Structural Engineers Association of Southern California/City of Los Angeles) Special Investigation Task Force*, Tilt-up Subcommittee. Final report dated September 25, 1994.

Shiotani, S., D. Hohbach, J. Roberts, 2011, *Lateral System for Multi-Unit Construction*, Wood Products Council Workshops.

Shipp, John and D. Thompson, 2001 *Timber Design I, II, and III, Volumes VIII, IX, and X.* Professional Engineering Development Publications, Inc., Irvine, California.

Simpson, William T. 1998. *Equilibrium Moisture Content of Wood in Outdoor Locations in the United States and Worldwide. Res. Note FPL-RN-0268.* Forest Products Laboratory, Madison, Wisconsin.

Skaggs, T.D. and Z.A. Martin, 2004. "Estimating Wood Structural Panel Diaphragm and Shear Wall Deflection." *Practice Periodical on Structural Design and Construction.* ASCE, May 2004.

Steinbrugge, J., 1994, "Standard of Care in Structural Engineering Wood Frame Multiple Housing," Proceedings: Annual SEAOC Convention. Structural Engineers Association of California, Sacramento, California.

Technical Coordinating Committee for Masonry Research (TCCMAR), 1985. James Noland – Chairman, *U.S.-Japan Coordinated Program for Masonry Building Research*, U.S. Research Plan.

Thompson, D.S., 2009, *Four-story Wood-frame Structure over Podium Slab.* Woodworks, Tacoma, Washington.

Thompson, D.S., 2012, *Five-story Wood-frame Structure over Podium Slab*, Woodworks, Tacoma, Washington.

Thompson, D.S., 2012, *2009 IBC Structural/Seismic Design Manual, Volume 2, Design Examples 1, 2 & 3* Structural Engineers Association of California. Sacramento, California.

VanDorpe, Tom and Andy Fennell. 2010, *2010 Building Code Update Re-tooling Your Office for Changes to the 2010 California Building Regulations that Affect Light-Frame Structures.* Orange, California.

Washington Association of Building Officials and Structural Engineers Association of Washington (WABO/SEAW) Liaison Committee, 2013, *White Paper 9-2013: Threaded Rod Holdown Systems in Wood Frame Buildings*, Seattle, Washington. www.wabo.org/waboseaw-white-papers

Western Wood Products Association (WWPA), November 2002, *Tech Notes Report No. 10-Shrinkage Calculations for Multi-Story Wood Frame Construction*, Portland, Oregon.

WWPA, 1990, Dimensional Stability of Western Lumber, Portland, Oregon.

Yousefi, Ben, Son, James, and Sabelli, Rafael, 2005. *Structural Engineering Review Manual* (2005 Edition), BYA Publications, Santa Monica, California.

How to Use This Document

Equation numbers in the right-hand margin refer to the one of the standards (e.g., ACI 318, ASCE 7, or IBC). The default standard is given in the heading of each section of each example; equation numbers in that section refer to that standard unless another standard is explicitly cited.

Abbreviations used in the "Code Reference" column are

§ – Section   T – Table

F – Figure   Eq – Equation

Design Example 1
Four-Story Wood Light-Frame Structure

OVERVIEW

This design example illustrates the seismic design of selected elements for a four-story wood-frame hotel structure. The gravity-load framing system consists of wood-frame bearing walls. The lateral-load-resisting system consists of wood-frame bearing shear walls (common box-type system). A typical building elevation and floor plan of the structure are shown in Figures 1-1 and 1-2, respectively. A typical section showing the heights of the structure is shown in Figure 1-3. The wood roof is framed with pre-manufactured wood trusses. The floor is framed with prefabricated wood I-joists. The floors have a 1½-inch lightweight concrete topping. The roofing is composition shingles.

When designing this type of mid-rise wood-frame structure, there are several unique design elements to consider. The following steps provide a detailed analysis of some of the important seismic requirements of the shear walls per the 2018 IBC. This design example represents a very simple wood-frame wood structure; most wood-frame structures have several unique features requiring engineering design and detailing not shown in this design example.

This design example is not a complete building design. Many aspects have not been included, specifically the gravity-load framing system, and only certain steps of the seismic design related to portions of a selected shear wall have been illustrated. In addition, the lateral requirements for wind design related to the selected shear wall have not been illustrated (only seismic). The steps that have been illustrated may be more detailed than what is necessary for an actual building design but are presented in this manner to help the design engineer understand the process. For a more detailed listing of the items not addressed, see Section 10.

OUTLINE

1. Building Geometry and Loads   ASCE 7

1.1 GIVEN INFORMATION

The roof is $^{15}/_{32}$-inch-thick DOC PS 1- or DOC PS 2-rated wood structural panel (WSP) sheathing, with a 32/16 span rating and Exposure I adhesive or waterproof adhesive.

The floor is $^{23}/_{32}$-inch-thick DOC PS 1- or DOC PS 2-rated Sturd-I-Floor 24 inches o.c. rating, with a 48/24 span rating (40/20 span rating with topping is also acceptable) and Exposure I adhesive or waterproof adhesive.

DOC PS 1 and DOC PS 2 are the US Department of Commerce (DOC) prescriptive and performance-based standards for plywood and oriented strand board (OSB), respectively.

Wall framing is a "modified balloon framing" where the joists hang from the walls in joist hangers. (See Figure 1-7 detail of this and an explanation of other common framing conditions.)

Framing lumber for studs and posts   NDS T 4A

Douglas Fir-Larch-No. 1 Grade unadjusted design values:

$F_b = 1,000$ psi

$F_c = 1,500$ psi

$F_{c\perp} = 625$ psi

$F_t = 675$ psi

$E = 1,700,000$ psi

$E_{min} = 620,000$ psi

$C_M = 1.0$ dry in-service conditions assumed

$C_t = 1.0$ normal temperature conditions assumed

Framing lumber used for studs and posts is designed per the National Design Specification® (NDS®) for Wood Construction and NDS Supplement: Design Values for Wood Construction. Only two end-use adjustment factors are shown here. Others will be defined and shown later in the design example.

Common wire nails are used for shear walls, diaphragms, and straps. When specifying nails on a project, specification of the penny weight, type, diameter, and length (example 10d common = 0.148 inch × 3 inches) are recommended.

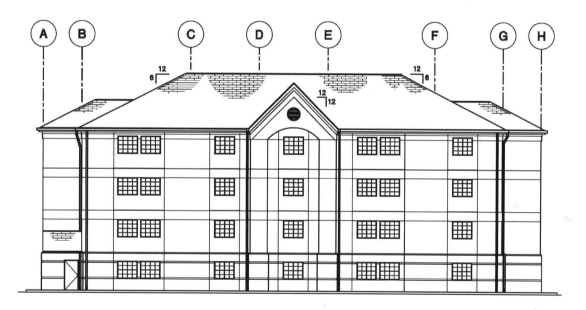

Figure 1-1. Building elevation

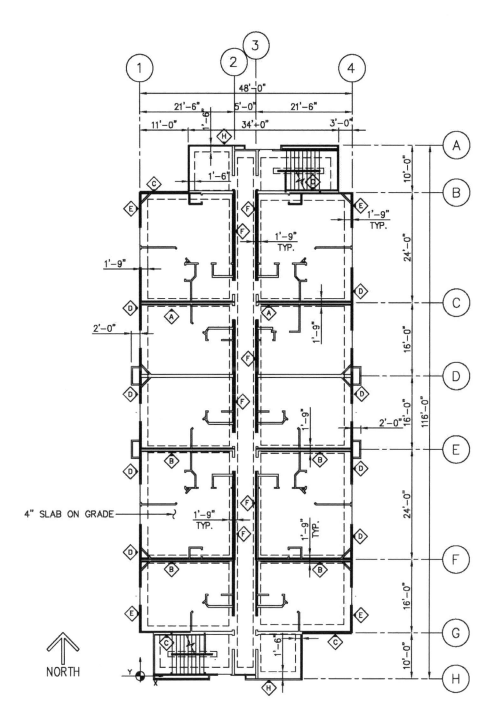

Figure 1-2. Typical foundation plan

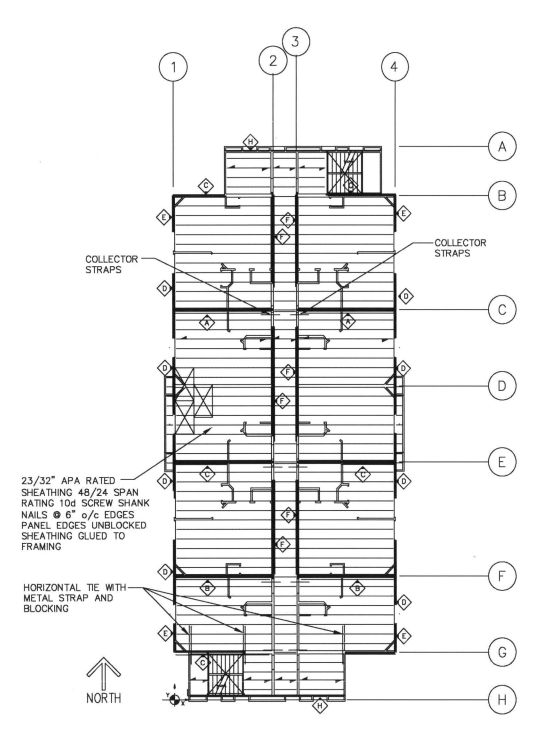

COLLECTOR
STRAPS

COLLECTOR
STRAPS

23/32" APA RATED
SHEATHING 48/24 SPAN
RATING 10d SCREW SHANK
NAILS @ 6" o/c EDGES
PANEL EDGES UNBLOCKED
SHEATHING GLUED TO
FRAMING

HORIZONTAL TIE WITH
METAL STRAP AND
BLOCKING

NORTH

Figure 1-3. Typical floor framing plan

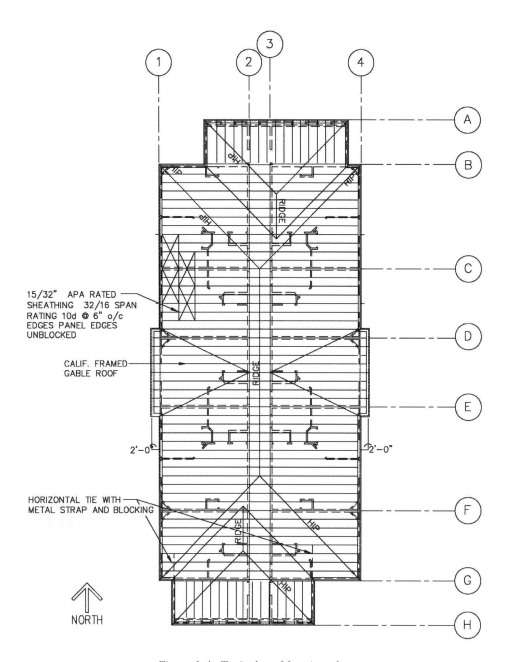

15/32" APA RATED SHEATHING 32/16 SPAN RATING 10d @ 6" o/c EDGES PANEL EDGES UNBLOCKED

CALIF. FRAMED GABLE ROOF

HORIZONTAL TIE WITH METAL STRAP AND BLOCKING

NORTH

Figure 1-4. Typical roof framing plan

Notes for Figures 1-2 through 1-4:

1. Nonstructural "pop-outs" on the exterior walls at lines 1, 4 need special detailing showing the wood structural panel sheathing running continuous at lines 1, 4 and the pop-outs framed after the sheathing is installed.

2. All walls stack from the foundation to the fourth floor.

3. ◇ Designates sheathed wall per shear-wall schedule (see Table 1-35).

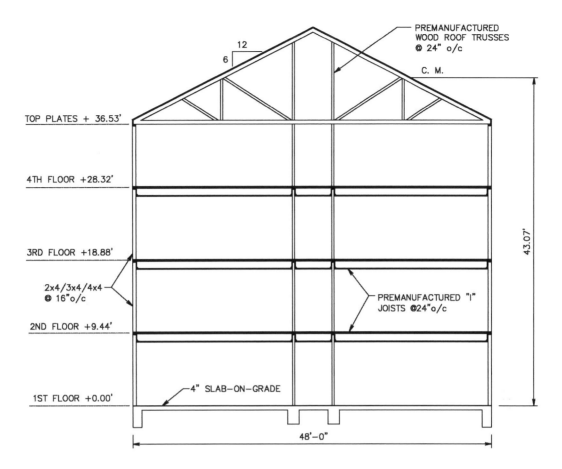

Figure 1-5. Typical building sections

Notes for Figure 1-5:

The center of mass of the roof is higher than one-third of the "triangle" shape plus the blocking height over the top plates due to the weight of the roofing re-roof, and sheathing is heavier than the weight of the ceiling. A conservative height equal to the center of the roof diaphragm (average height of the sloped roof) has been used in this design example.

1.2 FACTORS THAT INFLUENCE DESIGN

Prior to starting the seismic design of a structure, the following must be considered:

Good Shear-Wall Construction Detailing Guidance

Use oriented strand board (OSB) sheathing rather than plywood for improved stiffness.

Use distributed nailing to end studs and plates. This reduces the need to stitch multi-ply end studs and reduces potential framing split damage due to putting all nails in a single 2× end framing member. In a typical high-strength wall test, placing all the nails in the outermost stud tends to increase compression perpendicular to grain deformation in the bottom plate that is flush with the end stud.

Provide greater than minimum nail edge distance at OSB panel edges. Putting nails at ⅜ inch from the panel edge increases the potential for nonconforming construction, even in testing. Because some nails will be closer than ⅜ inch, it places panel edge fastening in the outermost stud of a multi-ply stud pack, which might lead to splitting damage even if the outermost row of nails is staggered (per above), and in some cases promotes earlier occurrence of panel edge tear out relative to distributed nailing.

Use concentric hold-downs or continuous tie-down systems rather than eccentric hold-downs. Data from both shear-wall testing with continuous rods and from prior wood shear-wall testing with conventional hold-down devices on both sides of a built-up 2 × 6 end stud performed better than tests with a single conventional hold-down on the inboard side of the wall.

Provide at least equivalent strength and stiffness (including the participation of finishes) at first-level lateral system elements as compared with the second level. Consider nonstructural walls (especially when such walls do not stack down to the building base) when evaluating lateral system layout for weak and/or soft story conditions.

Species of Lumber

The species of lumber used in this design example is Douglas Fir-Larch (DF-L), which is common on the west coast. The author does not intend to imply that this species can or should be used in all areas or for all markets. Species that are both appropriate for this type of construction and locally available vary by region and commonly include (among others) Southern Pine (SP) and Spruce Pine Fir (SPF).

Grade of Lumber

The lower two stories of the wood-frame structure carry higher gravity loads than the upper two stories. One approach is to use a higher grade of lumber for the lower two stories than the upper two stories. This approach can produce designs that yield a consistent wall construction over the height of the building. Another approach is to choose one grade of lumber for all four wood-frame stories. This approach produces the need to change the size and/or spacing of the studs based on the loading requirements. Sill-plate crushing may control stud sizing at lower levels. For simplicity, this design example illustrates the use of one lumber grade for all floor levels.

Figure 1-6. Typical grade stamp

Notes for Figure 1-6:

a. Certification Mark: Certifies association quality supervision

b. Mill Identification: Firm name, brand, or assigned mill number

c. Grade Designation: Grade name, number, or abbreviation

d. Species Identification: Indicates species by individual species or species combination

e. Condition of Seasoning: Indicates condition of seasoning at the time of surfacing

Moisture Service Condition of Lumber

There are three levels of wood seasoning (drying), which denote the moisture content of the lumber at the time of surfacing. The identification stamps are as follows:

S-GRN = over 19% moisture content (unseasoned)

S-DRY, KD or KD-HT = 19% maximum moisture content (seasoned)

MC 15 or KD 15 = 5% maximum moisture content

These designations may be found in the grade stamp.

Unseasoned lumber (S-GRN) is manufactured oversized so that when the lumber reaches 19 percent moisture content (MC), it will be approximately the same size as the dry (seasoned) size.

Heat-treated (HT) lumber is lumber that has been placed in a closed chamber and heated until it attains a minimum core temperature of 56°C for a minimum of 30 minutes.

The word "DRY" indicates that the lumber was either kiln or air dried to a maximum moisture content of 19 percent.

Kiln-dried (KD) lumber is lumber that has been seasoned in a chamber to a predetermined moisture content by having heat applied.

Kiln-dried heat-treated (KD-HT) lumber has been placed in a closed chamber and heated until it achieves a minimum core temperature of 56°C for a minimum of 30 minutes and is dried to a maximum moisture content of 19 percent or less.

Moisture-content restrictions apply at time of shipment as well as time of dressing if dressed lumber is involved, and at time of delivery to the buyer unless shipped exposed to the weather.

Platform Framed vs. Modified Balloon-framed Floors

Engineered I-joists framed in the modified balloon-frame fashion were used for this design example (see Figure 1-7); however, given the short span on the floor joists, sawn lumber could have been used. Many engineers and developers use the sawn lumber joists in these types of structures because they are cheaper than the engineered I-joists. In this case, the joist shrinkage perpendicular to the grain would need to be included in the overall shrinkage calculation. Also, sawn lumber joists can be supported in joist hangers so as to not contribute to the overall building shrinkage. The method of framing the floor joists and the type of floor joists used varies, depending on engineers' and developer's preferences. For this design example, sawn lumber is used for the stud-framed walls and premanufacurered roof trusses.

Vertical Displacement (Shrinkage) in Multilevel Wood Framing   **IBC §2303.7**

Vertical displacement can be a significant problem in multilevel wood framing unless special considerations are accounted for during design and construction. An estimate of shrinkage and consolidation per floor is required in order for the continuous tie-down rod system supplier to determine the amount of travel required for the shrinkage-device components. Vertical displacement may be caused by one or a combination of the following:

Moisture Content and Wood Shrinkage

From a serviceability and performance perspective, the most significant potential issue related to multistory wood-frame construction is wood shrinkage, which is impacted by the moisture content and, more specifically, whether the wood used is green or kiln dried. Wood shrinkage can be mitigated by proper detailing. For all wood-frame structures, the areas requiring attention are most commonly ensuring that the plumbing/electrical lines and the exterior finishes (stucco, veneer) accommodate the building shrinkage/settlement. Building shrinkage/settlement for the shear-wall hold-downs is accomodated by compensating devices that are discussed in Section 4.4C.

A more serious problem can be differential shrinkage between full-height steel frames and the wood-frame system or full-height concrete or masonry walls and the wood-frame system. Both of these conditions require special detailing.

The availability of both types of lumber (green and kiln-dried) is largely dependent on the region and associated market conditions. Typically, wood used in construction in the US southwest has both green (S-GRN) and kiln-dried (KD) wood, while other parts of the country have more kiln-dried wood. Kiln-dried lumber is available, and when the contractor needs to provide the product, this may mean a longer lead time in some areas to obtain it.

Wood Shrinkage

Shrinkage occurs when wood dries, changing the structural dimensions of the lumber. This is a factor in any wood structure, and the compounding (additive) effect of multiple stories can increase the potential to have a shrinkage problem. Shrinkage problems can be cracking of finishes, pinching of door and window frames, or buckling of piping and conduits.

Both the IBC and NDS require consideration be given to the effects of cross-grain dimensional changes (shrinkage) when lumber is fabricated in a green condition. In addition, IBC Section 2304.3.3 requires that bearing walls supporting more than two floors and a roof be analyzed for shrinkage of the wood framing and that possible adverse effects on the structure be satisfactorily remediated. This analysis and remediation is submitted to the building official.

The total shrinkage in wood-frame buildings can be calculated by summing the estimated shrinkage of the *horizontal* lumber members in walls and floors (wall plates, sills, and floor joists). Most of the shrinkage is cross grain. The amount of shrinkage parallel to grain (length of studs) is approximately 1/40 of the shrinkage perpendicular to grain (cross grain) and can be neglected.

This design example illustrates two methods for determining the amount of wood shrinkage:

Comprehensive Shrinkage Estimation

For a dimensional change with the moisture content limits of 6 to 14 percent, the formula is

$$S = D_i[C_T(M_F - M_i)]$$

where

S = shrinkage (in inches)

D_i = initial dimension (in inches)

C_T = dimension change coefficient, tangential direction

C_T = 0.00319 for Douglas Fir-Larch

C_T = 0.00323 for Hem-Fir

C_T = 0.00263 for Spruce-Pine-Fir

M_F = final moisture content (%)

M_i = initial moisture content (%)

The formulas are from the *Wood Handbook: Wood as an Engineering Material, Dimensional Stability of Western Lumber Products*, and *Accommodating Shrinkage in Multistory Wood-Frame Structures* (www.woodworks.org/wp-content/uploads/wood_solution_paper-Accomodating-Shrinkage.pdf).

The final moisture content (M_F) for a building is referred to as the equilibrium moisture content (EMC). The final equilibrium moisture content can be higher in coastal areas and lower in inland or desert areas. These ranges are normally from 6 to 15 percent (low to high).

For this design example, a final moisture content M_F (EMC) of 12 percent is used.

Project specifications call for all top plates and sill (sole) plates to be Douglas Fir-Larch kiln dried (KD) or surfaced dried (S-Dry). Kiln-dried or surfaced-dried lumber has a maximum moisture content of 19 percent and an average of 15 percent.

It might be more realistic to use a lower number than 19 percent in the calculation so as to not overestimate the shrinkage.

Typical floor framing has a 4 × 4 top plate and two 2 × 4 sole plates (see Figure 1-7).

Find the individual shrinkage of the two members:
Determine shrinkage of two 2 × 4 top plates and sill plates:
Since the initial MC (M_i) is 19 percent and the final MC (M_F) is 12 percent, the equation is

$$S = \frac{D_i(M_F - M_i)}{\dfrac{30(100)}{S_T} - 30 + M_i} = \frac{(2 \times 1.5) \times (12 - 19)}{\dfrac{30(100)}{7.775} - 30 + 19} = -0.06 \text{ in}$$

The final size of the two 2 × 4s is

$$(2 \times 1.5) - 0.06 = 2.94 \text{ in}$$

Quick Shrinkage Estimation

A close approximation that is much more easily used to determine amount of shrinkage is

$$S = CD_i(M_F - M_i)$$

where

S = shrinkage (inches)
C = average shrinkage constant
C = 0.002
M_F = final moisture content (%)
M_i = initial moisture content (%)

Determine shrinkage of the 4 × 4 top plate and two 2 × 4 sill plates:

For the two 2 × 4 sill plates, since the initial MC (M_i) is 19 percent and the final MC (M_F) is 12 percent, the equation is

$$S = CD_i(M_F - M_i) = 0.002 \times (2 \times 1.5) \times (12 - 19) = -0.4 \text{ in}$$

The final size of the two 2 × 4s is

$$(2 \times 1.5) - 0.04 = 2.96 \text{ in}$$

This quick estimation is within 0.5 percent of the actual calculated dimension of 2.94 inches using the comprehensive formulas.

For the 4 × 4 top plate

$$S = CD_i(M_F - M_i) = 0.002 \times (3.5) \times (12 - 19) = -0.05 \text{ in}$$

The final size of the 4 × 4 is

$$(3.5) - 0.05 = 3.45 \text{ in}$$

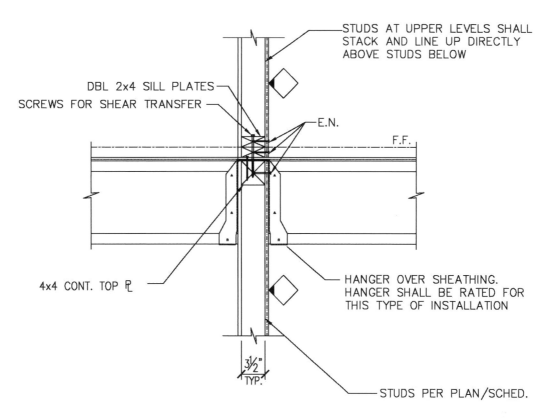

Figure 1-7. Floor framing at wall

Notes for Figure 1-7:

1. The double sill plate is to provide a nailing surface for the finishes. An alternative detail could use one sill plate and blocking between the studs for finish nailing.

2. Web stiffeners at joist hangers may be required, depending on joist size and manufacturer.

3. Hangers for the floor joist are installed over the sheathing (gypsum, plywood, or OSB) and must be rated/approved for this installation (e.g., Technical Bulletin from joist hanger manufacturer listing reduced allowable hanger loads).

4. For condition at shear wall with the floor joists parallel to the wall, see Figure 1-24.

Total shrinkage per floor level with the 4×4 top plate and two 2×4 sill plates:

$$S = 0.05 + 0.04 = 0.09 \text{ in}$$

Settlement-Under-Construction Gaps (Consolidation)

An estimate of shrinkage and consolidation per floor is required in order for the continuous tie-down rod system supplier to determine the amount of travel required for the shrinkage-device components. This may be calculated on each project, or a typical value may be used for buildings having similar construction and similar initial moisture content in the lumber.

Small gaps can occur between plates and studs, caused by (among other things) mis-cuts (short studs) and the lack of square-cut ends. These gaps can account for up to ⅛ inch per story, where "perfect" workmanship would be 0 inches, and a more "sloppy" workmanship would be ⅛ inch. Some settlement can be attributed to compression at joist and beam-hanger top flanges. This case study factors in gaps and compression at hanger flanges of ⅛ inch.

Deformation under Sustained Loading

Wood beams that support walls can creep from the sustained loading. The rate of creep can be higher for beams that are loaded while drying under load because the modulus of elasticity is lower for higher moisture contents. Appendix F of the NDS provides commentary related to creep in wood and recommends a (creep) deflection amplification factor of between 1.5 and 2.0 for computing deflections under sustained loads.

Table 1-1. Vertical displacements

Level	Vertical Displacement		Design Displacement (in)
	Per Floor (in)	Cumulative (in)	
4th Floor	0.22	0.65	3/4
3rd Floor	0.22	0.43	1/2
2nd Floor	0.22	0.22	1/4

where

shrinkage of 0.09 in + settlement of 0.125 in = 0.22 in

Methods to Reduce Vertical Displacement

1. Use kiln-dried plates (MC < 19 percent) or even MC15 (MC < 15 percent) lumber or engineered lumber for plates.

2. Consider a single top plate instead of a double top plate.

3. Consider balloon framing or a modified balloon framing.

4. Place floor joists in metal hangers bearing on beams or top plates instead of bearing on the top plates.

5. The site storage of the material stock can negate all design and planning when the material is not properly stored. Lumber should be kept away from moisture sources and rain.

Methods to Account for Vertical Displacement

1. Use continuous tie-down systems with shrinkage compensating devices in shear walls.

2. Architectural finish details near the floor lines need to account for vertical displacement.

3. Provide a ⅛-inch gap between window and door tops to the framing lumber.

Use of Premanufactured Metal-Plate-Connected Wood Trusses §2303.4

The permanent individual truss member restraint/bracing of wood trusses from individual truss to individual trusses is the responsibility of the truss designer/truss manufacturer. The responsibility of which party is required to design/detail the *restraint* of the lateral bracing is the problem. The truss submittal drawings (ANSI/TPI 1 Standard Section 2.3.2.4) are required to show the approximate location of the required lateral bracing on the *individual* truss members. ANSI/TPI 1 Standard Section 2.3.3.1.3 states that as an option, the building designer/engineer of record may design the *restraint* of this lateral bracing. Other options for the design of permanent lateral bracing are use of BCSI-B3, *Permanent Restraint/Bracing of Chords and Web Members* or BCSI-B7, *Guide for Handling, Installing, and Bracing of 3×2 and 4×2 Parallel Chord Trusses.* These documents are available from the Truss Plate Institute. IBC Section 2303.4.1.2 references industry standards for bracing without directly referencing the BCSI documents. These bracing forces are accumulated along the length of the brace and need to be detailed as to how they are resisted by the building. The problem is that when the building design is completed, the locations of the truss bracing are not known to the building designer because the truss designs done by the truss designer/truss manufacturer have not been completed. The current practice with building designers is that the truss design and truss bracing is by others.

It should be acknowledged that many prefabricated truss design submittals do not seem to take responsibility for certain design items that are shown in them, such as sizing truss-to-truss connections, setting cambers, or the bracing and connections of internal webs that may otherwise be slender. Often, notes are placed in the submittal documents indicating that another party, such as the "building designer," should be the one to take responsibility for these designs even though the design originated outside the office of the "building designer."

See Section 4.1 for further discussion about shear transfer (drag) trusses.

Effects of Box Nails on Wood Structural Panel Shear Walls

This design example uses common nails for fastening wood structural panels. Based on cyclic testing of shear walls and performance in past earthquakes, the use of common nails is preferred. The 2018 IBC no longer lists allowable shears for wood structural panel shear walls using nails; IBC Table 2306.3 lists allowable shears for wood structural panel shear walls for staples. The IBC directly references the *Special Design Provisions for Wind and Sesimic* (SDPWS) by the American Wood Council (AWC) for wood structural panel shear capacities with nails as fasteners.

SDPWS Table 4.3A lists nominal unit shear capacities for wood structural panel shear walls for common or galvanized box nails. Footnote 7 of Table 4.3A states that the galvanized nails shall be "hot-dipped" or tumbled, but these nails will not work in some power-driven fastener devices. Most contractors use power-driven fasteners for diaphragm and shear-wall installations.

Box nails have a smaller diameter shank and a smaller head size than common nails. Using 10d box nails results in a 19 percent reduction in allowable load for diaphragms and shear walls compared to 10d common nails. Using 8d box nails would result in a 22 percent reduction in allowable load for diaphragms and shear walls compared to 8d common nails. This is based on comparing allowable shear values listed in Table 12N in the National Design Specification (NDS) for Wood Construction for ¾-inch side member thickness, t_s, and Douglas Fir-Larch framing. In addition to the reduction of the shear wall and diaphragm capacities, where box nails are used, the walls will also drift more than where common nails are used. Alternatively, the engineer can consider using nail and sheathing thicknesses not listed in the IBC or SDPWS by using the values listed in ICC-ES report ESR-1539, available from the International Staple, Nail, and Tool Association (ISANTA).

A contributor to the problem is that when contractors buy large quantities of nails for nail guns, the words "box" or "common" do not appear on the carton label. Nail length and diameters are the most common listing on the labels. Thus, it is **extremely important** to list the required nail lengths and diameters on the structural drawings for all diaphragms and shear walls.

Some manufacturers of nails have developed a method of color coding and stamping of the nail head that allows the inspection of the nail size and length in the installed condition as opposed to someone either physically witnessing the installation of the nails or removing the installed nails for verification. These color-coded and stamped nails add only a nominal cost to the nails and are gaining in popularity with engineers, special inspectors, and building officials.

Another problem is that contractors prefer sinker and short nails because their use reduces splitting, eases driving, and costs less.

To illustrate a point, if an engineer designs for dry lumber (as discussed earlier) and common nails, and subsequently green lumber and box nails are used in the construction, the result is a compounding of the reductions. For example, for 10d nails installed into green lumber, the reduction would be 0.81 times 0.7 or a 43 percent reduction in capacity.

Wood Studs in Fire-Resistance-Rated Walls   IBC T504.4 and T601

The four-story building in this design example has rated walls and ceilings and is considered a Type V building. When wood-frame structures exceed the limits for Type V construction (e.g., five stories of wood-frame construction), the code requires either Type III or Type IV construction.

IBC Section 602.3 defines Type III construction as buildings with exterior walls made from noncombustible materials. Therefore, as an exception, use of fire-retardant-treated wood (FRTW) is allowed for the exterior load-bearing wall assemblies.

Fire-rated assemblies can be found in a number of sources, including the IBC, the Underwriters Laboratories (UL) *Fire-Resistance-Rated Systems and Products*, the UL *Fire Resistance Directory*, the Gypsum Association's *Fire Resistance Design Manual*, and AWC's Design for Code *Acceptance 3* (DCA 3) —*Fire-Resistance-Rated Wood-Frame Wall and Floor/Ceiling Assemblies*.

Table 721.1(2) of the IBC lists fire ratings for various wall construction types. Many of the wall construction types using wood construction reference Footnote m. Footnote m of the table requires the reduction of F_c' to be 78 percent of the allowable where the slenderness ratio $l_e/d > 33$. For studs with a slenderness ratio $l_e/d < 33$, the design stress shall be reduced to 78 percent of the adjusted stress F_c' calculated for studs having a slenderness ratio l_e/d of 33.

The AWC has tested a number of wood-frame fire-rated wall assemblies to 100 percent design load. There is a disparity between the IBC and publications such as AWC's DCA 3, *Fire-Resistance-Rated Wood-Frame Wall and Floor/Ceiling Assemblies*, which does not require the reduction in allowable stress. The building's architect and/or engineer should check with the local jurisdiction to determine the accepted approach. The AWC procedure is detailed at https://www.awc.org/faqs/fire/fire/what-is-the-background-behind-footnote-m-of-ibc-2012-table-721.1-(2).

The calculated stresses for F_c' used in this design example will not use the reductions for Footnote m.

1.3 WEIGHTS

Roof weights:		Floor weights:	
Roofing + re-roof	5.0 psf	Flooring	1.0 psf
Sheathing	2.5	Lt. wt. concrete	14.0
Trusses	3.0	Sheathing	2.8
Insulation + sprinklers	2.5	I-joist	4.0
2 layers gyp + misc	7.0	2 layers gyp + misc	8.2
	———		———
Dead load	20.0 psf		30.0 psf
Live load	20.0 psf		40.0 psf

Interior and exterior wall weights have not been included in the above loads; they have been included in the diaphragm weights shown in Table 1.2. Typical interior and exterior partition weights (for determining the *building* weights) can vary between 15 psf to 20 psf (based on the horizontal plan dimension), depending on room sizes, number of layers of gypsum board on walls, staggered studs, etc.

Weights of roof diaphragms are typically determined by taking one-half the height of the walls from the fourth floor level to the roof. Weights of floor diaphragms are typically determined by taking one-half the walls above and below for the fourth, third, and second floor diaphragms. The weights of all walls, including interior nonbearing partitions, are included in the respective weights of the various levels. The weight of parapets (where they occur) has been included in the roof weight.

Table 1-2. Weights of roof and floor diaphragms

Level	Assembly	Unit Wt (psf)	Area (ft²)	Weight (kips)	Story Wt (kips)
Roof	Roof	20	5288	105.7	165.7
	Ext wall	15	1350	20.25	
	Int wall	15	5288	39.66	
4th Floor	Floor	30	5288	158.6	284.5
	Ext wall	15	3100	46.50	
	Int wall	15	5288	79.32	
3rd Floor	Floor	30	5288	158.6	284.5
	Ext wall	15	3100	46.50	
	Int wall	15	5288	79.32	
2nd Floor	Floor	30	5288	158.6	284.5
	Ext wall	15	3100	46.50	
	Int wall	15	5288	79.32	

$W = 3(284.5 \text{ kips}) + 165.7 \text{ kips} = 1{,}019 \text{ kips}$

2. Calculation of the Design Base Shear   ASCE 7

2.1 CLASSIFY THE STRUCTURAL SYSTEM

From ASCE 7 Table 12.2-1 for bearing-wall systems using light-frame wood walls sheathed with wood structural panels rated for shear resistance:

$$R = 6.5 \quad \Omega_0 = 3.0 \quad C_d = 4.0$$

2.2 DESIGN SPECTRAL ACCELERATIONS

The spectral accelerations to be used in design are derived from soil profile and site location:

$$S_S = 1.540g \qquad S_1 = 0.568g$$

2.3 RESPONSE SPECTRUM

Determine the approximate fundamental building period using Section 12.8.2.1:

$C_t = 0.02$ and $x = 0.75$ T12.8-2

$T_a = C_t h_n^x = 0.02 \times 43^{0.75} = 0.34 \text{ sec}$ (see the following discussion)   Eq 12.8-7

$$T_a = 0.34 \text{ sec}$$

$$T_o = 0.2 \frac{S_{D1}}{S_{DS}} = 0.2 \frac{0.568}{1.026} = 0.11 \text{ sec}$$

$$S_a = S_{DS}\left(0.4 + 0.6\frac{T}{T_o}\right) = 0.4 + 5.6T \text{ for } T < T_o \qquad \text{Eq 11.4-5}$$

$$T_s = \frac{S_{D1}}{S_{DS}} = \frac{0.568}{1.026} = 0.55 \text{ sec} \qquad \S 11.4.6$$

$$S_a = \frac{S_{D1}}{T} = \frac{0.568}{T} \text{ for } T > T_s \qquad \text{Eq 11.4-6}$$

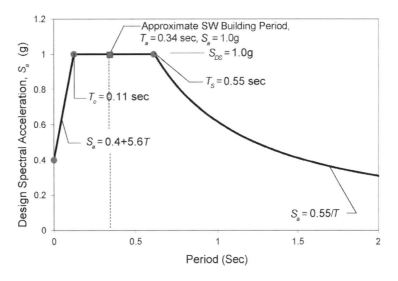

Figure 1-8. Design response spectrum for the example building

The long period equation for S_a does not apply here because the long period transition occurs at 12 seconds (from Figure 22-14).

As shown in Figure 1-8, the design spectral acceleration is between T_o and T_s, so the design spectral acceleration S_a is 1.0g. It is not required to construct the design response spectrum when using the equivalent lateral force procedure, since the response spectrum is implicit in the calculation of C_s in Section 12.8.1.1.

The response spectrum demonstrates the effect of the assumptions used in the calculation of building period. Values of $C_t = 0.02$ and $x = 0.75$ were selected as specified for shear wall buildings, which result in an approximate period, $T_a = 0.34$ sec. As shown later in this example, drifts are close to, if not at, the story drift limits of Section 12.12.

The period of the structure can be established through structural analysis. Section 12.8.2, however, limits the period that can be used to calculate spectral acceleration to a value of $T_{max} = C_u \times T_a$, where C_u is a factor found in Table 12.8-1. In this case, $T_{max} = 1.4 \times 0.34 = 0.48$ sec.

2.4 HORIZONTAL IRREGULARITIES   T12.3-1

1a. to 5.   By inspection, the building does not qualify for any of the horizontal structural irregularities.

NO HORIZONTAL STRUCTURAL IRREGULARITIES

2.5 VERTICAL IRREGULARITIES   T12.3-2

1a. to 5b.   By inspection, the building does not qualify for any of the vertical structural irregularities.

NO VERTICAL STRUCTURAL IRREGULARITIES

2.6 LATERAL FORCE PROCEDURE   T12.6-1

Design checklist:

1. Determine occupancy category and importance factor.

2. Determine S_s, S_1, and soil profile from site location.

3. Test for Seismic Design Category (SDC) E.

4. Determine S_{DS} and S_{D1}.

5. Determine T and test for short period exception on SDC. Determine if equivalent lateral force analysis is allowed.

6. Determine SDC (if not E).

7. Determine R and verify height.

8. Test for $S_s < 1.5$ and calculate C_s base shear.

9. Determine C_s.

   • Determine risk category and importance factor:

   Risk Category II   T1.5-1

   $I_e = 1.0$ T1.5-2

   • Determine S_s, S_1, and soil profile:

   Site Class D (based on geotechnical investigation)

   Per geotechnical investigation: Site Class D

   Location: Irvine, CA

   Longitude = −117.8320, Latitude = 33.6800

Therefore, from USGS website application:

$S_s = 1.540g \gg 0.15$

Therefore, not SDC A

$S_1 = 0.567g \gg 0.04$

Therefore, not SDC A

$S_1 = 0.567g < 0.75$

Therefore, not SDC E

$S_1 = 0.567g < 0.6$

Therefore, Equation 12.8-6 applies.

- Determine SDC:

Based on the geotechnical investigation, SDC = D.

The above additional checks were added for reference when an investigation has not determined the SDC.

- Determine R and verify height:

For light-frame walls with wood structural panels that are both shear walls and bearing walls:

$R = 6.5$ T12.2-1

Maximum height permitted in SDC D is 65 feet   T12.2-1

The building structure is less than 65 feet; therefore, it is permitted.

In addition, Equation 12.8-6 requires an additional check for C_s, the minimum for structures that are located where S_1 is equal to or greater than 0.6g:

$$C_s = \frac{0.5 S_1}{\left(\dfrac{R}{I}\right)} = \frac{0.5(0.567)}{\left(\dfrac{6.5}{1.0}\right)} = 0.04; \text{ therefore, it does not control}$$

$$\boxed{C_s = 0.158}$$

Therefore:

$V = C_s W = 0.158W$

Design base shear in ASCE 7 is based on a strength design basis.

Since the 2012 IBC, all tables for "nailed" wood diaphragms and shear walls have been removed from the IBC; the only tables that are left are for "stapled" wood diaphragms and shear walls and have allowable shears. All tables in the SDPWS are "dual format," and the nominal values must be adjusted for both strength and allowable stress design (ASD) loads. Since ASD is still predominantly practiced, it has been decided to have this design example in ASD format. In addition, all the manufacturers of metal hardware connectors currently publish ASD values.

1. Simplified alternative structural design criteria—According to Section 12.14.1.1, this analysis procedure can be used for bearing wall systems, but not for buildings over 3 stories—NOT PERMITTED.

2. Equivalent lateral force analysis—According to Table 12.6-1, since $T < 3.5T_s$ (0.34 sec < 1.93 sec), and the building is regular and Risk Category II— PERMITTED.

3. Modal response spectrum analysis—PERMITTED.

4. Seismic response history procedures—PERMITTED.

> USE EQUIVALENT LATERAL FORCE ANALYSIS

2.7 BASE SHEAR

$$C_s = 0.158$$

$$V = C_s W = 0.158 \times 1019 = 160.8 \text{ kips}$$ Eq 12.8-1

$$V = 160.8 \text{ kips}$$

2.8 VERTICAL DISTRIBUTION OF SHEAR

Table 1-3. Vertical distribution of shear from Section 12.8.3

Level	w_x (k)	h_x (ft)	$w_x h_x$ (k-ft)	C_{vx}	F_x (k)	$\dfrac{F_x}{w_x}$	F_{tot} (k)
Roof	165.67	43.07	7135	0.31	49.37	0.298	49.37
4th Floor	284.46	28.32	8056	0.35	55.74	0.196	105.1
3rd Floor	284.46	18.88	5371	0.23	37.16	0.131	142.2
2nd Floor	284.46	9.44	2685	0.12	18.58	0.065	160.8
Total	1019.1		23,247	1.00	160.8		457.47

The terms used in Table 1-3 are defined in Section 12.8.3. Since the period = 0.34 < 0.5 sec, the value for k is 1.0.

In this design example, $k = 1.0$. The distribution of story shear is carried out using

$$F_x = C_{vx}V, \text{ where } C_{vx} = \frac{w_x h_x^k}{\sum_{i=1}^{n} w_i h_i^k}$$

Eq 12.8-11 and Eq 12.8-12

2.9 REDUNDANCY FACTOR

According to Section 12.3.4, the redundancy factor should be calculated for each principal axis. The redundancy factor is 1.3 unless either Section 12.3.4.2(a) or 12.3.4.2(b) is shown to be true, in which case the redundancy factor can be taken as 1.0. Section 12.3.4.2(b) requires that there be two bays of shear walls on each perimeter line. Therefore, the redundancy factor is 1.0 for both the east-west direction and the north-south direction.

$\rho = 1.0$ FOR EAST-WEST DIRECTION

$\rho = 1.0$ FOR NORTH-SOUTH DIRECTION

3. Location of Shear Walls and Horizontal Distribution of Shear   ASCE 7

3.1 LOCATION OF SHEAR WALLS

The lateral-force-resisting system in this design example uses both interior and exterior walls for shear walls (see Figures 1-2 and 1-3). The seismic-force-resisting system for the transverse direction (north-south) utilizes the interior walls between the hotel guest rooms. A seismic design of a selected interior shear wall in the transverse direction is illustrated in this design example. The seismic-force-resisting system for the longitudinal direction (east-west) utilizes the long interior corridor walls located at the center of the structure, with shear walls on both sides of the corridor in addition to shear walls on the exterior walls and shear walls at the bathroom walls.

In a lateral-force-resisting system in the longitudinal direction for structures similar to this design example, some structural engineers will utilize only the interior corridor walls and not place shear walls on the exterior walls. In previous editions of the SDPWS, this type of design used a rigid diaphragm approach for the distribution of lateral forces to the shear walls. Also, previous editions of ASCE 7 and the SDPWS were not clear or specific on what was allowed by the code. The 2015 SDPWS has added language and requirements for a semirigid and envelope diaphragm analysis for open-front structures. These added requirements include length to width (L/W) limits with a maximum cantilever distance of 35 feet. In addition, in Seismic Design Categories B, C, D, E, and F the engineer must consider torsion, accidental torsion, and story drifts in conformance with ASCE 7, and diaphragm shear and bending deformation contributions to story drift at the open front.

3.2 FLEXIBLE VS. RIGID DIAPHRAGM ANALYSIS

ASCE 7 continues to allow the assumption of flexible diaphragms for most wood structures without a rigorous analysis if the conditions in Section 12.3.1.1 are satisfied. The engineer should use judgment in applying this code requirement in determining shear distributions to the shear walls since, in reality, all diaphragms behave as semirigid. Flexible diaphragm assumptions may be justifiable from a code-compliance perspective for this design example due to the overall uniformity of shear wall lengths and spacing for the building's transverse direction (north-south).

ASCE 7 and prior editions of the SDPWS did not have a definition of an envelope analysis approach for lateral analysis. The 2015 SDPWS states that the distribution of shear to the vertical resisting elements shall be based on an analysis where the diaphragm is modeled as semirigid, idealized as flexible, or idealized as rigid. As an alternative to a semirigid analysis, SDPWS also describes permissible use of an envelope analysis.

Recognizing that horizontal wood diaphragms are semirigid and are neither purely flexible nor purely rigid, an engineer using the envelope method analyzes the distribution of horizontal story forces twice, with diaphragms separately idealized as flexible and rigid. Whereby, the diaphragm shear to each vertical resisting element is the larger of the shear forces resulting from the analyses.

Commentary on Diaphragm Flexibility for Multistory Light-Frame Structures

In current practice, usually to accommodate larger openings and windows at the building perimeters, some design professionals have opted to omit or limit lateral-force-resisting elements from exterior wall lines and rely on the interior lines of lateral resistance, such as corridor walls. Some jurisdictions have not allowed the designer to disregard the results from a traditional flexible diaphragm approach. This practice is not recommended unless the engineer explicitly considers building performance, including the control of localized horizontal diaphragm deflections that could lead to instability. Regardless of the approach, the design shall comply with code limits for horizontal diaphragm cantilevers (shown in code reference SDPWS), deformation compatibility, stability, and seismic drift requirements. New research is underway that looks directly into the efficacy of this approach, which should be available to designers of mid-rise wood frame buildings in the near future.

For this design example, an envelope method of design is utilized.

Behavior of Cantilevered Diaphragms

Although allowed by Standards, use of cantilever diaphragms do not appear to have sufficient test data to justify wide-spread use. Previous write-ups have urged caution on the use of cantilever diaphragms without additional study and validating physical testing. Reportedly some jurisdictions, including the City of LA, are not allowing or are restricting cantilever diaphragm use.

3.3 USE OF CANTILEVER DIAPHRAGMS

The 2015 SDPWS had significant changes to the document related to the use of cantilever diaphragms. 2015 SDPWS open-front requirements have changed from the 2008 edition regarding allowable cantilever length. The 2008 edition limited the maximum cantilever length of an open-front structure to 25 feet; however, it had an exception that allowed an increase in the cantilever length where calculations show that diaphragm deflections can be tolerated. Consequently, there did not exist a hard limit on the cantilever length provided that the aspect ratio and all other requirements could be met. The 2015 edition limits the cantilevered length, L', to 35 feet with no exception provided. Section 4.2.5.2 of the 2015 SDPWS also has significantly changed from the requirements of the previous 2008 edition, requiring the following for cantilever diaphragms with seismic loading:

- Calculation of story drift at the edges of the structure.

- Verification that the building is not torsionally irregular.

- Calculations to justify that the diaphragm can be idealized as rigid (or modeled as semirigid).

The 2015 SDPWS and building codes prior had provisions for use of cantilever diaphragms; however, deflection equations for the cantilever case were never provided. The proposed 2021 SDPWS equations are to address two types of loading conditions of cantilever diaphragms (Case 2 and Case 3). The new deflection calculations utilize the shear stiffness properties, G_a. Loading Case 2 represents a uniformly loaded cantilever diaphragm as could be represented by distributed loads transferred from floors/roofs and walls. Loading Case 3 represents a condition where forces may be concentrated at the cantilever end such as from perimeter walls at the outside edge of the diaphragm. Calculations of diaphragm deflection account for bending and shear deflections, fastener deformation, chord splice slip, and other contributing sources of deflection. The diaphragm deflection, δ_{dia}, shall be permitted to be calculated by use of the following equations that are proposed for the 2021 SDPWS.

Three-Term Diaphragm Deflection Equations

Loading Case	Equation
1. Mid-span deflection of a single-span simply supported diaphragm with uniformly distributed load.	$\delta_{dia} = \dfrac{5vL^3}{8EAW} + \dfrac{0.25vL}{1000G_a} + \dfrac{\Sigma \Delta c x_c}{2W}$
2. End deflection of a cantilever diaphragm with uniformly distributed load.	$\delta_{dia} = \dfrac{3vL'^3}{EAW'} + \dfrac{0.5vL'}{1000G_a} + \dfrac{\Sigma \Delta c x_c}{W'}$
3. End deflection of a cantilever diaphragm with concentrated load at the end.	$\delta_{dia} = \dfrac{8vL'^3}{EAW'} + \dfrac{vL'}{1000G_a} + \dfrac{\Sigma \Delta c x_c}{W'}$

Four-Term Diaphragm Deflection Equations

Loading Case	Equation
1. Mid-span deflection of a single-span simply supported diaphragm with uniformly distributed load.	$\delta_{dia} = \dfrac{5vL^3}{8EAW} + \dfrac{vL}{4Gvtv} + 0.188Le_n + \dfrac{\Sigma \Delta c x_c}{2W}$
2. End deflection of a cantilever diaphragm with uniformly distributed load.	$\delta_{dia} = \dfrac{3vL'^3}{EAW'} + \dfrac{vL'}{2Gvtv} + 0.376L'e_n + \dfrac{\Sigma \Delta c x_c}{W'}$
3. End deflection of a cantilever diaphragm with concentrated load at the end.	$\delta_{dia} = \dfrac{8vL'^3}{EAW'} + \dfrac{vL'}{Gvtv} + 0.75L'e_n + \dfrac{\Sigma \Delta c x_c}{W'}$

where
E = modulus of elasticity of diaphragm chords, psi

A = area of chord cross-section, in^2

G_a = apparent diaphragm shear stiffness from nail slip and panel shear deformation, kips/in

L = diaphragm length, ft

L' = cantilever diaphragm length, ft

v = induced unit shear in diaphragm, lb/ft

W = diaphragm width, ft

W' = cantilever diaphragm width, ft

x_c = distance from chord splice to nearest support, ft

Δc = diaphragm chord slice slip (in) at the induced unit shear in diaphragm

δ_{dia} = maximum mid-span diaphragm deflection determined by elastic analysis, in

e_n = nail slip per SDPWS C4.2.2D for the load per fastener at v

$Gvtv$ = panel rigidity through the thickness

WoodWorks has recently released a new publication, *Seismic Design Example of a Cantilever Wood Diaphragm*. This publication has a comprehensive design example for calculating cantilever diaphragm deflections in light-frame construction.

3.4 WEAK AND SOFT STORIES IN LIGHT-FRAME STRUCTURES

A recent Applied Technology Project, ATC-116 Project: Solutions to the Issue of Short-Period Building Performance has additional guidance. The project's purpose was to:

1. Identify key missing elements of current modeling practice related to short-period buildings.

2. Develop a methodology to improve analytical modeling of short-period buildings.

3. Calibrate the methodology with observed performance of short-period buildings in recent earthquakes.

4. Simplify the methodology into practical solutions that can be implemented in codes and standards.

As part of the ATC-116 short-period project, numerical studies identified that when finish materials are included in analysis models, they can dramatically change both the strength and stiffness of light-frame shear wall structures and appear to result in the consistent occurrence of a first-story collapse mechanism.

Several factors are thought to be driving the first-story mechanism:

1. While the capacity of the designed shear wall varies over the height of the structure with demand, the capacity added by the finish material remains the same, which results in the overstrength (designed shear walls plus finish materials). However, these shear walls plus finish materials, due to common architectural and occupancy issues, contribute to providing the least strength at the first story. In other words, shear walls at the lowest level will have the highest demand-to-capacity ratio (DCR) and will therefore yield first.

2. Once inelastic behavior begins in the numerical studies, additional inelastic behavior tends to focus in that story and does not have the capacity to push yielding up into the upper levels as would be expected with a well-distributed and ductile lateral system.

This potential issue is thought to be amplified in multistory buildings with stacking shearwalls, where due to the desire for more open space at the base level (e.g., lobby, exercise room, meeting rooms, retail space), there are often fewer nonstructural bearing walls, resulting in a sometimes significant reduction in the actual stiffness and strength compared to the upper levels.

The wood industry is currently undertaking testing to expand the data available for numerical modeling; this could result in additional numerical modeling being available for consideration. It is therefore recommended that the designer evaluate the effects of the lower level layout of the structural and nonstructural finishes as well as the structural and nonstructural walls and where possible, provide extra strength in the first-story shear walls.

4. Mechanics of Multistory Segmented Shear Walls and Load Combinations

4.1 OVERTURNING EFFECTS OF SHEAR-TRANSFER (DRAG) TRUSSES

The structural design in this design example uses premanufactured wood roof trusses. Under seismic forces, these must transfer the lateral forces from the roof diaphragm to the tops of the interior shear walls. To accomplish this, special considerations must be made in the design and detailed on the plans. In particular, any trusses that are to be used as collectors or shear-transfer (drag) trusses should be clearly indicated on the structural framing plan(s). The magnitude of the forces, the means by which the forces are applied to the trusses, and the means by which the forces are transferred from the trusses to the shear walls must be shown on the plans. In addition, if the roof sheathing at the hip ends breaks above the joint between the end jack trusses and the supporting girder truss, the lateral forces to be resisted by the end jacks should be specified so that an appropriate connection can be provided to resist these forces. The drawings for the building also must specify the load combinations and whether or not a stress increase is permitted. If ridge vents are being used, special detailing for shear transfers must be included because normal diaphragm continuity is disrupted.

Method of Load Transfer

The trusses that transfer drag loads actually only transfer the loads from their top chord to their bottom chord. This is a fine point, but it is the engineer of record's (EOR) responsibility to get the loads from the diaphragm to the top chord and then from the bottom chord to the top plate (or wherever it goes from there). Also, the trusses do not, in general, transfer loads to the shear walls; they transfer the loads to the bottom chord and from there they may be transferred to the upper top plate, another truss, a strap at the corner, or many other types of mechanisms. The shear walls are usually at least one other link down the load path, sometimes many more than one.

ASD vs. Strength Loads for Trusses

Truss designers are typically going to assume ASD loads. It is not recommended that strength-level forces are given to the truss designers.

Ridge Vents

With current energy standards, ridge vents are becoming the new norm and are almost always used.

At ridge vents, the forces on diaphragms that transfer loads to the eaves are usually small, but if there are interior shear walls (like in this design example) with blocking panels between the trusses up to the roof, these forces can become much higher.

The truss metal connector plates are not designed for loads in this direction. Only limited testing on this condition has been done, and the capacity of the plates in this direction is generally large enough to carry the forces that result in the low range existing at the roof level. If the peak is not near the location of zero diaphragm shear, it is prudent to bump up the truss peak metal connector plate size.

Overturning of Drag Truss

The roof trusses that transfer lateral loads have overturning forces at their ends. These overturning forces are the only resultant vertical forces imposed on the structure. The lateral forces are transferred to the shear wall(s) by tension drag ties and/or framing clips. Where the shear wall is at the end of the truss, the tension and compression forces are additive to the overturning forces in the shear wall. Where the shear wall is in the interior part of the truss and does not extend to the end of the truss, there are no vertical effects on the shear wall.

This design example is only the simplest of cases. Most actual design conditions are more complex. When the condition of a bearing wall and/or shear wall is below the truss, the truss design software used when idealized as an infinitely rigid continuous support can yield bogus results. Quite often these results are deeply hidden in the computer-generated output and require close scrutiny. Many times the computer model needs to be manipulated to remove the erroneous uplift numbers the computer model yields because of the infinitely rigid continuous support model.

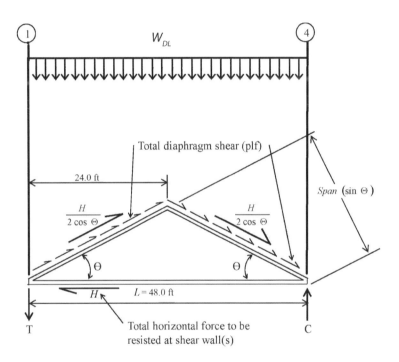

Figure 1-9. Overturning at shear-transfer (drag) truss

Notes for Figure 1-9:

T = uplift in lb

Slope = 3, 4, 5, 6, etc., in increments of 12 (e.g., for a 6:12 roof slope, slope = 6)

Spacing of roof trusses is 2.0 ft on center

Dead load on roof truss (includes both top chord and bottom chord loading):

W_{DL} = 20.0 psf × 2.0 ft = 40.0 plf

Slope of truss = 6

Span of truss = L = 48.0 ft

Determine uplift force T at line 1 due to seismic overturning forces on roof shear-transfer (drag) truss (see Figure 1-9).

$$\Sigma M_4 = 0$$

$$\frac{H\,L\sin\Theta}{2\cos\Theta} - \frac{W_{DL}(L)^2}{2} - T \times L = 0$$

$$T = C = \frac{\dfrac{H\,L\sin\Theta}{2\cos\Theta} - \dfrac{W_{DL}(L)^2}{2}}{L}$$

For gable-type trusses:

$$T = \frac{H(slope)}{24} - \frac{W_{DL} \times L}{2}$$

$$C = \frac{H(slope)}{24} - \frac{W_{DL} \times L}{2}$$

For single-slope-type trusses:

$$T = \frac{H(slope)}{24} - \frac{W_{DL} \times L}{2}$$

$$C = \frac{H(slope)}{24} - \frac{W_{DL} \times L}{2}$$

From Table 1-13, the total horizontal (strength) shear force for the wall at line C is:

$$H = 12,548 \text{ lb}$$

Determine strength level of vertical forces.

For tension force:

$$T = \frac{H(slope)}{24} - \frac{W_{DL} \times L}{2} = \frac{12,548 \times 6}{24} - \frac{27.8 \times 48.0}{2} = 3137 - 667 = 2470 \text{ lb}$$

where

$$(0.9 - 0.2S_{DS})D + \rho Q_E \qquad\qquad \text{ASCE 7 §2.3.6, Eq 7}$$
$$H = \rho Q_E = 12,548 \text{ lb} \qquad\qquad \text{Eq 12.4-3}$$
$$W_{DL} = (0.9 - 0.2S_{DS})W_{DL}$$
$$W_{DL} = 0.9 - (0.2 \times 1.026)W_{DL} = 0.69W_{DL}$$
$$W_{DL} = 0.69 \times 40.0 \text{ plf} = 27.8 \text{ plf}$$
$$L = 48.0 \text{ ft}$$

For compression force:

$$C = \frac{H(slope)}{24} + \frac{W_{DL} \times L}{2} = \frac{12{,}548 \times 6}{24} + \frac{56.0 \times 48.0}{2} = 3137 + 1344 = 4481 \text{ lb}$$

where

$(1.2 + 0.2S_{DS})D + \rho Q_E$	ASCE 7 §2.3.6, Eq 6
$H = \rho Q_E = 12{,}548 \text{ lb}$	Eq 12.4-3
$W_{DL} = (1.2 + 0.2S_{DS})W_{DL}$	
$W_{DL} = (1.2 + 0.2 \times 1.026)W_{DL} = 1.4W_{DL}$	
$W_{DL} = 1.4 \times 40.0 \text{ plf} = 56.0 \text{ plf}$	
$L = 48.0 \text{ ft}$	

Determine ASD level of vertical forces.

For tension force:

$$T = \frac{H(slope)}{24} - \frac{W_{DL} \times L}{2} = \frac{8784 \times 6}{24} - \frac{18.4 \times 48.0}{2} = 2196 - 442 = 1754 \text{ lb}$$

where

$(0.6 + 0.14S_{DS})D + 0.7\rho Q_E$	ASCE 7 §2.4.5, Eq 10
$H = 0.7\rho Q_E = 0.7 \times 12{,}548 = 8784 \text{ lb}$	Eq 12.4-3
$W_{DL} = (0.6 + 0.14S_{DS})W_{DL}$	
$W_{DL} = 0.6 - (0.14 \times 1.026)W_{DL} = 0.46W_{DL}$	
$W_{DL} = 0.46 \times 40.0 \text{ plf} = 18.4 \text{ plf}$	
$L = 48.0 \text{ ft}$	

For compression force:

$$T = \frac{H(slope)}{24} + \frac{W_{DL} \times L}{2} = \frac{8784 \times 6}{24} + \frac{44.0 \times 48.0}{2} = 2196 + 1056 = 3252 \text{ lb}$$

where

$(1.0 + 0.14S_{DS})D + 0.7\rho Q_E$	ASCE 7 §2.4.5, Eq 8
$H = 0.7\rho Q_E = 0.7 \times 12{,}548 = 8784 \text{ lb}$	Eq 12.4-3
$W_{DL} = (1.0 + 0.14S_{DS})W_{DL}$	
$W_{DL} = 1.0 + (0.14 \times 1.026)W_{DL} = 1.1W_{DL}$	
$W_{DL} = 1.1 \times 40.0 \text{ plf} = 44.0 \text{ plf}$	
$L = 48.0 \text{ ft}$	

4.2 SHEAR WALL CUMULATIVE OVERTURNING FORCES AND WALL STABILITY

Shear Wall Cumulative Overturning Forces

When designing overturning forces in multilevel structures, shear and the respective overturning forces due to seismic (or wind) must be carried down to the foundation (or base where a podium slab exists). While shear is resisted by the sheathing, overturning compression and tension forces are typically designed to be resisted by the boundary studs and continuous tie-down system, respectively. These forces are not only cumulative over the height of the building, but are also dependent on the height of the load application; shear forces applied at the upper levels will generate much larger base overturning moments than if the same shear forces were applied at the lower story.

The overturning forces (M_{OT}) for the horizontal loads on the shear wall (Figure 1-14) can be obtained by summing forces about the base of the wall for the level being designed.

The height at which the load is applied to the wall for determining overturning forces depends on the type of construction and the method used to apply the load to the shear wall.

For a sheathed wall that does not have a ribbon board at the floor line but has top plate(s) below the floor sheathing (modified platform framed, see Figures 1-10 and 1-11), the height of the wall is the distance between the bottom of the sill plate and the top of the top plate(s) (same as story height).

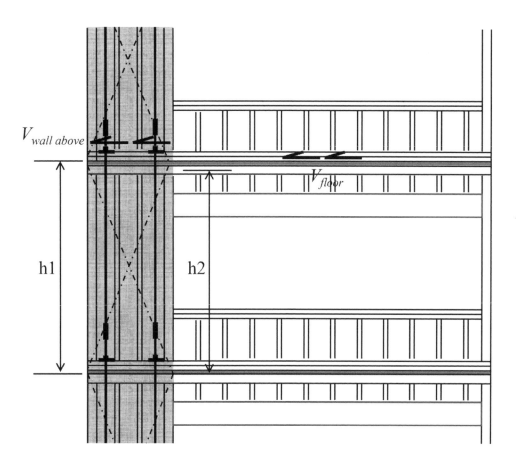

Figure 1-10. Overturning forces at floor level

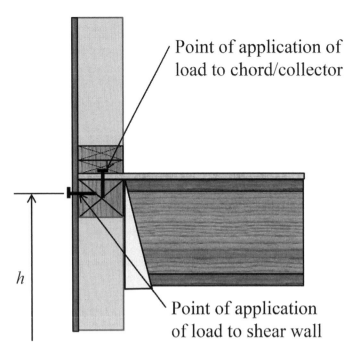

Figure 1-11. Framing section at floor

Notes on Figures 1-11 and 1-12:

1. Figure 1-11 is a wall elevation with a modified balloon framing system.

2. Figure 1-12 is a section cut in Figure 1-11 taken at the shear wall showing the 4×4 top plate (see also Figure 1-7 for additional notes).

Where a sheathed wall has a ribbon board at the floor line (see Figures 1-12 and 1-13) with the top plate(s) below the ribbon board (platform framed), and where the sheathing is not placed at the ribbon board, the height of the wall is not the same as the story height but rather is the distance between the bottom of the sill plate and top of the top plate(s) below the ribbon board (wall height). In this case, the point of application of the horizontal load to the shear wall is often considered to be below the floor level and thereby sometimes considered to reduce overturning moment as opposed to considering that the loads are applied at the floor line. As this percentage of force varies from shear wall to shear wall within the building, the potential reduction of the overturning forces may be a small percentage. This method of overturning reduction is not recommended as it can be time-consuming to account for all the overturning forces and may be inaccurate, depending on the actual bending stiffness and detailing of the ribbon board/floor framing and the location of the wall (at the end of building, adjacent to a window or large opening, and so on). Principles of statics also appear to be at odds with reducing the overturning height to that below the ribbon board (wall height) as opposed to floor height (story height).

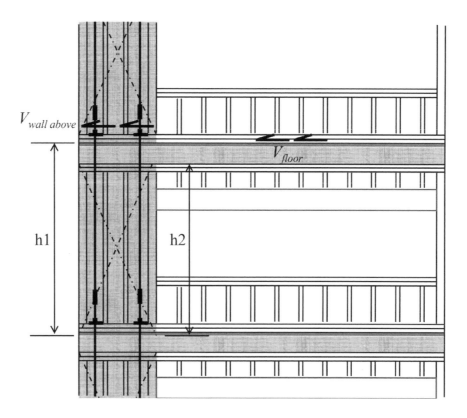

Figure 1-12. Overturning forces at floor level

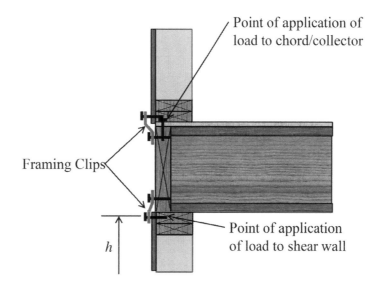

Figure 1-13. Framing section at floor

This design example will apply the lateral loads at the roof and floor levels (see Figure 1-14):

Cumulative overturning force for the roof level:

$$M_{OT} = F_4(H_4)$$

Cumulative overturning force for the fourth-floor level:

$$M_{OT} = F_4(H_4 + H_3) + F_3(H_3)$$

Cumulative overturning force for the third-floor level:

$$M_{OT} = F_4(H_4 + H_3 + H_2) + F_3(H_3 + H_2) + F_2(H_2)$$

Cumulative overturning force for the second-floor level:

$$M_{OT} = F_4(H_4 + H_3 + H_2 + H_1) + F_3(H_3 + H_2 + H_1) + F_2(H_2 + H_1) + F_1(H_1)$$

For overturning forces for the overturning effects of the shear-transfer (drag) trusses, see Section 4.1.

In shear walls with continuous tie-down systems, the overturning resistance in the shear wall is resisted by the posts and/or end studs resisting the compression forces and the tension rods resisting the tension forces.

In shear walls with conventional hold-down systems, the overturning resistance in the shear wall is resisted by the posts and/or end studs resisting the compression forces and the tension rods resisting the tension forces.

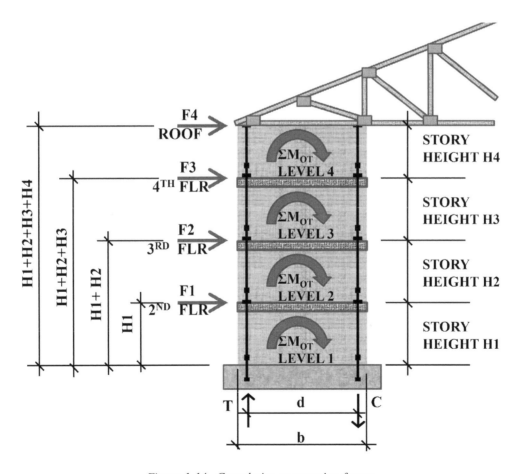

Figure 1-14. Cumulative overturning forces

Commentary on Tension and Compression Forces in Shear Walls

If a shear wall were an infinitely rigid body, all of the loads acting on the wall (dead loads including self-weight and live loads, based on load combinations, in addition to the overturning forces) would contribute to the compression force at the shear wall boundary. Recognizing that shear walls constructed out of wood structural panels are not infinitely rigid bodies, as soon as deformations occur, the loads to the compression posts change to the tributary loads on the compression members. Certainly a very tall aspect ratio shear wall can act as a rigid body and can have all the loads acting on the wall contributing to the compression force at the wall boundary. Likewise, very long walls do not act as a rigid body and will only see tributary loads to the wall boundary posts. It can be argued that if only tributary loads are used on the compression posts, then only tributary loads should be used at the opposite end for determining the tension force in the tie-down rods.

For determing the tension force in the tie-down rod, current industry practice is to use the net overturning moment divided by the resisting arm, where the net overturning force is gross overturning moment minus the resisting moment. The resisting moment is the sum of any dead load supported by the wall, including self-weight times the distance from the wall end to the center of gravity of the dead loads. For a uniformly distributed dead load, the lever arm is simply one-half the shear wall length

$$M_R = W_{DL}\left(\frac{b}{2}\right)$$

where W_{DL} or M_R have the appropriate load combinations of ASCE 7, and b is the overall length of the shear wall (see Figure 1-14).

The uplift force T is determined by

$$T = \frac{M_{OT} - M_R}{d}$$

where d is the distance between the tie-down rod and the center of mass of the boundary members (see Figures 1-15 and 1-16).

4.3 LOAD COMBINATIONS

Load Combinations Using the 2018 IBC

IBC Section 1605.3.2 has alternative basic load combinations to ASCE 7. For allowable stress design, the earthquake load combinations are

$$D + L + S + \frac{E}{1.4} \qquad \text{IBC Eq 16-21}$$

Since S is not present, the simplified load combination is

$$D + L + \frac{E}{1.4}$$

where E = the horizontal seismic force (F)

$$0.9D + \frac{E}{1.4} \qquad \text{IBC Eq 16-22}$$

Load Combinations Using ASCE 7 §2.4.5

Per Section 2.4.5, the following load combinations shall be used for basic combinations for allowable stress design:

$$(1.0 + 0.14S_{DS})D + H + F + 0.7\rho Q_E \qquad \text{ASCE 7 Eq 8}$$

$$(1.0 + 0.105S_{DS})D + H + F + 0.525\rho Q_E + 0.75L + 0.75(L_r \quad \text{or} \quad S \quad \text{or} \quad R) \qquad \text{ASCE 7 Eq 9}$$

$$(0.6 - 0.14S_{DS})D + 0.7\rho Q_E + H \qquad \text{ASCE 7 Eq 10}$$

where the dead load D is increased (or decreased) for vertical accelerations by the S_{DS} coefficient.

Since H, F, S, and R are not present, the simplified load combinations are

$$(1.0 + 0.14S_{DS})D + 0.7\rho Q_E \qquad \text{ASCE 7 Eq 8}$$

$$(1.0 + 0.105S_{DS})D + 0.525\rho Q_E + 0.75L + 0.75L_r \qquad \text{ASCE 7 Eq 9}$$

$$(0.6 - 0.14S_{DS})D + 0.7\rho Q_E \qquad \text{ASCE 7 Eq 10}$$

where Q_E = the horizontal seismic force F §12.4.2.1

$$0.105S_{DS} = 0.105(1.026) = 0.11$$

$$0.14S_{DS} = 0.14(1.026) = 0.14$$

4.4 DETERMINE MECHANICS OF SEGMENTED SHEAR WALL C

To help in the illustration of a design example, the shear wall located at grid line C will be used. Refer to other sections in this design example for the derivation of the forces to this wall.

4.4A SHEAR WALL CHORD (BOUNDARY) MEMBERS

The vertical members at the end of the shear walls are the walls' chords (boundary members). As in a diaphragm, the chords resist flexure, and the sheathing (web) resists the shear. The overturning moment is resolved into a T-C couple, creating axial tension and compression forces. When only the horizontal component of the seismic forces are considered, the tension and compression forces are equal and opposite for each load case. The overturning compressive force is determined by dividing the overturning moment by the distance b_{eff} between the center of the tension rod and the center work point of the compression posts (Figure 1-15). However, in most designs, the size and number of chords (boundary members) change from story to story, as shown in Figure 1-15, which can necessitate iterations to derive the actual distance b_{eff}. Many engineers will appropriately take a conservative average distance b_{eff} and use the same value for all cases to minimize iterations. The distance b_{eff} sometimes can be justified as being closer to the wall end where stresses are low in the boundary members.

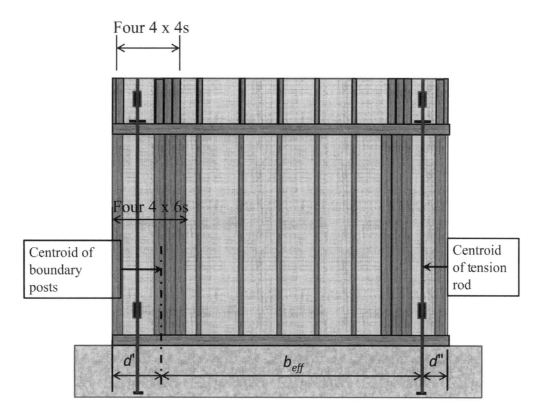

Figure 1-15. Tension and compression forces

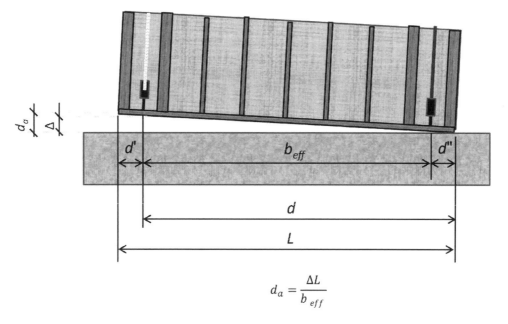

$$d_a = \frac{\Delta L}{b_{eff}}$$

Figure 1-15A. Rotation at wall base

Figure 1-16 illustrates multiple boundary members that are common to multilevel wood-frame shear walls.

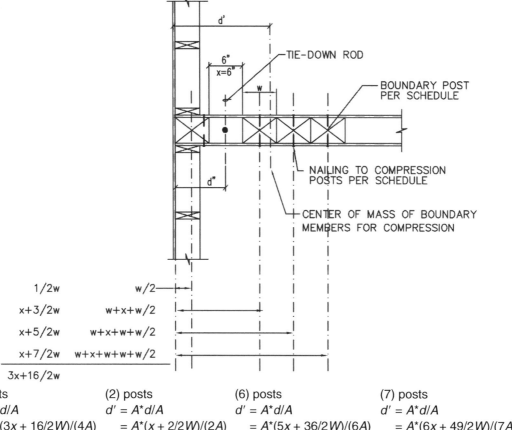

d′ = distance from edge of wall to center of compression post

(4) posts
$d' = A^*d/A$
$= A^*(3x + 16/2W)/(4A)$
$= 3/4x + 2W$

(2) posts
$d' = A^*d/A$
$= A^*(x + 2/2W)/(2A)$
$= 1/2x + W$

(6) posts
$d' = A^*d/A$
$= A^*(5x + 36/2W)/(6A)$
$= 5/6x + 3W$

(7) posts
$d' = A^*d/A$
$= A^*(6x + 49/2W)/(7A)$
$= 6/7x + 7/2W$

Figure 1-16. Example plan section at boundary members

Notes for Figure 1-16:

1. $d' = [(n - 1)^*x + n^2{}^*w/2]/n$

    n is the number of posts

    x is the gap distance for the threaded rod (in)

    w is the width of the posts (in)

    $d'_{Roof} = [(4 - 1)^*6 + 4^2{}^*2.5/2]/4 = 9.5$ in

    $n = 4$, $x = 6$ in, $w = 2.5$ in

    $d'_{Roof\,i} = 9.5$ in $+ 5.5$ in $= 15$ in $= 1.25$ ft

2. Edge nailing to boundary member posts is determined by dividing the differential load per floor (see Table 1-6) by the story height divided by the number of boundary members. For the second-floor level (differential load):

    Vertical shear force:

    $$\frac{6373 \text{ lb}}{9.44 \text{ ft}} = 675 \text{ plf}$$

The number of boundary posts is four (see Table 1-5); the vertical shear force per boundary post is:

$$\frac{675 \text{ plf}}{4 \text{ posts}} = 169 \text{ plf}$$

An edge nailing of 6 inches on center will be adequate for the four boundary posts. Having edge nailing equal to the nailing at the panel edges can be done, but the overnailing of the wall at the jambs can produce undesirable failure modes due to the concentration of strength at the jamb. It is common to have a boundary post nailing schedule that is placed on the drawings that specifies this special nailing pattern.

3. A gap of 6 inches is used at the tie-down rod. This dimension should be at least as wide as the bearing plate. For this design example, the widest bearing plate is 5.5 inches (see Table 1-8). Where the gap is narrower than the bearing plate width, it will force the "dapping" of the boundary posts for the bearing plates; in addition to the increased labor, it also produces reduced bearing areas for the boundary members.

4. The distance d'' remains a contant distance from the wall end. For the shear wall at line C in this design example, the distance d'' is determined at the second-floor level where there are four 4×6 boundary posts (see Table 1-5).

For this shear wall, the distance d'':

$$d'' = 5.5 + \frac{6.0}{2} = 8.5 \text{ in} = 0.71 \text{ ft}$$

Determine chord members for the shear wall at line C.

The axial loads to the bearing wall and boundary members are determined from the following loads:

Dead loads:

$$w_{Roof} = (20.0 \text{ psf})(2.0 \text{ ft}) = 40.0 \text{ plf}$$
$$w_{Floor} = (30.0 \text{ psf})(2.0 \text{ ft}) = 60.0 \text{ plf}$$

For the roof level:

$$w_{Wall} = 10.0 \text{ psf}(8.21 \text{ ft}) = 82.1 \text{ ft}$$

For the 2nd- through 4th-floor levels:

$$w_{Wall} = 10.0 \text{ psf}(9.44 \text{ ft}) = 94.4 \text{ plf}$$

The wall weight of 10 psf is different than the 15 psf used in determining the building weight based on plan dimensions (see Section 1.3).

Live loads:

$$w_{Roof} = (20.0 \text{ psf})(2.0 \text{ ft}) = 40.0 \text{ plf}$$
$$w_{Floor} = (40.0 \text{ psf})(2.0 \text{ ft}) = 80.0 \text{ plf}$$

Dead + live loads:

$$w_{Roof} = (20.0 \text{ psf} + 20.0 \text{ psf})(2.0 \text{ ft}) = 80.0 \text{ plf}$$
$$w_{Floor} = (30.0 \text{ psf} + 40.0 \text{ psf})(2.0 \text{ ft}) = 140.0 \text{ ft}$$

For the roof level:

$$w_{Wall} = 10.0 \text{ psf}(8.21 \text{ ft}) = 82.1 \text{ plf}$$

For the 2nd- through 4th-floor levels:

$$w_{Wall} = 10.0 \text{ psf}(9.44 \text{ ft}) = 94.4 \text{ plf}$$

For ASD compression on the chord members, the alternate basic load combination will be used:

$$D + L + \frac{E}{1.4} \qquad\qquad \text{IBC Eq 16-21}$$

For strength-level compression on the chord members, the ASCE 7 seismic load combination will be used. The strength-level compression loads are used later in this example to determine the shear wall deflection at strength loads (sill plate crushing). Per ASCE 7 Sections 12.8.6 and 12.12.1, strength-level forces are required for the determination of shear wall deflections:

$$(1.2 + 0.2S_{DS})D + \rho Q_E + L + 0.2S \qquad\qquad \text{ASCE 7 §2.3.6}$$

where

$$\rho Q_E = E$$

Since S is not present, the simplified load combination is

$$(1.2 + 0.2S_{DS})D + L + E \qquad\qquad \text{ASCE 7 §2.3.6}$$

where

$$(1.2 + 0.2S_{DS}) = (1.2 + 0.2 \times 1.026) = 1.4$$

Per ASCE 7 Section 2.3.6, the load factor on L is permitted to be 0.5 since the live load is equal to or less than 100 psf and not of public assembly. The 0.5 factor is used in the following live load determinations:

$$w_{Roof} = \left[(1.4 \times 20.0 \text{ psf}) + (0.5 \times 20.0) \right](2.0 \text{ ft}) = 76.0 \text{ plf}$$
$$w_{Floor} = \left[(1.4 \times 30.0 \text{ psf}) + (0.5 \times 40.0) \right](2.0 \text{ ft}) = 124.0 \text{ plf}$$

For the roof level:

$$w_{Wall} = 1.4 \times 10.0 \text{ psf}(8.21 \text{ ft}) = 115 \text{ plf}$$

For the 2nd- through 4th-floor levels:

$$w_{Wall} = 1.4 \times 10.0 \text{ psf}(9.44 \text{ ft}) = 132 \text{ plf}$$

For shear wall chord member force:

$$E = \frac{M_{OT}}{d}$$

Table 1-4. Determination of shear wall chord member forces at line C

Level	$M_{OT}^{(2)}$ (kip-ft)	ASD $P_{D}+_L$ (kips)	$d_i'^{(4,5)}$ (ft)	$b_{eff}^{(6)}$ (ft)	ASD Demand Compression $C = \dfrac{M_{OT}}{1.4d} + P_{D+L}$ (kips)	Strength Demand Compression $C = \dfrac{M_{OT}}{d} + (1.2 + 0.2S_{DS})P_{D+L}$ (kips)
Drag Truss	—	—	—	—	3.29	4.49
Roof	51.5	0.365	1.25	19.54	5.58	7.60
4th Floor	177.6	0.892	1.25	19.54	10.78	14.69
3rd Floor	348.3	1.630	1.42	19.38	17.92	24.81
2nd Floor	541.2	2.812	1.75	19.04	26.63	37.57

Notes for Table 1-4:

1. Drag truss compression force is determined in Section 4.1 and is applied at the one end of the shear wall. For simplicity in design and detailing, the force will be applied to both ends of the shear wall.

2. Moment overturning forces (M_{OT}) are based on horizontal forces from Table 1-13 for shear wall at line C. Since there are two shear walls at line C, the horizontal force from Table 1-13 is divided by 2.

3. Compression forces for ASD demand and strength demand are determined from load combinations listed plus the compression force from the drag truss.

4. The overall out-to-out wall length is 21.5 feet (see Table 1-13). The d' dimension is the distance from the approximate center of mass of the multiple boundary posts to the continuous tie-down rod (see Figure 1-12).

5. The distance d_i', shown in Table 1-4, uses a (conservatively) larger distance of 5.5 inches more than the actual distance. Unless the engineer manually computes this distance or uses a computer program that automatically computes this distance, the design process would involve recalculating the distance d' and then redetermining/checking the boundary post, bearing plates, tension rods, elongations, and crushing effects for minute adjustments in post sizes, which can be an iterative process to say the least. Also, see Footnote 4 for Table 1-36 about possible additional iteration of shear wall loads due to the rigid/flexible ratio being greater than 100 percent. The initial estimate of d' using an additional 5.5 inches is only used for determining the force in this example. Once the posts have been chosen, the actual d' is used.

6. The distance b_{eff} (distance from the center of mass of the boundary posts to the tension rod, see Figure 1-15) is determined by

$$b_{eff} = b - d' - d''$$

where

b is the length of the shear wall

d' is the distance from the wall end to the center of compression posts

d'' is the distance from the wall end to the tension rod (see Figure 1-16)

7. Determine ASD compression load.

$$P_{D+L} = w(d')2$$

For ASD demand:

$$P_{D+L\ Roof} = (80\ plf + 82.1\ plf)(1.13 \times 2) = 0.365\ kips$$

$$P_{D+L\ 4th\ Floor} = (140\ plf + 94.4\ plf + 80 + 82.1)(1.13 \times 2) = 0.892\ kips$$

$$P_{D+L\ 3rd\ Floor} = \left[((140\ plf + 94.4\ plf) \times 2) + (80 + 82.1)\right](1.29 \times 2) = 1.630\ kips$$

$$P_{D+L\ 2nd\ Floor} = \left[((140\ plf + 94.4\ plf) \times 3) + (80 + 82.1)\right](1.63 \times 2) = 2.812\ kips$$

For strength demand:

$$(1.2 + 0.02S_{DS})D + L = 1.4D + L$$

$$P_{D+L\ Roof} = (76\ plf + 124\ plf)(1.13 \times 2) = 0.452\ kips$$

$$P_{D+L\ 4th\ Floor} = (124\ plf + 132\ plf + 76 + 124)(1.13 \times 2) = 1.030\ kips$$

$$P_{D+L\ 3rd\ Floor} = \left[((124\ plf + 132\ plf) \times 2) + (76 + 124)\right](1.29 \times 2) = 1.837\ kips$$

$$P_{D+L\ 2nd\ Floor} = \left[((124\ plf + 132\ plf) \times 3) + (76 + 124)\right](1.63 \times 2) = 3.155\ kips$$

Table 1-5. Determination of shear wall chord members at line C

Level	Chord Posts	Total Area	l_e (ft)	C_F	C_P	Bearing Capacity (kips)	ASD Demand (kips)	Stability Capacity (kips)	D/C Ratio
Roof	Four 3 × 4s	35.0	7.82	1.15	0.258	21.88	5.58	24.93	0.26
4th Floor	Four 3 × 4s	35.0	8.84	1.15	0.192	21.88	10.78	18.54	0.58
3rd Floor	Four 4 × 4s	49.0	8.84	1.15	0.192	30.63	17.92	25.96	0.69
2nd Floor	Four 4 × 6s	77.0	8.84	1.1	0.200	48.13	26.63	40.70	0.65

Notes for Table 1-5:

1. See the following example for determination of compression member capacity.

2. The typical interior stud wall is framed with 4-inch nominal framing studs.

3. Interior bearing walls for this design example are nonrated (fire) and, as such, would not require the reduction in allowable stresses required for FRTW.

4. The shear wall has sheathing on one side of the studs (not both sides); some engineers consider the overturning compression force with sheathing on one side as eccentrically loading the posts. Some engineers will combine the compressive force with the 5 psf lateral loading (IBC Section 1607.15), but this load combined with seismic forces does not appear to be the intent of the code. It is recognized that combining in-plane compression loads with out-of-plane lateral loads or eccentric loads (NDS Sections 3.9.2 and 3.9.3) would reduce the vertical capacity of the boundary posts. The possible eccentric loading from the sheathing on one side or out-of-plane loading on the compression posts has not been considered in this design example.

5. The bearing capacity for the 3 × 4 posts at the roof level controls over the stability capacity.

Example Compression Member Capacity Determination

4 × 4 post – Douglas Fir-Larch No. 1:

where

$$A = 12.25 \text{ in}^2$$
$$C_D = 1.6$$
$$E_{min} = 620{,}000 \text{ psi}$$
$$d_1 = 3.5 \text{ in}$$

The following coefficients for C_M and C_t are not referenced in the NDS formulas (for simplicity).

$$C_M = 1.0$$
$$C_t = 1.0$$
$$K_{e1} = 1.0$$

The members' span between the top of the two 2 × 4 sill plates and the underside of the 4 × 4 top plate (see Figure 1-7) is

$$\frac{(1.5 \times 2) + (23/32) + 3.5}{12} = 0.60 \text{ ft}$$
$$l = 9.44 - 0.60 = 8.84 \text{ ft}$$
$$l_{e1} = 8.84 \times 12 = 106 \text{ in}$$

Assuming WSP sheathing is nailed to all posts to prevent lateral buckling of the posts parallel to the shear wall, the post dimension perpendicular to the shear wall will be used for buckling calculations (see NDS A.11.3). In all cases, this is the 3.5-inch dimension.

$$\frac{l_{e1}}{d_1} = \frac{106}{3.5} = 30.3$$

Compression parallel to grain (only applicable adjustment factors shown):

$$F_c' = F_c' C_F C_D C_P$$

$$F_c^* = F_c C_D C_F = 1500 \times 1.6 \times 1.15 = 2760 \text{ psi}$$

$$C_P = \frac{1 + \left(\dfrac{F_{cE}}{F_c^*}\right)}{2c} - \sqrt{\left[\frac{1 + \left(\dfrac{F_{cE}}{F_c^*}\right)}{2c}\right]^2 - \frac{\dfrac{F_{cE}}{F_c^*}}{c}} = 0.192 \qquad \text{NDS Eq 3.7-1}$$

where

$c = 0.8$

$$F_{cE} = \frac{0.822E_{min}}{\left(\dfrac{l_e}{d}\right)^2} = \frac{0.822 \times 620,000}{30.3^2} = 555 \text{ psi}$$ NDS §3.7.1.5

$$\frac{F_{cE}}{F_c^*} = \frac{555}{2760} = 0.201$$

$$F_c' = F_C C_D C_F C_P = 1500 \times 1.6 \times 1.15 \times 0.192 = 530 \text{ psi}$$

For a 4×4 post:

$$P_{allow} = A \times F_c' = 12.25 \times 530 = 6493 \text{ lb}$$

Compression perpendicular to grain:

$$F_{c\perp}' = F_{c\perp}(C_b) = 625 \text{ psi where } C_b = 1.0 \text{ due to assumed bearing length} > 6 \text{ in}$$ NDS §3.10.4

For a 4×4 post:

$$P_{allow} = A \times F_{c\perp}' = 12.25 \times 625 = 7656 \text{ lb}$$

4.4B DETERMINATION OF RESISTING MOMENTS AND UPLIFT FORCES

The resisting moment M_R is determined from the following dead loads:

$$w_{Roof} = 20.0 \text{ psf}(2.0 \text{ ft}) = 40.0 \text{ plf}$$
$$w_{Floor} = 30.0 \text{ psf}(2.0 \text{ ft}) = 60.0 \text{ plf}$$

For the roof level:

$$w_{Wall} = 10.0 \text{ psf}(8.21 \text{ ft}) = 82.1 \text{ plf}$$

For the 2nd-floor through 4th-floor levels:

$$w_{Wall} = 10.0 \text{ psf}(9.44 \text{ ft}) = 94.4 \text{ plf}$$

Table 1-6. Determine shear wall uplift forces using ASCE 7 load combinations at line C

| Level | M_R (ft-lb) | b_{eff} (ft) | Strength | | ASD Uplift | Differential Load per Floor (lb) |
			M_{OT} (ft-lb)	$M_R(0.6 - 0.14S_{DS})^{(1)}$ (ft-lb)	$\dfrac{(M_{OT} \times 0.7) - (0.6 - 0.14S_{DS})M_R}{b_{eff}}$ (lb)	
Drag Truss	—	—	—	—	1758	—
Roof	31,063	19.54	51,511	14,176	2878	0
4th Floor	66,749	19.54	177,607	30,462	6561	3684
3rd Floor	102,435	19.38	348,283	46,747	11,928	5367
2nd Floor	138,120	19.04	541,249	63,033	18,345	6416

Notes for Table 1-6:

1. Where $(0.6 - 0.14S_{DS}) = (0.6 - 0.14 \times 1.026) = 0.46$

2. Drag truss uplift (tension) force is determined in Section 4.1 and is applied at the one end of the shear wall. For simplicity in design and detailing, the force will be applied to both ends of the shear wall.

3. Overturning forces (M_{OT}) are from Table 1-4.

4.4C SHEAR WALL TIE-DOWN SYSTEM COMPONENTS

Tie-Down Rod

Tie-down rods are usually made from A36/A307 steel. This is called *standard rod strength*. Unless marked, rods should be considered standard rod strength. High-strength rods are ASTM A449 or A193-B7 and are usually marked on the end with an embossed stamp, though some rod manufacturers stamp the rod grade on the side. If the rod is stamped at the end and is cut, it needs to be re-marked. There should be a special inspection of high-strength rods to confirm the rod type since the ends of these rods may be embedded into a coupler where the marks cannot be seen after installation. High-strength rods are usually not weldable without special welding procedures. Proprietary systems have special rod colors and markings on the sides; some rods are proprietary, the manufactured components are proprietary.

Rod Elongation

The net tensile area, A_e, is used in the rod strength and elongation calculations. However, to facilitate rod strength design, AISC 360 Table J3.2 tabulates the nominal tensile strength, F_{nt}, so the designer may use the nominal bolt area, A_b. The Commentary states "$F_{nt} = 0.75F_u$" and "The factor of 0.75 included in this equation accounts for the approximate ratio of the effective tension area of the threaded portion of the bolt to the area of the shank of the bolt for common sizes." Some jurisdictions have limits on the amount of rod elongation that can occur between restraints and/or stories, and some require that the allowable stress area (A_e vs. A_g) be used in rod elongation calculations. As such, local building department requirements should always be checked. This design example uses A_e for rod elongation and A_g or A_n for rod capacity.

Many continuous rod system manufacturers try to determine the most cost-effective solution for a given tension load considering rod strength and diameter. The use of a higher-strength rod will increase the drift of the shear wall if used in place of a standard-strength rod due to increased rod elongation from the smaller rod diameters, and the modulus of elasticity of the steel, which does not change, is the same for both standard- and high-strength rods.

Tie-down rod elongation is computed between bearing plates (restraints). This design example has bearing plates located at each floor. Table 1-7 computes the rod capacities and elongations (per floor) between the bearing plates.

Table 1-7. Determine rod sizes, capacities, and elongations at line C

Level	Plate Height (ft)	ASD Tension Demand (kips)	Rod Dia. d (in)	Eff. Dia. d_e (in)	A_g (in^2)	A_e (in^2)	F_u (ksi)	F_y (ksi)	ASD Rod Capacity $\dfrac{0.75 \times F_u \times A_g}{2}$ (kips)	ASD Rod Elong. (in)
Roof	8.21	2.88	0.625	0.527	0.307	0.226	58	36	6.68	0.043
4th Floor	9.44	6.56	0.625	0.527	0.307	0.226	58	36	6.68	0.113
3rd Floor	9.44	11.93	0.875	0.755	0.601	0.462	58	36	13.07	0.101
2nd Floor	9.44	18.34	1.00	0.865	0.785	0.606	120	105	35.33	0.118

Notes for Table 1-7:

1. Tension demand (ASD uplift) values are computed in Table 1-6.

2. Rod area: $A_g = \dfrac{3.14d^2}{4}$

3. Net tensile area:

$$A_e = 0.7854 \times \left(d_b - \frac{0.9743}{n} \right)^2$$

where n = the number of threads per inch per AISC Table 7-17

4. For ASD design, the allowable rod capacity for the AISC 360-10 Section J3.6 is

$$\frac{F_u \times A_b}{\Omega}$$

and $A_e = 0.75A_b$

$\Omega = 2.0$ for ASD

Therefore,

$$\frac{0.75 \times F_u \times A_b}{2}$$

5. Standard rod is ASTM A36 rod with minimum $F_u = 58$ ksi, $F_y = 36$ ksi. High-strength rod is ASTM A193-B7 rod with minimum $F_u = 125$ ksi; $F_y = 105$ ksi for rods up to 2½ inches in diameter and A449 rod with minimum $F_u = 120$ ksi; $F_y = 92$ ksi for rods up to 1 inch in diameter then drops to $F_u = 105$ ksi, $F_y = 81$ ksi (per ASTM A449) for rods from 1 to 1½ inches in diameter and drops to $F_u = 90$ ksi, $F_y = 58$ ksi (per ASTM A449) for rods from 1¾ to 3 inches in diameter.

6. Rod elongation: $\Delta = \dfrac{PL}{A_e E}$

    where

    Δ = the elongation of the rod in inches

    P = the accumulated uplift tension force on the rod in kips (tension demand)

    L = the length of the rod in inches from bearing restraint to bearing restraint, with the bearing restraint being where the load is transferred to the rod

    E = 29,000 ksi

    A_e = the effective area of the rod in square inches. Where smooth rods are used, the area is equal to the gross area (A_g). Where threaded (all-thread) rods are used, the area is equal to the tension area (A_e) of the threaded rod. Since many of the proprietary systems that have smooth rods have long portions threaded at the ends, it is recommended that A_e be used when calculating rod elongation.

7. Rod elongation from allowable stress design forces is based on using the effective area (A_e) and the following lengths:

    a. For the first level, the anchor bolt is projecting 4 inches above the foundation (the height of the coupler nut to the anchor bolt at the floor slab). The small amount of elongation of the rod anchored in the concrete foundation and projecting 4 inches above is neglected in the computation.

    b. For the framed floors, the rod from below is projecting 6 inches above the sole plate.

8. Rod elongations for determination of shear wall drifts will be factored up by 1.4 (see Table 1-12).

Rod Couplers

Couplers are used to connect the rods. Couplers can either be straight or reducing and can be supplied in different strengths or grades. Couplers for high-strength rods need to be of high-strength steel and are marked with notches or marks on the coupler. Also, high-strength nuts or couplers are not weldable. For a rod to develop its full strength, the rod must be embedded a set amount into the coupler (usually the depth of a standard nut). It is recommended that where couplers are used, they have pilot or witness holes in the side so the inspector can witness the threads of the rods in the holes to ensure proper embedment.

Reducing couplers are used where the rod size is changed. In reducing couplers, the size of the threading changes at the middle of the coupler device. It is intended that the rods be embedded until they bottom out at the center of the coupler. If the rods are installed in this fashion, witness holes will not be necessary; however, it is recommended that couplers with witness holes be used so that proper installation can be confirmed by an inspector. Some couplers have rod stops in them to ensure the proper length of bolt is in the coupler. Reducing couplers should have the same notches and identifying marks as straight couplers when used with high-strength rods.

Bearing Plates

Bearing plates transfer the differential overturning forces into the continuous tie-down system through bearing and compression in the floor framing through the sill plate(s) or the top plates and ribbon board (when used) into the rod (see Figure 1-17). Premanufactured bearing plates are usually identified by paint color or by a number marked on the plate. However, paint colors or unpainted plates vary among different rod system manufacturers.

Table 1-8. Determine bearing-plate sizes and capacities at line C

| Level | Bearing Plate | | | | | Bearing Factor C_b | Bearing Load (kips) | Allowable Capacity (kips) |
	Width (in)	Length (in)	Thickness (in)	Hole dia. (in)	A_{Brg} (in^2)			
Roof	3.0	5.5	0.6	0.8125	15.98	1.07	2.878	10.69
4th Floor	3.0	3.5	0.4	0.8125	9.98	1.11	3.684	6.92
3rd Floor	3.0	5.5	0.6	1.0625	15.61	1.07	5.367	10.44
2nd Floor	3.0	5.5	0.6	1.1875	15.39	1.07	6.416	10.29

Notes for Table 1-8:

1. Bearing plate is based on ASTM A36 steel with $F_y = 36$ ksi.

2. Bearing area factor for $l_b < 6$ inches $C_b = \dfrac{(l_b + 0.375)}{l_b}$ NDS §3.10.4

3. Bearing area factor for $l_b \geq 6$ inches: $C_b = 1.0$

4. Bearing plate thicknesses shall be checked for bending using lengths governed by the area satisfaction check and the associated hole in the plate (see Figure 1-17).

Example Bending Check of Bearing Plate at Second Floor

Bearing plate size = 3.0 in × 5.5 in × 0.6 in thick

Bearing load = 6373 lb (Table 1-6)

Bearing area for wood: subtracting for $^3/_{16}$-inch oversized hole in wood plates

$(16.5 - 0.887) = 15.6$ in^2

$f_{c\perp} = \dfrac{6.416}{15.6} = 411\,\text{psi}$

$F'_{c\perp} = F_{c\perp}C_b = 625 \times 1.07 = 669\,\text{psi} > 411\,\text{psi} \ \ldots\ \text{OK}$

Steel plate bending check:

$(411 \times 3.0) \times \dfrac{\left(\dfrac{5.5}{2}\right)^2}{2} = 4662$ in-lb

$Z_{plate} = \dfrac{bd^2}{4} = \dfrac{(3.0 - 1.0625) \times 0.6^2}{4} = 0.174$ in^3

$\dfrac{M}{Z} = \dfrac{4662}{0.174} = 26.8$ ksi $\ \ldots\ $ OK

5. Bearing load = differential load from Table 1-6.

Bolted Tie-Down Device Elements

Another type of tie-down device utilizes bolts instead of bearing plates to transfer the overturning forces to the continuous rods. In this system, posts need to transfer tension forces. Although this type of system is still available, most framing contractors prefer the bearing-plate devices due to quicker and easier installation in the field.

Shrinkage Compensating or Take-Up Devices

Most continuous rod systems have methods of compensating for shrinkage with proprietary expanding or contracting devices.

The purpose of these devices is to minimize the clearance created between the hold-down, tension tie connector, or plate washer and the anchor bolt/nut due to building settlement or wood shrinkage (resulting from a reduction in moisture content). The nut is rotated down (or compression spring is used) on the rod so the hold-down, tension tie, or bearing plate remains tight to the wood surface.

There are several different types of devices available, as defined in Acceptance Criteria (AC) 316:

Compression-Controlled Shrinkage Compensating Device (CCSCD): A device controlled by compression loading where the rod passes uninterrupted through the device, and that is used to compensate for localized wood shrinkage.

Tension-Controlled Shrinkage Compensating Coupling Device (TCSCCD): A device controlled by tension loading that connects rods or anchors together, and that is used to compensate for localized wood shrinking. This product is a continuously varying travel device.

Tension-Controlled Shrinkage Compensating Device (TCSCD): A device controlled by tension loading where the rod is attached to or engaged by the device, and that is used to compensate for localized wood shrinkage. The product may be an incremental or ratcheting travel device or a continuously varying travel device.

Other definitions defined by AC316:

Device Average Travel and Seating Increment (Δ_R) is the average of the movement required to cause incremental motion from a seated position and the opposite movement required to reseat the device after the actuation (or ratcheting).

Allowable Deflection Limit (Δ_A) of Device Loaded at Allowable Deflection Limit is the maximum allowable deflection limit of a shrinkage device.

ICC-Evaluation Service (ICC-ES) has acceptance criteria (AC316) for shrinkage compensating (take-up) devices. The design engineer should check to see that the proprietary devices conform to these criteria.

The use of take-up devices is highly desirable in multilevel wood-frame construction. Since the total shrinkage of the building has to be accounted for in the tie-down displacement (d_a), it is very difficult to meet the code drift requirements for most shear walls without take-up devices, especially for short-length shear walls.

Take-up devices deflect under load just like the conventional hold-down. The reported take-up device (connector) deflection found in the evaluation report is per AC155 the computed deflection and fastener slip at the maximum rated load for the device. The deflection can be reduced based on actual device loads that are less than the maximum for the device.

The deformation or initial slack of these devices needs to be considered in the overall tie-down displacement (d_a).

Take-up devices have moving parts and may jam if not properly installed. Jamming typically occurs as a result of excessive continuous tie rod angle (out-of-plumb). See the manufacturer's instructions for proper installation.

While shrinkage compensating or take-up devices do not distinguish between the gaps created by initial shrinkage or settlement or the gaps created at other times or by other causes, ICC-ES AC316 for shrinkage compensating devices states they are used to "compensate for movement in a connection due to settlement or wood shrinkage, since the codes do not specify procedures for qualifying and installing such products." Similar statements are in shrinkage compensating device ICC-ES evaluation reports. The designer could specify what settlement should be considered on the plans. Settlement cannot be calculated, only estimated.

TCSCD (e.g., ratcheting devices) move along a tension rod's length with no maximum gap limitation. However, the device average travel and seating increment (Δ_R) (deflection) of these devices increases significantly as the tension rod diameter increases, making it difficult to comply with deflection limitations.

While there is no current system to evaluate the acceptable long-term performance of shrinkage or take-up devices, ICC-ES AC316 Section 4.5 requires that "[d]ocumentation shall be submitted showing how the CCSCD, TCSCCD or TCSCD will be protected from moisture and contamination during construction, or data shall be submitted, demonstrating that exposure to moisture and contamination during construction will have no long-term adverse effects on the device." Many of the device manufacturers perform corrosion testing in order to provide information to the designer regarding the device's corrosion-resistance capability.

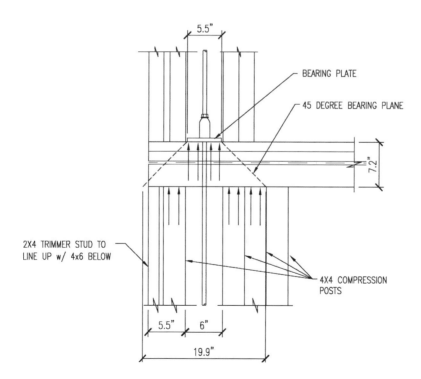

Figure 1-17. Bearing zone through framing from uplifting posts to bearing device

4.4D BEARING ZONE THROUGH FRAMING

Compression loads to the boundary members (posts) are achieved by nailing the shear wall sheathing to each boundary member, thus transferring the overturning (compression) forces, and are accumulative to the stories below. As the shear wall transfers the overturning (tension) forces to the boundary members, these forces collect at each level between restraint devices and transfer the differential loads (see Table 1-6) to the bearing plates at the level above (see Figure 1-17). The engineer should consider how the differential uplift forces are transferred from the boundary members to the bearing plate. As a general rule, where the differential uplift forces can be transferred within a bearing area located within a 45-degree plane from the bearing plate, no further investigation is necessary (see Figure 1-17). Where the transfer of forces requires an area larger than the 45-degree plane, some sort of further investigation is necessary (e.g., bending and shear checks of top plates).

Example Bearing Check (See Figure 1-17)

Differential load at third-floor level = 5367 lb (from Table 1-6)
Thickness of framing at floor = $(2 \times 1.5) + (23/32) + 3.5 = 7.2$ in
Bearing plate width = 5.5 in (from Table 1-8)
Bearing width at bottom of 4×4 top plate = $(5.5 + 7.2 + 7.2) = 19.9$ in
Neglecting the trimmer stud, there are three 4×4 compression posts within the bearing area:

        Bearing area = $(3.5 \times 3.5) \times 3 = 36.7$ in^2
        Bearing stress = $5367/36.7 = 146$ psi < 625 psi ... OK

Since the bearing area is more than 3 inches from the end of the top plate(s), an increase in bearing stress (NDS 3.10.4) can be considered. However, the length of the bearing area is greater than 6 inches, so the bearing factor is $C_b = 1.0$.

4.4E SILL PLATE CRUSHING

Per NDS Section 4.2.6, where compression perpendicular to grain $f_{c\perp}$ is less than 0.73 $F'_{c\perp}$, crushing will be approximately 0.02 inch. Where $f_{c\perp} = F'_{c\perp}$, crushing is approximately 0.04 inch. The effect of sill plate crushing is the downward effect at the opposite end of the wall (resulting from the boundary chords) and has the same rotational effect as the tie-down displacement (d_a). Short walls that have no (net) uplift forces will still have a crushing effect at wall boundaries and contribute to rotation of the wall.

The crushing effect on wood is not linear; a graph of load versus deformation is shown in Figure 1-18. The values of 0.02 inch and 0.04 inch are based on a *metal plate* bearing on wood perpendicular to the grain. These values are limit-state values and are not adjustable for the duration of load (C_D).

NDS Commentary Section C4.2.6 states that when a joint made of two wood members are both loaded perpendicular to grain, the amount of deformation will be approximately two and one-half times that of a metal plate bearing joint. Table 1-9 lists the deformation adjustment factors for different bearing conditions. Excepting post caps and bases, most connections in wood construction do not have metal plates for bearing. In the case of the shear wall in this design example, the only metal plates in the wall construction are the bearing plates at the continuous tie-down rods. Accordingly, the crushing values of the boundary posts should be increased by the deformation adjustment factor shown in Table 1-9.

Table 1-9. Deformation adjustment factor for bearing condition

Bearing Condition	Deformation Adjustment Factor
1. Wood-to-wood (both perpendicular to grain)	2.5
2. Wood-to-wood (one parallel to grain and one perpendicular to grain)	1.75
3. Metal-to-wood (wood loaded perpendicular to grain)	1.0

$F_{c\perp}$ Load Deformation Curve

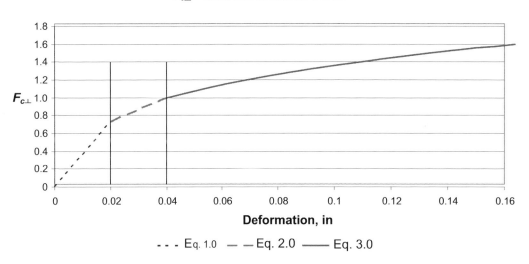

Figure 1-18. $F_{c\perp}$ load deformation curve (Eq. 3.0 derived from Bendtsen-Galligan, 1979)

For the three different regions of the load versus deformation curve shown in Figure 1-18, equations for determining compression perpendicular to grain deformation (Δ) may be calculated as follows:

where $f_{c\perp} \leq F_{c\perp 0.02''}$

$$\Delta = 0.02 \times \left(\frac{f_{c\perp}}{F_{c\perp 0.02''}} \right) \qquad \text{Eq 1.0}$$

where $F_{c\perp 0.02''} < f_{c\perp} < F_{c\perp 0.04''}$

$$\Delta = 0.04 - 0.02 \times \frac{\left(\frac{1 - f_{c\perp}}{F_{c\perp 0.04''}} \right)}{0.27} \qquad \text{Eq 2.0}$$

where

$$f_{c\perp} > F_{c\perp 0.04''}$$

$$\Delta = 0.04 \times \left(\frac{f_{c\perp}}{F_{c\perp 0.04''}} \right)^3 \qquad \qquad \text{Eq 3.0}$$

where

Δ = deformation, in

$f_{c\perp}$ = induced stress, psi

$F_{c\perp 0.04''} = F_{c\perp}$ = reference design value at 0.04-inch deformation, psi ($F_{c\perp}$)

$F_{c\perp 0.02''}$ = reference design value at 0.02-inch deformation, psi ($0.73F_{c\perp}$)

In the case of the shear wall in this design example (Figure 1-17), the boundary posts bear on the top plate (bearing condition 2), and the steel bearing plate resists this upward movement and bears on the sill plate and floor sheathing, which in turn bear down on the underside of the top plate (bearing condition 2). The crushing effect is coming from two directions at the same time, thus doubling the amount of deformation. In addition, there is the crushing effect of the floor sheathing. Since there are wood-to-wood bearing conditions, the deformation adjustment factor (Table 1-9) is 1.75. NDS does not have a crushing value for the wood structural panel floor sheathing, and it is assumed to be higher than for sawn lumber. As a way of accounting for this crushing effect of the floor sheathing, a deformation adjustment factor of 2.5 will be used in lieu of the 1.75 factor, producing a compounding effect of $2 \times 2.5 = 5.0$ times the values computed in Eq. 1.0, Eq. 2.0, or Eq. 3.0.

Crushing Effects of Uplift Boundary Members

Differential strength uplift forces for the boundary chords transfer the story uplift forces to the metal bearing plate at the floor above (Figure 1-17); however, these differential uplift forces are less than the cumulative strength compression downward forces. Since the crushing effects have already been considered for the higher downward forces, there is no need to consider the lesser crushing effects of the uplift forces.

Table 1-10. Determine sill plate crushing at line C

Level	Chord Posts	ASD Demand (kips)	Strength Demand (kips)	Total Area (in²)	$F_{c\perp}$ (ksi)	$0.73F'_{c\perp}$ (ksi)	Crush (in)
Roof	Four 3 × 4	5.58	7.60	35.0	0.217	0.456	0.048
4th Floor	Four 3 × 4	10.78	14.69	35.0	0.420	0.456	0.092
3rd Floor	Four 4 × 4	17.92	24.81	49.0	0.506	0.456	0.130
2nd Floor	Four 4 × 6	26.63	37.57	77.0	0.488	0.456	0.119

Notes for Table 1-10:

1. ASD demand and strength (LRFD) demand values are obtained from Table 1-4.

2. Allowable compression perpendicular to grain values $F_{c\perp}$ are not allowed to be increased for the duration of the load; therefore, $F'_{c\perp} = F_{c\perp}$

       For Douglas Fir-Larch: $F_{c\perp}$ = 625 psi

       For Hem-Fir: $F_{c\perp}$ = 405 psi (a 35% reduction from Douglas Fir).

For both Douglas Fir and Hem-Fir, the allowable compression perpendicular to the grain is the same for the various grades within the species.

For Southern Pine, the allowable compression perpendicular to the grain varies by grade within the species from 480 to 660 psi.

For laminated veneer lumber (LVL), the values vary between manufacturers and have a value for allowable compression perpendicular to the grain of approximately 480 psi.

For laminated strand lumber (LSL), the values vary between manufacturers and have a value for allowable compression perpendicular to the grain of approximately 435 psi.

3. Crushing value ranges from 0.00 to 0.02 inch when $f_{c\perp}$ ranges from 0.0 psi to $0.73F'_{c\perp}$ and ranges from 0.02 to 0.04 inch when $f_{c\perp}$ ranges from $0.73F'_{c\perp}$ to $F'_{c\perp}$. Values are interpolated to obtain the crushing values listed (crush).

4. Crushing values have been multiplied by $2 \times 2.5 = 5.0$.

Table 1-11. Determine bearing plate crushing at line C

Level	ASD Bearing Load (kips)	Strength Bearing Load (kips)	Bearing Plate A_{Brg} (in²)	$f_{c\perp}$ (ksi)	$0.73F'_{c\perp}$ (ksi)	Crush (in)
Roof	2.878	4.111	15.98	0.257	0.456	0.011
4th Floor	3.684	5.262	9.98	0.527	0.456	0.028
3rd Floor	5.367	7.667	15.61	0.491	0.456	0.024
2nd Floor	6.416	9.166	15.39	0.595	0.456	0.037

Notes for Table 1-11:

1. ASD bearing load values are obtained from the differential loads of Table 1-6.

2. Strength (LRFD) bearing loads are obtained by dividing ASD bearing loads by the conversion factor of 0.7.

3. The allowable $F'_{c\perp}$ may be exceeded; however, this design example uses strength (LRFD) loads where the bearing resistance is

$$F'_{c\perp} = \lambda \varphi_c K_F F_{c\perp} C_b = 1.0 \times 0.9 \left(\frac{1.875}{0.9} \right) 625 \times 1.11 = 1300 \text{ psi}$$

4. ASD bearing-plate capacities and bearing are from Table 1-8.

4.4F DETERMINE TIE-DOWN ASSEMBLY DISPLACEMENT

Table 1-12. Determine tie-down assembly displacements at line C

Level	Strength Rod Elong. (in)	Seating Increment (Vertical Displacement Δ_R) (in)	Chord Crushing (in)	Bearing-Plate Crushing (in)	Take-Up Device Initial Δ_A & Design Deflection, Δ_T (in)	Total Displacement, d_a (in)
Roof	0.061	0.031	0.048	0.011	0.030	0.181
4th Floor	0.159	0.031	0.092	0.028	0.030	0.340
3rd Floor	0.141	0.031	0.130	0.024	0.030	0.356
2nd Floor	0.166	0.031	0.119	0.037	0.030	0.382

Notes for Table 1-12:

1. Displacement values are taken out to three figures to avoid unwanted compounding of rounding up for each term.

2. Rod elongation values are obtained from Table 1-7 and factored up by 1.4 for strength-level (LRFD) elongations.

3. Seating increment values (vertical displacement) are obtained from Table 1-1; for most devices, this value is zero as take-up devices are used and initial (seating), Δ_R, take-up device deflection is taken into account as well as the device design deflection, Δ_A, in the device deflection value. These values should be obtained from the manufacturer's evaluation report evaluated to the ICC-ES AC316 criteria. For this design example, a value of $\frac{1}{32}$ inch is used, recognizing that the device used will have to travel a distance before the device gets to the next groove in the device to readjust.

4. Chord crushing (crush) values are obtained from Table 1-10.

5. Bearing-plate (crush) values are obtained from Table 1-11.

6. Without shrinkage compensators (Table 1-1), the tie-down assembly displacements are accumulative from floor-to-floor level.

4.5 SEGMENTED SHEAR WALL DEFLECTION   SDPWS

A considerable amount of monotonic and cyclic testing has been done (and continues to be done) on cantilever wood structural panel shear walls in the last two decades. Tests results and testing protocols used for the testing can be found in the references listed in Commentary Section C4.3 of the SDPWS. To date, there has been very limited testing on multistory shear walls and therefore there is not a significant amount of information on the deflection characteristic of multistory shear walls, specifically on the contribution of the floor framing on the wall deflection and whether to model the wall calculations on a structure that is assumed to have significant rotation at each floor level (not perfectly rigid), have no (or insignificant) rotation at each level (has fixity), or is somewhere in between the two. Certainly, the type and detailing of framing at the floor and the magnitudes of spans of the floor elements would be expected to affect the floor's contribution to the wall fixity.

Past physical testing of shear walls and current state of practice tends to ignore the finish materials and nonstructural walls' contribution to stiffness; however, limited whole building shake table testing on wood and cold-formed steel light-frame structures confirms that the finish materials and other nonstructural elements can contribute significantly to the deflections and can have a measurable effect (both positive and negative) on the overall lateral performance of multistory buildings.

Currently there are two primary methods used to determine shear wall deflections in mid-rise wood-frame structures. One method is to assume fixity only at the base of the building and consider the shear wall to cantilever up from the base with no fixity at each floor. Essentially considering the wall as one tall cantilever element with applied lateral loads at each floor. The second method is to assume that the wall elements have fixity at each floor level and cantilever up to the floor level directly above, and thereby determine the wall deflection on a story-by-story basis. This design example uses the second method, which is to assume fixity at the bottom of each floor level.

A well-known expression for determining (segmented) shear wall deflection using four sources of deflection is in IBC Section 2305.3; however, the 2018 IBC now requires only the four-term equation for *stapled* shear walls. For determining the calculated deflection for a *nailed* shear wall, the SDPWS defines a three-term equation for calculating shear wall deflection, as shown here.

$$\delta = \frac{8vh^3}{EAb} + \frac{vh}{1000G_a} + d_a\frac{h}{b_{eff}} \qquad\qquad \text{Eq 4.3-1}$$

This equation is a simplified form of the four-term equation, which adds the effects of four different sources contributing to the deflection: the cantilever (beam) bending of the vertical wall element, including the contribution of the boundary members; the shear deformation of the wood structural panels; the bending and slip of the fasteners; and the additional deflection due to the anchorage (tie-down) deformation. The original four-term shear wall deflection formula is shown here.

$$\delta = \frac{8vh^3}{EAb} + \frac{vh}{Gt} + 0.75he_n + d_a\frac{h}{b_{eff}} \qquad\qquad \text{Eq C4.3.2-1}$$

The simplified expression using three terms (Eq 4.3-1) combines the second and third terms of the four-term equation into one term. Computed deflections by using either the four-term equation or the three-term equation produce nearly identical results at the critical strength level (1.4 times the allowable shear values for seismic). Thus, either equation may be used for computing the deflection of a shear wall.

For determination of shear wall deflections with sheathing on the entire wall, see Sections 5.4 and 5.5.

Although Equation 4.3-1 is easier to use, the deflections computed will be larger than the actual deflections since the apparent shear wall stiffness (G_a) listed in Tables 4.3A, 4.3B, 4.3C, and 4.3D is based on the shear in the wall being at its capacity for the given nailing.

For the calculated shear-wall deflection to be more accurate, the computations for shear wall deflections in this design example will use the four-term equation (SDPWS Eq. C4.3.2-1).

Height of the Sheathed Wall *(h)*

See Section 4.2 for shear-wall cumulative overturning forces for determination of height.

For a sheathed wall that does not have a ribbon board at the floor line but has top plates below the floor sheathing (or modified platform framed, see Figure 1-19), the height of the wall is the distance between the sill plate and the top plate(s) below the ribbon board (story height).

For a sheathed wall that has a ribbon board at the floor line with a top plate(s) below the ribbon board (platform framed), and the sheathing is not placed at the ribbon board (see Figure 1-20), the height of the wall is not the story height but the distance between the sill plate and the top plate(s) below the ribbon board.

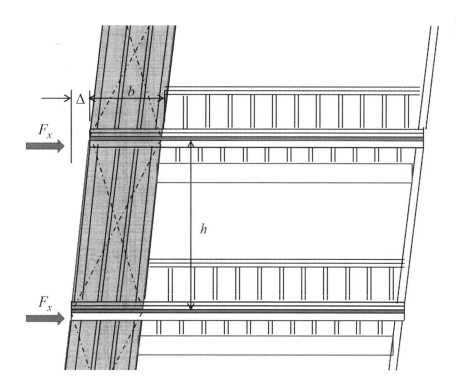

Figure 1-19. Shear wall height—modified balloon framing

Note:
For a section cut at the floor line at Figure 1-19, see Figure 1-11.

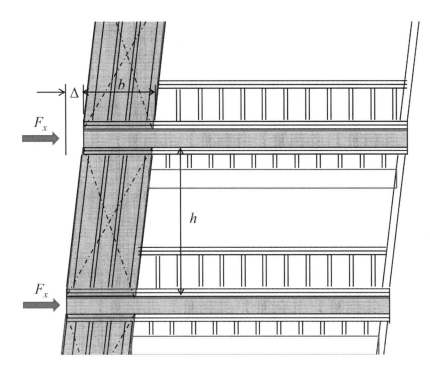

Figure 1-20. Shear wall height—platform framing

Note:

For a section cut at the floor line in Figure 1-20, see Figure 1-13.

Fastener Slip/Nail Deformation Values (e_n)

The two basic equations for fastener slip from SDPWS Table C4.2.2D for 10d common nails used in this example are shown here.

When nails are driven into green lumber: $e_n = (V_n/977)^{1.894}$ T C4.2.2D

When nails are driven into dry lumber: $e_n = (V_n/769)^{3.276}$ T C4.2.2D

where

V_n = fastener load in pounds per fastener

e_n = fastener slip in inches

Values of fastener slip from the above formulas are based on the performance with Structural-I sheathing and must be increased by 20 percent for other sheathing types.

Many engineers have expressed concern that if the contractor installs the nails at a different spacing (too many or too few), the rigidities will be significantly different from those calculated. However, based on past testing, a nominal changing of the nail spacing in a given wall does not appear to significantly change the stiffness.

Δ_a vs. d_a

For decades, the *Uniform Building Code*, *International Building Code*, APA documents, text books, earlier editions of the *Structural/Seismic Design Manual*, and earlier editions of SDPWS used a notation of d_a for the tie-down assembly displacement. In the 2008 SDPWS, notation changed to Δ_a. This design example uses both terms as most engineers will take a while to change what has become ingrained.

Continuous Tie-Down Assembly Displacement

The continuous tie-down assembly displacement (d_a) is a collective accumulation of the deformation of tie-down elements. Each of these elements within the assembly deforms, elongates, and/or compresses. See Figure 1-21A for the effect of the tie-down assembly displacement on the shear wall deflection.

The 2018 IBC and the 2015 SDPWS define d_a as follows:

d_a = Total vertical elongation of wall anchorage system (such as fastener slip, device elongation, rod elongation) at the induced unit shear in the wall (v)

It is uncertain whether the d_a factor is intended to include wood floor vertical deformation and crushing due to shear wall rotation, as the code is not specific. Based on test results of wood-frame shear walls, the crushing effect of wood at the panel ends *can be significant*. This design example includes vertical wood deflection and crushing in the d_a factor. The inclusion of vertical wood deformation and crushing in the d_a factor can be significant especially for higher aspect ratio shear walls, while less significant for lower aspect ratio shear walls.

Some engineers will argue that only the maximum value of elongation at the tension side (tie-down assembly displacement) versus the maximum value of the wood deflection/crushing on the compression side need be used. As the shear wall rotates from the induced shear, the tension side moves up and the compression side moves down, producing an additive effect on the shear wall rotation (d_a).

The net effect of the tie-down assembly displacement plus the wood deflection/crushing is an additional rotation of the shear wall, as a rigid body, with the additional lateral displacement at the top of the wall (Δ) equal to the aspect ratio (h/d) of the wall multiplied by the calculated tie-down assembly displacement (d_a) projected to the outside edge of the wall. See Figures 1-15A and 1-21.

$$\Delta = d_a \frac{h}{b_{eff}}$$

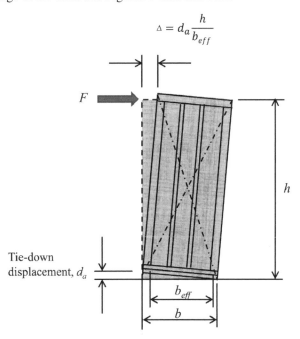

Figure 1-21. Project d_a

Notes for Figure 1-21:
h = height of shear wall
b = the out-to-out dimension of the shear wall
b_{eff} = the distance between centroid of tension hold-down and centroid of boundary element

Maximum Computed d_a Term

Over the last 10 years, several municipal jurisdictions adopted policies limiting the allowable contribution of the tie-down displacement to the overall shear wall lateral drift. Although similar in magnitude, in many cases the limitations adopted varied. In order to provide for a more uniform approach and to provide consistency for both the engineers designing the systems and the manufacturers, ICC-ES modified AC316 to include a maximum design limit of 0.2 inch for the calculated vertical deformation of the continuous tie-down system, including the shrinkage compensating devices, when resisting lateral overturning forces (ICC-ES 2012c). This 0.2-inch limit is defined at ASD forces. The limit is for each story or between restraint devices, regardless of the wall aspect ratio. Now calculations must be submitted that confirm that the total tie-down assembly (vertical) displacement (rod elongation, connector device elongation, wood crushing, etc.) is not exceeded. It is noted that the requirement is for ASD forces even though the engineers' deflection calculations need to be based on strength-level forces when checking building drifts.

AC316 allows the 0.2-inch limit to be exceeded provided that the total shear wall story drift is in compliance with the requirements of the building code. Note that with regard to added lateral drift, the 0.2-inch limit may be very conservative for low aspect ratio shear walls, but may be unconservative for narrow, high aspect ratio walls. For example, for a shear wall with a 2-to-1 (height-to-length) aspect ratio, 0.2 inch of vertical displacement at ASD level will result in an additional 2.3 inches of lateral drift when converted to strength level and calculated with the C_d factor. For a 10-foot story height, this results in 1.9 percent additional drift (not accounting for nail slip, wall bending, and shear deformation), where the code level drift for 5-story wood construction is limited to 2 percent.

Tables 1-15, 1-20, 1-24, and 1-28 list the total tie-down assembly displacement Δ_a (d_a) using strength-level forces. The ASD-level displacements are not listed but can be approximated by multiplying the values by 0.7. Many of the values exceed the limit of 0.2 inches; however, as allowed in the AC316 criteria, drift checks of the shear walls at the roof level are listed in Table 1-19.

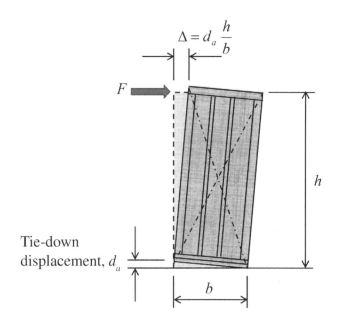

Figure 1-21A. Effect of d_a on drift

Note:
h = height of shear wall
b = the out-to-out dimension of the shear wall

Stiffness of Plywood vs. Oriented Strand Board (OSB)

For shear walls with wood structural panels, there can be a significant difference in the shear wall deflection, depending on which type of structural use panels are used for the construction of the shear wall. The difference comes from the apparent shear wall stiffness value (G_a). This apparent shear wall stiffness is a combination of nail slip and panel shear deformation. Most engineers are not aware of the difference and can mistakenly allow or approve a change to the different wood structural panels without knowledge of the true impact. The ratio of the apparent shear wall stiffness value varies, depending on the fastener spacing, where the closer the fastener spacing, the greater the difference. In addition to shear walls, the difference in G_a between plywood and OSB can have a measurable effect on diaphragm deflection. This could significantly affect the expected performance of cantilever or rigid diaphragms.

The following is a comparison of apparent shear wall stiffness values for $^{15}\!/_{32}$-inch Structural I wood structural panels using 10d common nails:

Fastener Spacing	G_a		Ratio OSB/PLY
	PLY	OSB	
6″	16	22	1.4
4″	20	29	1.5
3″	22	36	1.6
2″	28	51	1.8

For other thicknesses of sheathing applied directly to stud framing, different fastener sizes, and so on, refer to SDPWS Table 4.3A.

Example using three-term equation:

$$\delta = \frac{8vh^3}{EAb} + \frac{vh}{1000G_a} + d_a\frac{h}{b} \qquad\qquad \text{SDPWS Eq 4.3-1}$$

where

$v = 750$ plf

$h = 9.0$ ft

$E = 1.7 \times 106$

$A = 5.26 \times 2 = 10.52$ in^2

$b = 8.0$ ft

$d_a = 0.188$ in

Sheathing thickness $= {}^{15}\!/_{32}$ in

Fasteners $= 10$d common nails at 2-in spacing

$G_a = 28$ PLY

$G_a = 51$ OSB

Using Structural I plywood sheathing:

$$\delta = \frac{8 \times 750 \times (9.0)^3}{1.7 \times 10^6 \times 10.52 \times 8.0} + \frac{750 \times 9.0}{1000 \times 28} + 0.188 \frac{9.0}{8.0} = 0.48 \text{ in}$$

Using Structural I OSB sheathing:

$$\delta = \frac{8 \times 750 \times (9.0)^3}{1.7 \times 10^6 \times 10.52 \times 8.0} + \frac{750 \times 9.0}{1000 \times 51} + 0.188 \frac{9.0}{8.0} = 0.37 \text{ in}$$

Using 10d box nails would result in a 19 percent reduction in allowable load for diaphragms and shear walls compared to 10d common nails. Using 8d box nails would result in a 23 percent reduction in allowable load for diaphragms and shear walls compared to 8d common nails. This is based on comparing allowable shear values listed in Table 12N in the NDS-15 for ¾-inch side member thickness, t_s, and Douglas Fir-Larch framing. In addition to the reduction of the shear wall and diaphragm capacities, where box nails are used, the walls will also drift more than where common nails are used. Alternatively, the engineer can consider using nail and sheathing thicknesses not listed in the IBC or SDPWS by using the values listed in ICC-ES report ESR-1539, available from the International Staple, Nail, and Tool Association (ISANTA).

A contributor to the problem is that when contractors buy large quantities of nails (for nail guns), the words *box* or *common* do not appear on the carton label. Nail length and diameters are the most common listing on the labels. Thus, it is *extremely important* to list the required nail lengths and diameters (not just specifying 8d common or 10d common nails) on the structural drawings for all diaphragms and shear walls.

5. Mechanics of Multistory Shear Walls with Force Transfer around Openings

5.1 DESIGN OF WALL FRAME WITH FORCE TRANSFER AROUND OPENINGS   SDPWS

Section 4.3.5 of the SDPWS lists the three basics types of shear walls: segmented method, force-transfer, and perforated. The following method illustrates force-transfer shear walls, which is more commonly referred to in the industry as force transfer around openings, or FTAO. Section 4.3.5.2 states that this type of design shall be based on "a rational analysis," leaving the type of analysis to be chosen by the building engineer/engineer of record. There are basically four types of analysis techniques that are generally accepted as rational analysis: the drag strut, the cantilever beam, the "Diekmann method," and the SEAOC/ Thompson method. The engineer is encouraged to refer to the *SEAOC Blue Book* article "Wood-framed Shear Walls with Openings."

Until recently, there has not been adequate testing of these types of shear walls to justify the rational analysis methods available, but APA and the Forest Products Laboratory have now tested full-size walls with openings. The testing focused on determining the horizontal tension strap forces at the opening corners. One of the conclusions in the testing report is that either the Diekmann method or the SEAOC/ Thompson method most accurately estimates the actual tension strap forces in the shear walls, while the other two methods can either produce overly nonconservative or overly conservative tension strap-force estimates. The method illustrated in this design example, the SEAOC/Thompson method, uses the Diekmann method with variations. Many engineers will arbitrarily add tie-downs at the window jamb members (Figure 1-40). However, with this type of design, the tie-downs at these locations are not necessary and may result in higher shear stresses above and below the window. However, adding tie-downs at the window jambs will increase the wall frame performance and help prevent sill plate uplift at the window jambs, which occurs (to some degree) when they are not provided.

It is possible to get the mistaken impression from SDPWS Figure 4E that all a designer needs to do to reduce the *h/w* ratio is add some blocking and straps. This design example has a structure with 9-foot plate heights, which makes using a wall frame feasible. However, when the plate height is 8 feet, there are chord development and panel nailing capacity problems. Most often, the wall shears above and below the opening will be higher than in the wall piers. These design examples analyze the wall frame and neglect gravity loads. Although correct from a technical standpoint, some engineers will argue that vertical loads need to be considered when determining wall shears. The standard practice of neglecting gravity loads when considering wall shears is deemed appropriate.

Three-dimensional finite element analysis computer programs are now being used to model structural-use panels on horizontal diaphragms and lateral-resisting elements. These programs model the structural-use panels as continuous without panel splices. Depending on the size and location of the panel splices, the computer model may not accurately model the field conditions. Recent full-scale tests have shown that even locating a panel splice at the window corners versus away from the window corners (cut corners) can produce different test results.

The 2012 and earlier editions of *SEAOC Structural/Seismic Design Manual* Volume 2, Design Example 1 illustrated a method where the inflection points in the wall piers as well as the wall segments above and below the window openings were assumed to be at the mid-point of the opening. The methods illustrated in this edition of the *Design Manual* proportion the inflection point location based on wall lengths of the adjacent wall segments. All of the full-scale testing to date of shear walls with force transfer around openings has yet to determine where the inflection points occur; thus, these methods of analysis are considered approximate and within the intent of providing a rational analysis. Proportioning the inflection point locations produces uniform shears at the wall piers and wall segments above and below the openings. To some degree, the inflection points should be based on stiffness, which would tend to attract more load to the wall segment above the opening than the segment below the opening due to the header beam that is above the opening. Likewise, the full-scale testing to date has not determined whether the shear stresses in wall piers is proportional to wall lengths or based on the stiffnesses of the wall piers.

Due to the indeterminate nature of calculating inflection points and wall stiffnesses, the current practice for force transfer around openings is to distribute the forces to the wall piers based on wall length as opposed to wall stiffness.

Figure 1-22 illustrates a generic wall frame with four wall piers. Where there are more than three wall piers, wall pier "L2" (the wall pier between two adjacent openings) repeats as necessary. Where there are two wall piers, wall pier "L2" does not exist. The wall frame used in this design example has more wall area and less window area than many projects and has been chosen to illustrate force transfer around openings in large multistory walls. Building structures that have sliding glass doors to balconies or wall-mounted air-conditioner units below the windows, such as those in hotels, usually cannot utilize force transfer around openings because there is not enough wall length above and below the openings (dimension "H1" and "H2"). In these cases, a segmented shear wall with continuous tie-downs may be necessary.

A more global approach for whether a wall face should be designed with the segmented method or the force-transfer method should be based on capacities. In other words, if the wall shear forces are significantly higher above and below the openings, then the use of force transfer may not be the appropriate choice.

5.2 THOMPSON METHOD

A new method of force transfer is illustrated in this design example and is different than the SEAOC/ Thompson method illustrated in previous editions. This method first appeared in the 2012 SSDM edition and has been illustrated in more detail in the 2015 and 2018 editions and will be referred to as the Thompson method.

Due to the relatively uniform wall lengths on the exterior walls, this design example uses a uniform distribution of wall shear forces in the wall frame. This method may not be appropriate on other building wall faces, and its use will be up to the engineering judgment of the building designer/engineer of record.

The Thompson method assumes the following:

- The unit shear at the sides of the opening is uniform.

- The location of the inflection points above and below the openings is proportional to the wall pier lengths adjacent to that specific opening.

- The location of the inflection points at the sides of the window openings is proportional to the wall lengths above and below that specific opening.

- The vertical shear forces above and below the opening are determined by static free body equilibrium of the free body of that wall pier element.

Determine Shear Forces around Openings for the Roof Level

Using statics, determine the shears and forces in each free body panel.

Figure 1-22 is generic in nature and depicts three window openings. For this design example, the shear wall design for the piers between grid lines B and D will be illustrated where the wall frame continues for several openings, making the right side of the figure look like the center of the figure.

Lateral (strength level) forces to wall line 1 (see Table 1-14):

Roof level: $F_{tot} = 11,223$ lb

Fourth-floor level: $F_{tot} = 23,893$ lb

Third-floor level: $F_{tot} = 32,340$ lb

Second-floor level: $F_{tot} = 36,563$ lb

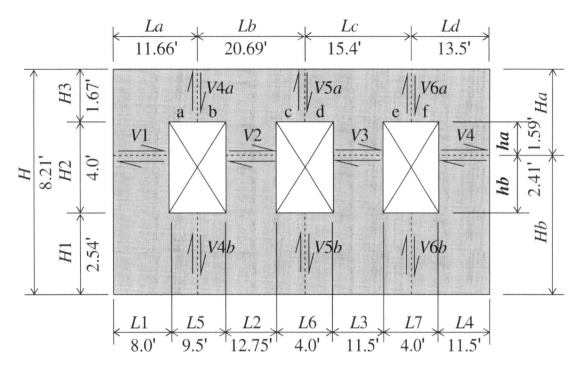

Figure 1-22. Wall force determination

First: Determine wall dimensions for the wall frame.

$L1 = 8.0$ ft, $L2 = 12.75$ ft, $L3 = 11.5$ ft, $L4 = 11.5$ ft, $L5 = 9.5$ ft, $L6 = 4.0$ ft, $L7 = 4.0$ ft

Total wall length including openings on grid lines 1 and 4 (see Figure 1-1):

$L = 96.0$ ft

Total wall length for wall piers on grid lines 1 and 4:

$\Sigma L = 8.0 + 12.75 + 11.5 + 11.5 + 12.75 + 8.0 = 64.5$ ft

Total length of wall piers shown in Figure 1-16:

$\Sigma L = 8.0 + 12.75 + 11.5 + 11.5 = 43.75$ ft

Total shear to wall piers shown in Figure 1-22 is proportional to the total wall length in the same wall line:

$$\frac{\Sigma L}{\text{Total } \Sigma L} = \left(\frac{43.75}{64.5}\right)11{,}223 \text{ lb} = 7612 \text{ lb}$$

$H = 8.21$ ft, $H1 = 2.54$ ft, $H2 = 4.0$ ft, $H3 = 1.67$ ft

$$a = \left(\frac{L1}{L1+L2}\right)L4 = \left(\frac{8.0}{8.0+12.75}\right)9.5 = 3.66 \text{ ft}$$

$$b = L4 - a = 9.5 - 3.66 = 5.84 \text{ ft}$$

$$c = \left(\frac{L2}{L2+L3}\right)L5 = \left(\frac{12.75}{12.75+11.5}\right)4.0 = 2.10 \text{ ft}$$

$$d = L5 - c = 4.0 - 2.1 = 1.90 \text{ ft}$$

$$e = \left(\frac{L3}{L3+L4}\right)L6 = \left(\frac{11.5}{11.5+11.5}\right)4.0 = 2.0 \text{ ft}$$

$$f = L6 - e = 4.0 - 2.0 = 2.0 \text{ ft}$$

Determine the inflection points above and below the openings:

$$La = L1 + a = 8.0 + 3.66 = 11.66 \text{ ft}$$

$$Lb = b + L2 + c = 5.84 + 12.75 + 2.1 = 20.69 \text{ ft}$$

$$Lc = d + L3 + e = 1.9 + 11.5 + 2.0 = 15.4 \text{ ft}$$

$$Ld = L4 + f = 11.5 + 2.0 = 13.5 \text{ ft}$$

Check the sum of the lengths:

$$11.66 + 20.69 + 15.4 + 13.5 = 61.25 \text{ ft} => checks$$

Determine the inflection points at the sides of the openings:

$$Ha = \left(\frac{H3}{H1+H3}\right)H = \left(\frac{1.67}{2.54+1.67}\right)8.21 = 3.26 \text{ ft}$$

$$Hb = H - Ha = 8.21 - 3.26 = 4.95 \text{ ft}$$

$$ha = Ha - H3 = 3.26 - 1.67 = 1.59 \text{ ft}$$

$$hb = H2 - ha = 4 - 1.59 = 2.41 \text{ ft}$$

Label the upper and lower free-body portions of the wall frame (see Figure 1-23).

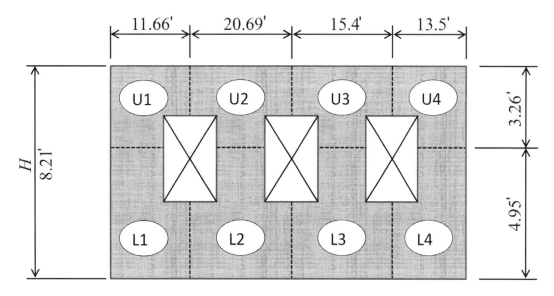

Figure 1-23. Wall frame showing upper and lower free-body portions

Second: Find forces acting on wall piers and shear in-wall piers.

Shear forces to the wall piers are proportioned based on the length of the pier in relation to the total length of the piers (Figure 1-22).

$$V1 = \left(\frac{L1}{\Sigma L}\right)V = \left(\frac{8.0}{64.5}\right)11{,}223 = 1392 \text{ lb}$$

$$v1 = \frac{V1}{L1} = \frac{1392}{8.0} = 174 \text{ plf}$$

$$V2 = \left(\frac{L2}{\Sigma L}\right)V = \left(\frac{12.75}{64.5}\right)11{,}223 = 2218 \text{ lb}$$

$$v2 = \frac{V2}{L2} = \frac{2218}{12.75} = 174 \text{ plf}$$

$$V3 = \left(\frac{L3}{\Sigma L}\right)V = \left(\frac{11.5}{64.5}\right)11{,}223 = 2001 \text{ lb}$$

$$v3 = \frac{V3}{L3} = \frac{2001}{11.5} = 174 \text{ plf}$$

$$V4 = \left(\frac{L4}{\Sigma L}\right)V = \left(\frac{11.5}{64.5}\right)11{,}223 = 2001 \text{ lb}$$

$$v4 = \frac{V4}{L4} = \frac{2001}{11.5} = 174 \text{ plf}$$

Check the sum of the shears in the piers:

$$V1 + V2 + V3 + V4 = 1392 + 2218 + 2001 + 2001 = 7612 \text{ lbs} => checks$$

Third: Find the vertical shear forces acting above and below the openings and the unit shear forces (see Figure 1-24).

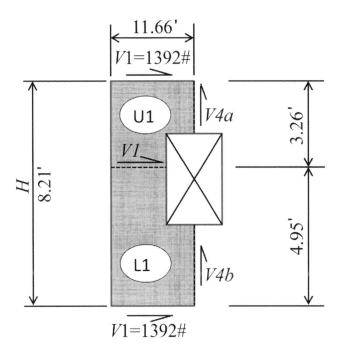

Figure 1-24. Vertical shear forces acting above and below opening

$$V4a + V4b = \frac{V1 \times H}{La} = \frac{1392 \times 8.21}{11.66} = 980 \text{ lb}$$

$$V4a = (V4a + V4b)\left(\frac{H3}{H1 + H3}\right) = 980 \times \left(\frac{1.67}{2.54 + 1.67}\right) = 389 \text{ lb}$$

$$v4a = \frac{V4a}{H3} = \frac{389}{1.67} = 233 \text{ plf}$$

$$V4b = (V4a + V4b)\left(\frac{H1}{H1 + H3}\right) = 980 \times \left(\frac{2.54}{2.54 + 1.67}\right) = 592 \text{ lb}$$

$$v4b = \frac{V4b}{H1} = \frac{592}{2.54} = 233 \text{ plf}$$

Fourth: Determine shear and tie forces (see Figure 1-25).

Free body U1:

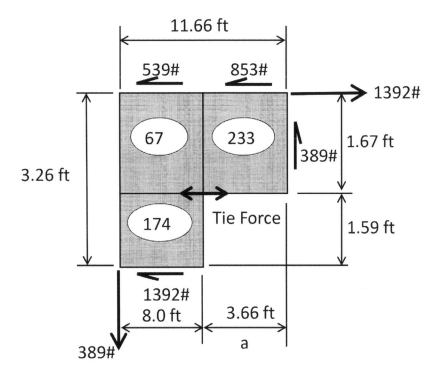

Figure 1-25. Free-body diagram U1

Determine horizontal shear force at the top of the wall above "a":

$$Va = V4a \times \left(\frac{a}{H3}\right) = 389 \times \left(\frac{3.66}{1.67}\right) = 853 \text{ lb}$$

Determine horizontal shear force at upper left corner:

$$V = V1 - Va = 1392 - 853 = 540 \text{ lb}$$

$$v = \frac{V}{L1} = \frac{540}{8.0} = 67 \text{ plf}$$

Determine horizontal tie force from header to wall pier $V1$:

$$\text{Tie} = V4a \times \frac{a}{H3} = 389 \times \frac{3.66}{1.67} = 853 \text{ lb}$$

Free body L1:

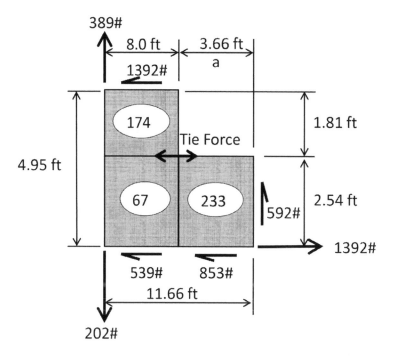

Figure 1-26. Free-body diagram L1

Determine horizontal shear force at the bottom of the wall at "a":

$$Va = V4b \times \left(\frac{a}{H1}\right) = 592 \times \left(\frac{3.66}{2.54}\right) = 853 \text{ lb}$$

Determine horizontal shear force at the lower left corner:

$$V = V1 - Va = 1392 - 853 = 539 \text{ lb}$$

$$v = \frac{V}{L1} = \frac{539}{8.0} = 67 \text{ plf}$$

Determine horizontal tie force from window sill to wall pier *V*1:

$$\text{Tie} = V4b \times \frac{a}{H1} = 592 \times \frac{3.66}{2.54} = 853 \text{ lb}$$

Determine vertical tie force at lower corner of wall pier *V*1:

$$\text{Tie } T1 = V4b - V4a = 591 - 389 = 202 \text{ lb}$$

Free body U2:

$$V4a + V4b = V5a + V5b = \frac{V2 \times H}{Lb} = \frac{2218 \times 8.21}{20.7} = 880 \text{ lb}$$

$$V4a = (V4a + V4b)\left(\frac{H3}{H1 + H3}\right) = 880 \times \left(\frac{1.67}{2.54 + 1.67}\right) = 349 \text{ lb}$$

$$V5a = (V4a + V4b)\left(\frac{H3}{H1 + H3}\right) = 880 \times \left(\frac{1.67}{2.54 + 1.67}\right) = 349 \text{ lb}$$

$$v4a = v5a = \frac{V4a}{H3} = \frac{349}{1.67} = 209 \text{ plf}$$

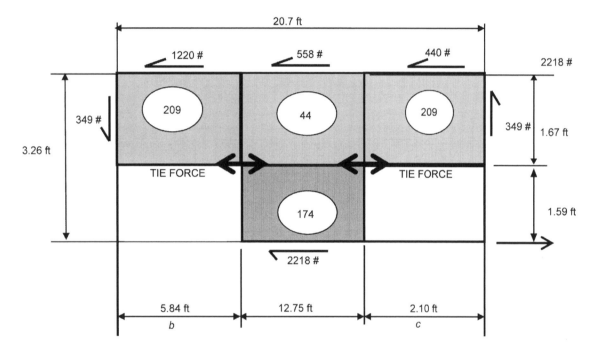

Figure 1-27. Free-body diagram U2

Determine horizontal shear force at the top of the wall above "b":

$$Vb = V4a \times \left(\frac{b}{H3}\right) = 349 \times \left(\frac{5.84}{1.67}\right) = 1220 \text{ lb}$$

$$Vc = V5a \times \left(\frac{c}{H3}\right) = 349 \times \left(\frac{2.1}{1.67}\right) = 440 \text{ lb}$$

Determine horizontal shear force at upper left *V2* portion:

$$V = Vb - Vc = 1220 - 440 = 558 \text{ lb}$$

$$v = \frac{V}{Lb} = \frac{558}{12.75} = 44 \text{ plf}$$

Determine horizontal tie force from header to wall pier $V2$ (left side):

$$\text{Tie} = V4a \times \frac{b}{H3} = 349 \times \frac{5.84}{1.67} = 1220 \text{ lb}$$

Determine horizontal tie force from header to wall pier $V2$ (right side):

$$\text{Tie} = V5a \times \frac{c}{H3} = 349 \times \frac{2.1}{1.67} = 440 \text{ lb}$$

Free body diagram L2:

$$V4b = V5b = (V4a + V4b)\left(\frac{H1}{H1+H3}\right) = 880 \times \left(\frac{2.54}{2.54+1.67}\right) = 531 \text{ lb}$$

$$v4b = v5b = \frac{V5b}{H1} = \frac{531}{2.54} = 209 \text{ plf}$$

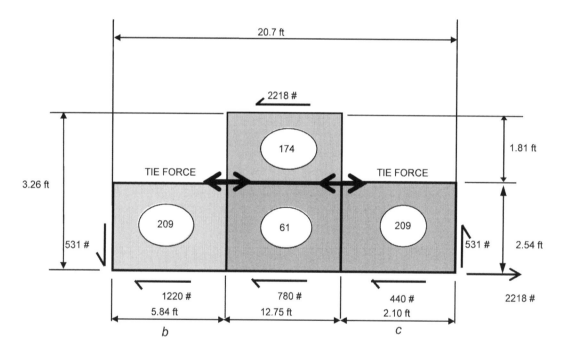

Figure 1-28. Free-body diagram L2

Determine horizontal shear force at the bottom of the wall below "b":

$$Vb = V4b \times \left(\frac{b}{H1}\right) = 531 \times \left(\frac{5.84}{2.54}\right) = 1220 \text{ lb}$$

Determine horizontal shear force at "c":

$$Vc = V5b \times \left(\frac{c}{H1}\right) = 531 \times \left(\frac{2.1}{2.54}\right) = 440 \text{ lb}$$

Determine horizontal shear force at lower center $V2$ portion:

$$V = Vb - Vc = 1220 - 440 = 780 \text{ lb}$$

$$v = \frac{V}{Lb} = \frac{780}{12.75} = 61 \text{ plf}$$

Determine horizontal tie force from window sill to wall pier $V2$ (left side):

$$\text{Tie} = V4b \times \frac{b}{H1} = 531 \times \frac{5.84}{2.54} = 1220 \text{ lb}$$

Determine horizontal tie force from window sill to wall pier $V2$ (right side):

$$\text{Tie} = V5b \times \frac{c}{H1} = 531 \times \frac{2.1}{2.54} = 440 \text{ lb}$$

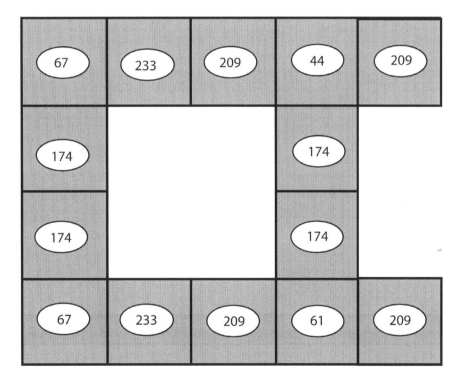

Figure 1-29. Shear forces in wall

Determine strap forces and boundary forces around openings.

Design horizontal tie straps above and below windows.

Determine the tie force for the horizontal strap for window header to wall pier (from Figures 1-25 through 1-28). Tie force (strength level) is maximum at the header beam.

$$F_{tie} = 1220 \text{ lb}$$

Determine the tie force for the horizontal strap for window sill to wall pier (from Figures 1-25 through 1-28). Tie force (strength level) is maximum at the window sill.

$$F_{tie} = 1220 \text{ lb}$$

Consult ICC Evaluation Reports for the allowable load capacity of premanufactured straps.

Check minimum penetration for full nail capacity in accordance with NDS Table 12P Footnote 3.

For 10d nails through 16-gage strap and ½-inch sheathing penetration = 3.0 − 0.060 − 0.5 = 2.4 in.

Required penetration for full value = $10D = 10 \times 0.148 = 1.5 < 2.4$ in ... OK

Allowable load per 10d common nails with 16-gage metal side plate = 116 lb   NDS T 12P

$$Z' = 116 \text{ lb/nail} \times C_D = 116 \times 1.6 = 185 \text{ lb/nail}$$

For ASD design:

Number of 10d nails required each end = $(1220 \times 0.7)/184 = 4.6$ nails

Use a continuous 16-gage by 1¼-inch strap across the opening head and sill to blocking.

Allowable strap load is the area times the allowable stress:

$$(1.25)(0.06)(0.6 \times 33,000) = 1485 \text{ lb} > 1220 \times 0.7 = 854 \text{ lb} \ldots \text{OK}$$

An allowable stress increase has not been used for the metal strap.

5.3 THE DIEKMANN METHOD

This method first appeared in the 2018 SEAOC Convention Proceedings and was presented at that convention.

The method assumes the following:

- The unit shear above and below the opening is uniform.
- The corner forces are based on the shear above and below the openings and only the piers adjacent to that specific opening.
- The tributary length of the opening is the basis for calculating the shear to each pier. This tributary length is the ratio of the length of the pier multiplied by the length of the opening it is adjacent to, divided by the sum of the length of the pier and the length of the pier on the other side of the opening.
  For example, $T_1 = (L_1 * L_{o1})/(L_1 + L_2)$
- The shear in each pier is the total shear divided by the *L* of the wall, multiplied by the sum of the length of the pier and its tributary length, divided by the length of the pier:
  $(V/L)(L_1 + T_1)/L_1$
- The unit shear of the corner zones is equal to subtracting the corner forces from the panel resistance, *R*. *R* is equal to the shear of the pier multiplied by the pier length:
  $Va_1 = (v_1 L_1 − F_1)/L_1$

Lateral (strength level) forces to wall lines 1 and 4 (see Table 1-14):

Roof level: $F_{tot} = 11{,}223$ lb

Fourth-floor level: $F_{tot} = 23{,}893$ lb

Third-floor level: $F_{tot} = 32{,}340$ lb

Second-floor level: $F_{tot} = 36{,}563$ lb

Design the wall with the first four wall piers on line 1 between grid lines B and E (see Figures 1-1 and 1-2).

First: Determine wall dimensions for the wall frame (Figure 1-30).

$$L_1 = 8.0 \text{ ft}, L_2 = 12.75 \text{ ft}, L_3 = 11.5 \text{ ft}, L_4 = 11.5 \text{ ft}, L_{o1} = 9.5 \text{ ft}, L_{o2} = 4.0 \text{ ft}, L_{o3} = 4.0 \text{ ft}$$

Total wall length for wall piers and openings on grid lines 1 and 4 (see Figure 1-1):

$$L = 96.0 \text{ ft}$$

Total wall length for wall piers shown in Figure 1-30:

$$\Sigma L = 8.0 + 12.75 + 11.5 + 11.5 = 43.75 \text{ ft}$$

The total shear to wall piers shown in Figure 1-30 is proportional to the total wall length in the same wall line:

$$V = \frac{\Sigma L}{\text{Total } \Sigma L} = \left(\frac{43.75}{64.5}\right) 11{,}223 \text{ lb} = 7612 \text{ lb}$$

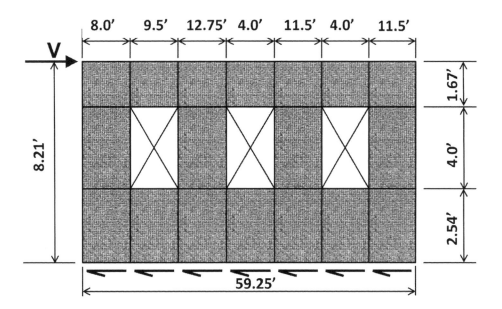

Figure 1-30. Wall elevation

Figure 1-31 is generic in nature and depicts three window openings. For this design example, the shear wall design for the piers between grid lines B and D will be illustrated where the wall frame continues for several openings, making the right side of the figure look like the center of the figure.

For lengths in Figure 1-31:

$L_1 = 8.0$ ft, $L_2 = 12.75$ ft, $L_3 = 11.5$ ft, $L_4 = 11.5$ ft

$L_{o1} = 9.5$ ft, $L_{o2} = 4.0$ ft, $L_{o3} = 4.0$ ft

$h = 8.21$ ft, $h_b = 2.54$ ft, $h_o = 4.0$ ft, $h_a = 1.67$ ft

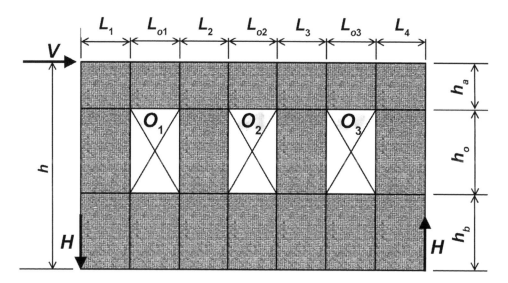

Figure 1-31. Tie-down forces

Second: Calculate tie-down forces.

$$H = V_h/L = 7612 \text{ lb} \times 8.21 \text{ ft}/61.25 \text{ ft} = 1020 \text{ lb}$$

Solve for shear above and below openings:

$$v_a = v_b = H/(h_a + h_b) = 1020 \text{ lb}/(1.67 \text{ ft} + 2.54 \text{ ft}) = 242 \text{ plf}$$

Find total boundary forces:

$$O_1 = v_a \times (L_{o1}) = 242 \text{ plf} \times 9.5 \text{ ft} = 2299 \text{ lb}$$
$$O_2 = v_a \times (L_{o2}) = 242 \text{ plf} \times 4.0 \text{ ft} = 968 \text{ lb}$$
$$O_3 = v_a \times (L_{o3}) = 242 \text{ plf} \times 4.0 \text{ ft} = 968 \text{ lb}$$

Third: Determine corner forces.

The corner forces are based on the shear above and below the openings and only the piers adjacent to that specific opening.

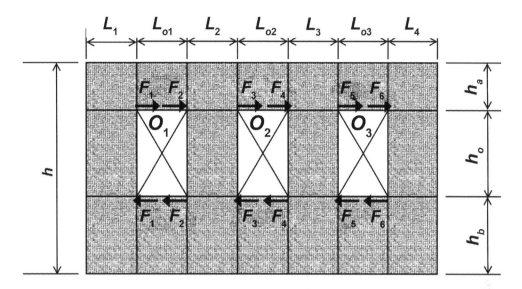

Figure 1-32. Corner forces

Calculate corner forces:

$$F_1 = O_1(L_1)/(L_1 + L_2) = 2299 \text{ lb} \times 8.0/(8.0 + 12.75) = 886 \text{ lb}$$

$$F_2 = O_1(L_2)/(L_1 + L_2) = 2299 \text{ lb} \times 12.75/(8.0 + 12.75) = 1413 \text{ lb}$$

$$F_3 = O_2(L_2)/(L_2 + L_3) = 968 \text{ lb} \times 12.75/(12.75 + 11.5) = 509 \text{ lb}$$

$$F_4 = O_2(L_3)/(L_2 + L_3) = 968 \text{ lb} \times 11.5/(12.75 + 11.5) = 459 \text{ lb}$$

$$F_5 = O_3(L_3)/(L_3 + L_4) = 968 \text{ lb} \times 11.5/(11.5 + 11.5) = 484 \text{ lb}$$

$$F_6 = O_3(L_4)/(L_3 + L_4) = 968 \text{ lb} \times 11.5/(11.5 + 11.5) = 484 \text{ lb}$$

Fourth: Calculate tributary lengths.

The tributary length is the product of the pier length and the opening length, divided by the sum of the pier lengths on each side of the opening.

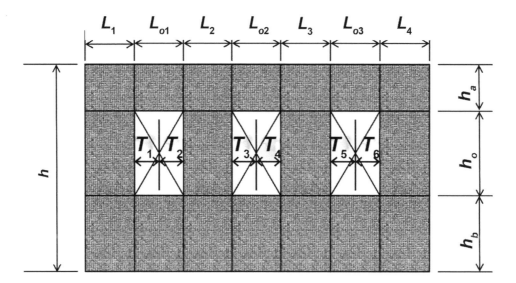

Figure 1-33. Tributary lengths

$T_1 = L_1 \times L_{o1}/(L_1 + L_2) = 8.0 \times 9.5/(8.0 + 12.75) = 3.66$ ft

$T_2 = L_2 \times L_{o1}/(L_1 + L_2) = 12.75 \times 9.5/(8.0 + 12.75) = 5.84$ ft

$T_3 = L_2 \times L_{o2}/(L_2 + L_3) = 12.75 \times 4.0/(12.75 + 11.5) = 2.10$ ft

$T_4 = L_3 \times L_{o2}/(L_2 + L_3) = 11.5 \times 4.0/(12.75 + 11.5) = 1.90$ ft

$T_5 = L_3 \times L_{o3}/(L_3 + L_4) = 11.5 \times 4.0/(11.5 + 11.5) = 2.0$ ft

$T_6 = L_4 \times L_{o3}/(L_3 + L_4) = 11.5 \times 4.0/(11.5 + 11.5) = 2.0$ ft

Fifth: Determine unit shears at sides of openings.

The shear force in each pier is the total shear divided by the length of the wall, multiplied by the sum of the pier length and its tributary length, divided by the length of the pier.

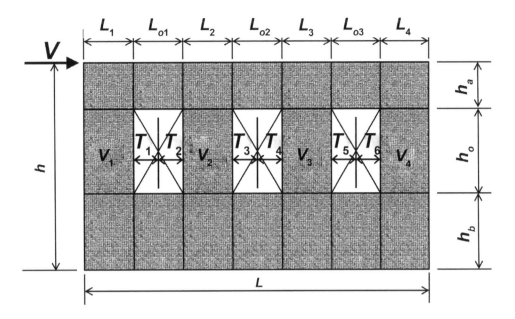

Figure 1-34. Unit shears determination

$V_1 = (V/L)(L_1 + T_1)/L_1$

$V_1 = (7612/61.25)(8.0 + 3.66)/8.0 = 181$ plf

$V_2 = (V/L)(T_2 + L_2 + T_3)/L_2$

$V_2 = (7612/61.25)(5.84 + 12.75 + 2.10)/12.75 = 202$ plf

$V_3 = (V/L)(T_4 + L_3 + T_5)/L_3$

$V_3 = (7612/61.25)(1.90 + 11.5 + 2.0)/11.5 = 166$ plf

$V_4 = (V/L)(T_6 + L_4)/L_4$

$V_4 = (7612/61.25)(2.0 + 11.5)/11.5 = 146$ plf

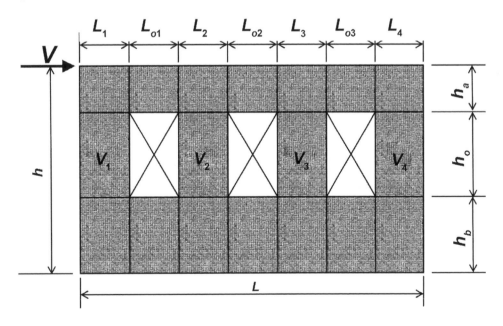

Figure 1-35. Sum forces in piers

Sixth: Check sum of shears in the piers.

$$V_1 \times L_1 = 181 \times 8.0 = 1448 \text{ lb}$$
$$V_2 \times L_2 = 202 \times 12.75 = 2576 \text{ lb}$$
$$V_3 \times L_3 = 166 \times 11.5 = 1909 \text{ lb}$$
$$V_4 \times L_4 = 146 \times 11.5 = 1679 \text{ lb}$$

Sum forces:

$$V_1 + V_2 + V_3 + V_4 = 1448 + 2576 + 1909 + 1679 = 7612 \text{ lb} \Rightarrow \text{checks}$$

Design horizontal tie straps above and below windows.

Determine the tie force for the horizontal strap for window header to wall pier (Figure 1-32). Tie force (strength level) is maximum at the header beam.

$$F_{tie} = 1413 \text{ lb}$$

Determine the tie force for the horizontal strap for window sill to wall pier (Figure 1-32). Tie force (strength level) is maximum at the window sill.

$$F_{tie} = 1413 \text{ lb}$$

Consult ICC Evaluation Reports for the allowable load capacity of premanufactured straps. Check minimum penetration for full nail capacity in accordance with NDS Table 12P Footnote 3.

For 10d nail through 16-gage strap and ½-inch sheathing penetration = 3.0 − 0.060 − 0.5 = 2.4 in.

Required penetration for full value = 10d = 10 × 0.148 = 1.5 < 2.4 in ... OK

Allowable load per 10d common nail with a 16-gage metal side plate = 116 lb   NDS T 12P

$$Z' = 116 \text{ lb/nail} \times C_D = 116 \times 1.6 = 185 \text{ lb/nail}$$

For ASD design:

Number of 10d nails required each end = (1413 × 0.7)/185 = 5.3 nails

Use a continuous 16-gage by 1¼-inch strap across the opening head and sill to blocking.

Allowable strap load is the area times the allowable stress:

$$(1.25)(0.06)(0.6 \times 33{,}000) = 1485 \text{ lb} > 1413 \times 0.7 = 989 \text{ lb} \dots \text{ OK}$$

An allowable stress increase has not been used for the metal strap.

5.4 COMPARISON OF THOMPSON METHOD WITH DIEKMANN METHOD

Thompson method shears at sides of openings and above and below openings:

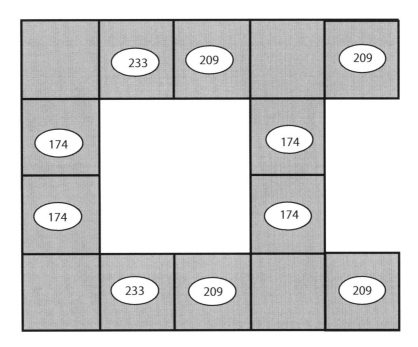

Figure 1-36. Sum forces in piers—Thompson method

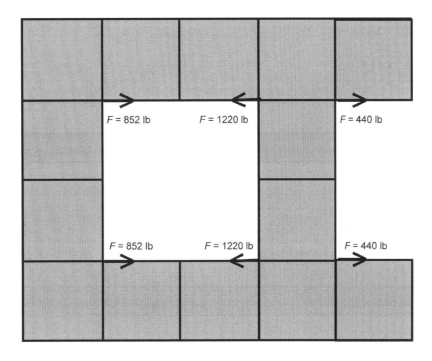

Figure 1-37. Tie forces—Thompson method

Diekmann Method shears at sides of openings and above and below openings:

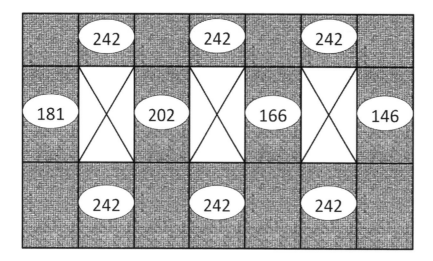

Figure 1-38. Shear forces in segments—Diekmann method

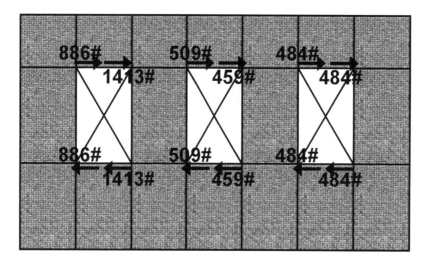

Figure 1-39. Shear forces in segments—Diekmann method

5.5 SHEAR WALL DEFLECTION USING WINDOW STRIPS (UNIT STRIP METHOD)

The deflection for a shear wall can be approximated by using an analysis similar to computing the stiffness for a concrete wall with an opening in it. The deflection for the solid wall is computed, then a deflection for a horizontal window strip is subtracted, and the deflection for the wall piers added back in.

Engineering judgment may be used to simplify this approximation. However, the method shown in Figure 1-40 is one method to approximate the deflection.

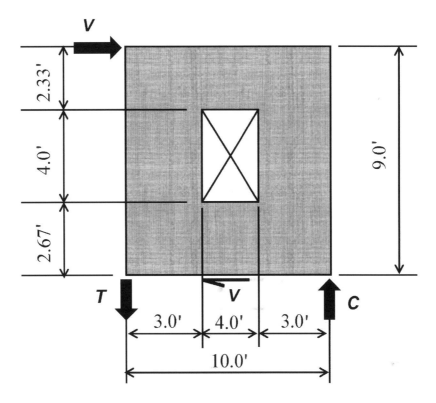

Figure 1-40. Elevation of wall frame with opening

The method illustrated here neglects any rotation of the wall piers due to any displacements of the sill plate below the window jambs. These amounts can be calculated but are extremely time-consuming.

First, determine deflection of the entire wall, without an opening.

$$\delta = \frac{8vh^3}{EAb} + \frac{vh}{1000G_a} + d_a\frac{h}{b_{eff}}$$

Eq 4.3-1

Second, determine deflection of window strip.

Since the boundary elements are connected to continuous posts that extend above and below the opening, the value of Δ_a equals the sheathing-nail deformation value calculated above (boundary element chord elongation is neglected).

This deflection is negative because it is subtracted from the sum of the deflections, as shown later.

Third, determine deflection of wall piers.

Since the boundary elements are connected to continuous posts that extend above and below the opening, the value of Δ_a equals the sheathing-nail deformation value calculated for the wall piers.

Last, determine the sum of the deflections.

The deflection is the sum of the solid wall (first step) minus the deflection of the window strip (second step) plus the deflection of the wall piers (third step).

Using the window strip method for determining shear wall deflection for the shear wall illustrated in Figure 1-20, the wall has 92 percent of stiffness of the same wall without the opening.

5.6 SHEAR WALL DEFLECTION USING PERFORATED SHEAR WALL METHOD   SDPWS

The deflection for a shear wall can be approximated by using the method of perforated shear walls in SDPWS Section 4.3.2.1, where v in Equation 4.3-1 is equal to v_{max} obtained in Equation 4.3-9 and b is taken as ΣL_i.

First, determine v_{max}.

$$v_{max} = \frac{V}{C_0 \Sigma L_i}$$
Eq 4.3-9

where

C_0 = shear capacity adjustment factor from Table 4.3.3.5 or can be calculated with Equations 4.3-5 and 4.3-6:

$$C_0 = \left(\frac{r}{3 - 2r}\right)\frac{L_{tot}}{\Sigma L_i}$$
Eq 4.3-5

$$r = \frac{1}{1 + \dfrac{A_0}{h\Sigma L_i}}$$
Eq 4.3-6

where

    r = sheathing area ratio

    L_{tot} = total length of a perforated shear wall including the lengths of perforated shear wall segments and the lengths of segments containing openings

    A_0 = total area of openings in the perforated shear wall individual opening areas calculated as the opening width times the clear opening height

    h = height of the perforated shear wall

    ΣL_i = sum of perforated shear wall segment lengths, ft

Using the perforated wall method for determining shear wall deflection for the shear wall illustrated in Figure 1-20, the wall has 59 percent of stiffness of the same wall without the opening.

The window strip method for determining shear wall deflection appears to overestimate the stiffness of the wall and is more time-consuming than the perforated wall method.

For determining shear wall deflections and stiffnesses, this design example will use the perforated wall method. Testing has shown the shear walls with openings have good stiffness degradation and performance compared to shear walls without openings.

6. The Envelope Process   ASCE 7

6.1 ASSUMPTION OF FLEXIBLE DIAPHRAGMS   §12.3.1.1

ASCE 7 Section 12.3.1.1 allows wood structural panel diaphragms to be idealized as flexible if any of the following conditions exist:

1. In structures where the vertical elements are steel-braced frames; steel and concrete composite-braced frames; or concrete, masonry, steel, or steel and concrete composite shear walls.

2. In one- and two-family dwellings.

3. In structures of light-frame construction where all of the following conditions are met:

   a. Topping of concrete or similar materials is not placed over wood structural panel diaphragms except for nonstructural topping not greater than 1½ inches thick.

   b. Each line of vertical elements of the seismic-force-resisting system complies with the allowable story drift of Table 12.12-1.

In this design example, condition 3 is met since the structure does not exceed the 1½ inches of lightweight concrete.

Section 6.4 of this design example for drift check of typical shear wall complies with the allowable story drift.

6.2 LATERAL FORCES ON SHEAR WALLS AND SHEAR WALL NAILING IDEALIZED AS FLEXIBLE DIAPHRAGMS

In this step, forces on shear walls due to seismic forces will be determined. As was customary in the past, this portion of the example assumes flexible diaphragms. ASCE 7 Section 12.8.4.1 does not require torsional effects to be considered for flexible diaphragms. The effects of torsion and wall rigidities will be considered in Part 6.5 of this design example.

Under diaphragms idealized as flexible, loads to shear walls are determined based on tributary areas with simple spans between supports. Another method of determining loads to shear walls assumes a continuous beam. This design example uses the total building weight *W* applied to each respective direction. The results shown will be slightly conservative since the building weight *W* includes the wall weights for the direction of load, which can be subtracted out. This example converts the story forces into seismic forces per square foot of floor or roof area. This may result in the loss of a certain amount of precision, but it also results in much simpler calculations. This approach is generally considered acceptable unless there appears to be a concentration of dead load in a particular area (e.g., a mechanical penthouse).

A detailed analysis will include the derivation of these tributary weights, which include the tributary exterior and interior wall weights.

Using forces from Table 1-3 and the area of the floor plan = 5288 square feet, calculate tributary weights.

For roof diaphragm:
Roof area = 5288 ft^2

$$f_{p\,Roof} = \frac{49.37 \times 1000}{5288} = 9.34 \text{ psf}$$

For fourth-floor diaphragm:
Floor area = 5288 ft^2

$$f_{p\,4th} = \frac{55.74 \times 1000}{5288} = 10.54 \text{ psf}$$

For third-floor diaphragm:
Floor area = 5288 ft^2

$$f_{p\,3rd} = \frac{37.16 \times 1000}{5288} = 7.03 \text{ psf}$$

For second-floor diaphragm:
Floor area = 5288 ft^2

$$f_{p\,2nd} = \frac{18.58 \times 1000}{5288} = 3.51 \text{ psf}$$

Table 1-13. Forces to walls and required panel nailing for east-west direction[1,2,3]

Wall	Trib. Area (ft^2)	ΣF_{Above} (lb)	ΣF_x (lb)	F_{tot} (lb)	b[4] (ft)	$v = \dfrac{F_{tot}}{b}$	$v = \dfrac{F_{tot}}{(1.4)\,b}$ (plf)[5]	Sheathed 1 or 2 Sides	Allowable Shear[6] (plf)	Edge Nail Spacing (in)
Shear Walls at Roof Level[7]										
A	170	0	1587	1587	12.5	127	91	1	340	6
B	746	0	6965	6965	22.0	317	226	1	340	6
C	1344	0	12,548	12,548	43.0	292	208	1	340	6
E	1344	0	12,548	12,548	43.0	292	208	1	340	6
F	960	0	8963	8963	43.0	208	149	1	340	6
G	554	0	5172	5172	22.0	235	168	1	340	6
H	170	0	1587	1587	12.5	127	91	1	340	6
Σ	5288	0	49,372	49,372						
Shear Walls at Fourth-Floor Level										
A	170	1587	1792	3379	12.5	270	193	1	655	3
B	746	6965	7864	14,829	22.0	674	481	1	510	4
C	1344	12,548	14,167	26,715	43.0	621	444	1	510	4
E	1344	12,548	14,167	26,715	43.0	621	444	1	510	4
F	960	8963	10,119	19,082	43.0	444	317	1	655	3
G	554	5172	5840	11,012	22.0	501	358	1	510	4
H	170	1587	1792	3379	12.5	270	193	1	655	3
Σ	5288	49,372	55,741	105,112						
Shear Walls at Third-Floor Level										
A	170	3379	1195	4574	12.5	366	261	1	870	2
B	746	14,829	5242	20,071	22.0	912	652	1	665	3
C	1344	26,715	9445	36,160	43.0	841	601	1	665	3
E	1344	26,715	9445	36,160	43.0	841	601	1	665	3
F	960	19,082	6746	25,829	43.0	601	429	1	655	3
G	554	11,012	3893	14,905	22.0	678	484	1	655	3
H	170	3379	1195	4574	12.5	366	261	1	870	2
Σ	5288	105,112	37,161	142,273						
Shear Walls at Second-Floor Level										
A	170	4,574	597	5171	12.5	414	295	1	870	2
B	746	20,071	2621	22,692	22.0	1031	737	1	870	2
C	1344	36,160	4722	40,882	43.0	951	679	1	870	2
E	1344	36,160	4722	40,882	43.0	951	679	1	870	2
F	960	25,829	3373	29,202	43.0	679	485	1	870	2
G	554	14,905	1947	16,852	22.0	766	547	1	870	2
H	170	4,574	597	5171	12.5	414	295	1	870	2
Σ	5288	142,273	18,580	160,853						

Notes for Table 1-13:

1. In SDC D, E, or F, SDPWS Section 4.3.7.1 requires 3× nominal thickness stud framing at abutting panels or two 2× members where the required nominal shear exceeds 700 plf, or the nail spacing is 2 inches on center or less at adjoining panel edges, or 10d common nails having penetration into framing members and blocking of more than 1½ inches are 3 inches on center or less.

2. Refer to Section 7.3 in this design example for sill-plate anchorage.

3. IBC Section 1705.12 requires special inspection where the nail spacing is 4 inches on center or closer with SDC C and higher.

4. The shear wall length used for wall shears is the "out-to-out" wall length.

5. Forces are strength level and the shear in wall is divided by 1.4 to convert to allowable stress design.

6. APA or TECO performance-rated Structural-I-rated wood structural panels may be either plywood or OSB. The allowable shear values are from SDPWS Table 4.3A using 10d common nails with a minimum 1½-inch penetration and $^{15}\!/_{32}$-inch panel thickness and divided by the ASD reduction factor of 2.0.

7. Shear walls at lines C, E, and F extend to the bottom of the prefabricated wood trusses at the roof level. Shear transfer is obtained by framing clips from the bottom chord of the trusses to the top plates of the shear walls. Project plans call for trusses at these lines to be designed for these horizontal forces (see also comments in Section 1.2). Roof shear forces are also transferred to lines A, B, G, and H.

Table 1-14. Forces to walls and required panel nailing for north-south direction[1, 2, 3]

Wall	Trib. Area (ft²)	ΣF_{Above} (lb)	ΣF_x (lb)	F_{tot} (lb)	$b^{(4)}$ (ft)	$v = \dfrac{F_{tot}}{b}$	$v = \dfrac{F_{tot}}{(1.4)b}$ (plf)[5]	Sheathed 1 or 2 Sides	Allowable Shear[6] (plf)	Edge Nail Spacing (in)
Shear Walls at Roof Level										
1	1202	0	11,223	11,223	64.5	174	124	1	340	6
2	1442	0	13,463	13,463	60.0	224	160	1	340	6
3	1442	0	13,463	13,463	60.0	224	160	1	340	6
4	1202	0	11,223	11,223	64.5	174	124	1	340	6
Σ	5288	0	49,372	49,372						
Shear Walls at Fourth-Floor Level										
1	1202	11,223	12,670	23,893	64.5	370	265	1	510	4
2	1442	13,463	15,200	28,663	60.0	478	341	1	340	6
3	1442	13,463	15,200	28,663	60.0	478	341	1	340	6
4	1202	11,223	12,670	23,893	64.5	370	265	1	510	4
Σ	5288	49,372	55,741	105,112						
Shear Walls at Third-Floor Level										
1	1202	23,893	8447	32,340	64.5	501	358	1	510	4
2	1442	28,663	10,133	38,797	60.0	647	462	1	510	4
3	1442	28,663	10,133	38,797	60.0	647	462	1	510	4
4	1202	23,893	8447	32,340	64.5	501	358	1	510	4
Σ	5288	105,112	37,161	142,273						
Shear Walls at Second-Floor Level										
1	1202	32,340	4223	36,563	64.5	567	405	1	655	3
2	1442	38,797	5067	43,864	60.0	731	522	1	665	3
3	1442	38,797	5067	43,864	60.0	731	522	1	665	3
4	1202	32,340	4223	36,563	64.5	567	405	1	655	3
Σ	5288	142,273	18,580	160,853						

Notes for Table 1-14:

1. In SDC D, E, or F, SDPWS Section 4.3.7.1 requires 3× nominal thickness stud framing at abutting panels or two 2× members where the required nominal shear exceeds 700 plf, or the nail spacing is 2 inches on center or less at adjoining panel edges, or 10d common nails having penetration into framing members and blocking of more than 1½ inches are 3 inches on center or less.

2. Refer to Section 7.3 in this Design Example for sill-plate anchorage.

3. IBC Section 1705.12 requires special inspection when the nail spacing is 4 inches on center or closer with SDC C and higher.

4. The shear wall length used for wall shears is the "out-to-out" wall length.

5. Forces are strength level and shear in wall is divided by 1.4 to convert to allowable stress design.

6. APA or TECO performance-rated Structural-I-rated wood structural panels may be either plywood or OSB. The allowable shear values are from SDPWS Table 4.3A using 10d common nails with a minimum 1½-inch penetration and ¹⁵/₃₂-inch panel thickness and divided by the ASD reduction factor of 2.0.

6.3 CALCULATION OF SHEAR WALL RIGIDITIES

In this example, shear wall rigidities are calculated using the three- or four-term code deflection equation. These calculations are facilitated by the use of a spreadsheet program, which eliminates possible arithmetic errors from the many repetitive computations that must be made.

The first step is to calculate the displacement (i.e., vertical elongation and deflection) of the tie-down assembly elements and the crushing effect of the boundary element. This is the term d_a. The force considered to act on the tie-down assembly is the net uplift force determined from the flexible diaphragm analyses. These forces are summarized in Tables 1-15, 1-20, 1-24, and 1-28 for the roof, the fourth floor, the third floor, and the second floor, respectively.

After the tie-down assembly displacements are determined, the four-term deflection equation is used to determine the deflection, Δ, of each shear wall. These are summarized in Tables 1-16 and 1-17 for the roof level, in Tables 1-21 and 1-22 for the fourth-floor level, in Tables 1-25 and 1-26 for the third-floor level, and in Tables 1-29 and 1-30 for the second-floor level.

Finally, the rigidities of the shear walls are summarized in Tables 1-18, 1-23, 1-27, and 1-31 for the roof, fourth floor, third floor, and second floor, respectively. For both strength and allowable stress design, ASCE 7 now requires building drifts to be determined by earthquake forces without multiplying by 0.7.

Using strength-level forces for wood design utilizing ASCE 7 and the IBC means that the engineer will use both strength-level forces and allowable stress forces. This can create some confusion because the code requires drift checks to be strength-level forces. However, most engineers design wood using allowable stress design. Drift and shear wall rigidities should be calculated from the strength-level forces. Remember that the structural system factor R is based on using strength-level forces.

Rigidities of Shear Walls

Determination of wood shear wall rigidities is not a simple task. In practice, approximate methods are often used. The method illustrated in this example is by far the most rigorous method used. There are other, more simplified methods, and their use is often appropriate.

It must be emphasized that, at the present time, *every* method is approximate, particularly for multistory structures such as those in this example as there has been only very limited testing on performance of multistory wood-sheathed shear walls. Until more definite general procedures are established through further testing and research, the designer must exercise judgment in selecting the appropriate method to be used for a given structure.

When in doubt, consult with the local building official regarding methods acceptable to the jurisdiction. At the time of this publication, the type of seismic design required for a project of this type varies greatly from one jurisdiction to another.

Wall rigidities (stiffness) are approximate. The initial rigidity of the structure can be significantly higher because of stucco, drywall, brick, and stone veneers, stiffening effects of walls not considered, and areas over doors and windows. During an earthquake, some low-stressed walls may maintain their stiffness while others degrade in stiffness. Some walls and their collectors may attract significantly more lateral load than anticipated in semi-flexible diaphragm analysis. The method of analyzing a structure using inflexible diaphragms takes significantly more engineering effort. However, use of the rigid-diaphragm method indicates that some lateral-resisting elements can attract significantly higher seismic demands than tributary area (i.e., flexible diaphragm) analysis methods. Yet with the limited testing data on multistory wall performance and the often approximate methods available for determining wood-sheathed wall and floor diaphragm deflections, engineers are asked to design more complex lateral systems that include multistory narrow shear walls, cantilevered diaphragms, and/or rigid diaphragms to accommodate open-front designs.

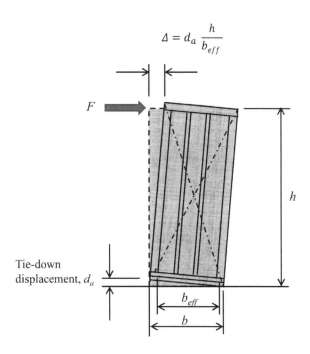

Figure 1-41.

In this example, shear wall rigidities, k, are computed using the basic stiffness equation

$$F = k\Delta$$

or

$$k = \frac{F}{\Delta}$$

Estimation of Roof-Level Rigidities

To estimate roof-level wall rigidities, roof-level displacements must first be determined. The following are a series of calculations in table form to estimate the roof-level drifts, Δ, in each shear wall. First, the shear wall tie-down assembly displacements are determined (Table 1-15). These and the parameters given in Table 1-15 are used to arrive at the drifts, Δ, for each shear wall at the roof level (Tables 1-16 and 1-17). Rigidities are estimated in Table 1-18 for walls in both directions. Once the drifts are known, a drift check is performed. This is summarized in Table 1-19.

Table 1-15. Determine tie-down assembly displacements at the roof level[1]

Wall	Tie-Down Device[6]	ASD Uplift[2] (lb)	Uplift[2] (lb)	Strength Design Tie-Down[3] Elongation (in)	Takeup Device Elongation (in)	Shrink[4] (in)	Chord Crush[5] (in)	Bearing Plate Crush (in)	Δ_a[7] (in)
A	Rod	0	0	0.000	0.030	0.031	0.003	0.000	0.064
B1	Rod	1922	2691	0.040	0.030	0.031	0.009	0.008	0.118
B2	Rod	1922	2691	0.040	0.030	0.031	0.009	0.008	0.118
C1	Rod	2878	4029	0.061	0.030	0.031	0.048	0.011	0.340
C2	Rod	2878	4029	0.061	0.030	0.031	0.048	0.011	0.340
E1	Rod	2878	4029	0.061	0.030	0.031	0.048	0.011	0.340
E2	Rod	2878	4029	0.061	0.030	0.031	0.048	0.011	0.340
F1	Rod	1848	2588	0.039	0.030	0.031	0.005	0.007	0.113
F2	Rod	1848	2588	0.039	0.030	0.031	0.005	0.007	0.113
G1	Rod	1922	2691	0.040	0.030	0.031	0.009	0.008	0.118
G2	Rod	1922	2691	0.040	0.030	0.031	0.009	0.008	0.118
H	Rod	0	0	0.000	0.030	0.031	0.009	0.000	0.064
1	None	0	0	0.000	0	0.000	0	0	0
2a	None	0	0	0.000	0.030	0.031	0.003	0.000	0.065
2b	None	0	0	0.000	0.030	0.031	0.004	0.000	0.065
2c	None	0	0	0.000	0.030	0.031	0.013	0.000	0.065
3a	None	0	0	0.000	0.030	0.031	0.003	0.000	0.065
3b	None	0	0	0.000	0.030	0.031	0.004	0.000	0.065
3c	None	0	0	0.000	0.030	0.031	0.013	0.000	0.065
4	None	0	0		0	0.000	0	0	0

Notes for Table 1-15:

1. Tie-down assembly displacements for the roof level are calculated for the tie-downs at the fourth-floor level.

2. Uplift force is determined by using the *net* overturning moment (Mot-MR) divided by the distance between the *centroids* of the boundary elements with 4× members at the ends of the shear wall where MR uses load combinations outlined in Part 4.2 of this design example. Using allowable stress design, tie-down devices need only be sized by using the ASD uplift force. The strength design uplift force is used to determine tie-down assembly displacement and then to determine strength-level displacements.

3. The continuous tie-down (rod) system selected for this structure will have a shrinkage compensating system. Most of these systems have shrinkage compensation by either pre-tensioning of cables or a self-ratcheting hardware connector and are proprietary. The device selected in this design example has adjusting grooves at $\frac{1}{10}$-inch increments, meaning the most the system will not have compensated for in shrinkage and crushing will be $\frac{1}{10}$ inch. If the selected device does not have a shrinkage compensating device, then shrinkage of floor framing, sill plates, compression bridges, crushing of bridge support studs, and collector studs will need to be considered.

4. Wood shrinkage is based on a change in moisture content (MC) from 19 percent to 12 percent, with 19 percent MC being assumed for S-Dry lumber per project specifications. The MC of 12 percent is the assumed final MC at equilibrium with ambient humidity for the project location. The final equilibrium value can be higher in coastal areas and lower in inland or desert areas. This equates to $(0.002)(d)(19 - 12)$, where d is the dimension of the lumber (see Figure 1-7). Pressure-treated lumber has a moisture content of less than 16 percent at treatment completion. Shrinkage of the 4× top plate + 2× DBL sill plate = $(0.002)(3.5 + 2 \times 1.5)(19 - 12) = 0.078$ inch. Since shrinkage compensating devices are used, a value of $\frac{1}{32}$ inch is used, recognizing that most devices have to travel a distance before they get to the next groove in the device to readjust.

5. Per NDS Section 4.2.6, when compression perpendicular to grain $f_{c\perp}$ is less than $0.73F_{c\perp}$, crushing will be approximately 0.02 inch. When $f_{c\perp} = 0.73F_{c\perp}$, crushing is estimated at 0.04 inch. The effect of sill plate crushing is the downward effect at the opposite end of the wall with uplift force and has the same rotational effect as the tie-down displacement. Short walls that have no uplift forces will still have a crushing effect and contribute to rotation of the wall.

6. If bolted-type tie-down devices are used, the displacement for the bolt slip can be determined by NDS Section 11.3.6 load/slip modulus $\gamma = (270,000)(D^{1.5})$, plus an additional $\frac{1}{16}$ inch for the oversized hole for bolts. For nails, values for e_n can be used.

7. Δ_a is the total tie-down assembly displacement. This also could include miscuts (short studs) and lack of square-cut ends.

Table 1-16. Deflections of shear walls at the roof level in the east-west direction

Wall	Strength v (plf)	h (ft)	A (in^2)	E (psi)	b (ft)	b_{eff} (ft)	$G_v t_v$ (psi)	Nail Spacing (in)	V_n (lb)	e_n (in)	Δ_a (in)	Δ (in)
A	127	8.21	17.5	1,700,000	12.5	11.6	45,500	6	63	0.0003	0.064	0.072
B1	317	8.21	17.5	1,700,000	11.0	10.1	45,500	6	158	0.0056	0.118	0.19
B2	317	8.21	17.5	1,700,000	11.0	10.1	45,500	6	158	0.0056	0.118	0.19
B					22.0	—						
C1	292	8.21	35.0	1,700,000	21.5	20.3	45,500	6	146	0.0043	0.180	0.15
C2	292	8.21	35.0	1,700,000	21.5	20.3	45,500	6	146	0.0043	0.180	0.15
C					43.0	—						
E1	292	8.21	35.0	1,700,000	21.5	20.3	45,500	6	146	0.0043	0.180	0.15
E2	292	8.21	35.0	1,700,000	21.5	20.3	45,500	6	146	0.0043	0.180	0.15
E					43.0	—						
F1	208	8.21	35.0	1,700,000	21.5	20.3	45,500	6	104	0.0014	0.113	0.09
F2	208	8.21	35.0	1,700,000	21.5	20.3	45,500	6	104	0.0014	0.113	0.09
F					43.0	—						
G1	235	8.21	17.5	1,700,000	11.0	10.1	45,500	6	118	0.0021	0.118	0.16
G2	235	8.21	17.5	1,700,000	11.0	10.1	45,500	6	118	0.0021	0.118	0.16
G					22.0	—						
H	127	8.21	17.5	1,700,000	12.5	11.6	45,500	6	63	0.0003	0.064	0.072

Table 1-17. Deflections of shear walls at the roof level in the north-south direction

Wall	v (plf)	h (ft)	A (in^2)	E (psi)	b (ft)	b_{eff} (ft)	$G_v t_v$ (psi)	Nail Space (in)	V_n (lb)	e_n (in)	d_a (in)	A_0	r	C_0	v_{max}	Δ (in)
1, 4	174	8.21	11.55	1,700,000	64.5	—	45500	6	87	0.0008	0.00	112	0.83	0.91	191	0.04
1, 4				$\Sigma L_i = 64.5$												
2a,3a	224	8.21	38.50	1,700,000	18.0	16.6	45500	6	112	0.0018	0.07					0.08
2b,3b	224	8.21	38.50	1,700,000	24.0	22.6	45500	6	112	0.0018	0.07					0.08
2c,3c	224	8.21	38.50	1,700,000	18.0	16.6	45500	6	112	0.0018	0.07					0.08
2, 3					60.0											

Table 1-18. Shear wall rigidities at the roof level[1]

Wall	$\Delta^{(2)}$ (in)	F (lb)	$k_i = \dfrac{F}{\Delta}$ (k/in)	K_{total} (k/in)
A	0.072	1587	22.1	22.1
B1	0.19	3483	18.2	
B2	0.19	3483	18.2	36.2
B		6965	36.2	
C1	0.15	6274	40.9	
C2	0.15	6274	40.9	81.7
C		12,548	82.0	
E1	0.15	6274	40.9	
E2	0.15	6274	40.9	81.7
E		12,548	82.0	
F1	0.09	4482	48.3	
F2	0.09	4482	48.3	97.0
F		8963	97.0	
G1	0.15	2586	16.7	
G2	0.15	2586	16.7	33.4
G		5172	33.4	
H	0.07	1587	22.1	22.1
1, 4	0.04	11,223	281.0	281.0
2a, 3a	0.08	4039	47.5	
2b, 3b	0.08	5385	70.8	166.0
2c, 3c	0.08	4039	47.5	
2, 3		13,463	166.0	

Notes for Table 1-18:

1. Deflections and forces are based on strength-force levels.

2. Δs are the design-level displacements from Tables 1-16 and 1-17.

Estimation of Fourth-Floor Level Rigidities

Shear wall rigidities at the fourth floor are estimated in the same manner as those at the roof. The calculations are summarized in Tables 1-19, 1-20, 1-21, and 1-22. A drift check is not shown.

Table 1-19. Tie-down assembly displacements at the fourth-floor level[1]

Wall	Tie-Down Device	ASD Uplift[2] (lb)	Uplift[2] (lb)	Strength Design Tie-Down[3] Elongation (in)	Takeup Device Elongation (in)	Shrink[4] (in)	Chord Crush[5] (in)	Bearing Plate Crush (in)	$\Delta_a^{(7)}$ (in)
A	Rod	8	11	0.000	0.030	0.031	0.009	0.002	0.072
B1	Rod	7117	9964	0.172	0.030	0.031	0.047	0.057	0.337
B2	Rod	7117	9964	0.172	0.030	0.031	0.047	0.057	0.337
C1	Rod	6561	9186	0.159	0.030	0.031	0.092	0.028	0.340
C2	Rod	6561	9186	0.159	0.030	0.031	0.092	0.028	0.340
E1	Rod	6561	9186	0.159	0.030	0.031	0.092	0.028	0.340
E2	Rod	6561	9186	0.159	0.030	0.031	0.092	0.028	0.340
F1	Rod	4241	5938	0.103	0.030	0.031	0.012	0.015	0.191
F2	Rod	4241	5938	0.103	0.030	0.031	0.012	0.015	0.191
G1	Rod	7117	9964	0.172	0.030	0.031	0.047	0.057	0.337
G2	Rod	7117	9964	0.172	0.030	0.031	0.047	0.057	0.337
H	Rod	8	11	0	0.030	0.031	0.009	0.002	0.072
1	None	0	0	0	0	0	0	0	0
2a	None	0	0	0	0.030	0.031	0.009	0.000	0.074
2b	None	0	0	0	0.030	0.031	0.012	0.000	0.074
2c	None	0	0	0	0.030	0.031	0.013	0.000	0.074
3a	None	0	0	0	0.030	0.031	0.009	0.000	0.074
3b	None	0	0	0	0.030	0.031	0.012	0.000	0.074
3c	None	0	0	0	0.030	0.031	0.013	0.000	0.074
4	None	0	0	0	0	0	0	0	0

Notes for Table 1-19:

1. Tie-down assembly displacements for the third-floor level are calculated for the tie-downs at the second-floor level.

2. Footnotes 2 through 7, see Table 1-15.

Table 1-20. Deflections of shear walls at the fourth-floor level in the east-west direction

Wall	Strength v (plf)	h (ft)	A (in^2)	E (psi)	b (ft)	b_{eff} (ft)	$G_v t_v$ (psi)	Space (in)	V_n (lb)	e_n (in)	Δ_a (in)	Δ (in)
A	270	9.44	17.5	1,700,000	12.5	11.6	45,500	3	68	0.0003	0.072	0.12
B1	674	9.44	17.5	1,700,000	11.0	10.1	45,500	4	225	0.0178	0.332	0.59
B2	674	9.44	17.5	1,700,000	11.0	10.1	45,500	4	225	0.0178	0.332	0.59
B					22.0							
C1	621	9.44	35.0	1,700,000	21.5	20.3	45,500	4	207	0.0136	0.338	0.39
C2	621	9.44	35.0	1,700,000	21.5	20.3	45,500	4	207	0.0136	0.338	0.39
C					43.0							
E1	621	9.44	35.0	1,700,000	21.5	20.3	45,500	4	207	0.0136	0.338	0.39
E2	621	9.44	35.0	1,700,000	21.5	20.3	45,500	4	207	0.0136	0.338	0.39
E					43.0							
F1	444	9.44	35.0	1,700,000	21.5	20.3	45,500	3	111	0.0018	0.182	0.20
F2	444	9.44	35.0	1,700,000	21.5	20.3	45,500	3	111	0.0018	0.182	0.20
F					43.0							
G1	501	9.44	17.5	1,700,000	11.0	10.1	45,500	4	167	0.0067	0.332	0.48
G2	501	9.44	17.5	1,700,000	11.0	10.1	45,500	4	167	0.0067	0.332	0.48
G					22.0							
H	270	9.44	17.5	1,700,000	12.5	11.6	45,500	3	68	0.0003	0.072	0.12

Table 1-21. Deflections of shear walls at the fourth-floor level in the north-south direction

Wall	v (plf)	h (ft)	A (in^2)	E (psi)	b (ft)	b_{eff} (ft)	$G_v t_v$ (psi)	Space (in)	V_n (lb)	e_n (in)	d_a (in)	A_0	r	C_0	v_{max}	Δ (in)
1, 4	370	9.44	11.55	1,700,000	—		45,500	4	123	0.0025	0	112	0.84	0.96	386	0.10
1, 4				$\Sigma L_i = 64.5$												
2a,3a	478	9.44	38.50	1,700,000	18.0	16.6	45,500	6	239	0.0217	0.07	—	—	—	—	0.30
2b,3b	478	9.44	38.50	1,700,000	24.0	22.6	45,500	6	239	0.0217	0.07	—	—	—	—	0.29
2c,3c	478	9.44	38.50	1,700,000	18.0	16.6	45,500	6	239	0.0217	0.07	—	—	—	—	0.30
2, 3					60.0											

Table 1-22. Shear wall rigidities at the fourth-floor level[1]

Wall	$\Delta^{(2)}$ (in)	F (lb)	$k_i = \dfrac{F}{\Delta}$ (k/in)	K_{total} (k/in)
A	0.12	3379	27.6	27.6
B1	0.59	7414	12.5	
B2	0.59	7414	12.5	24.9
B		14,829	24.9	
C1	0.39	13,358	34.5	
C2	0.39	13,358	34.5	69.0
C		26,715	69.0	
E1	0.39	13,358	34.5	
E2	0.39	13,358	34.5	69.0
E		26,715	69.0	
F1	0.22	9541	48.7	
F2	0.22	9541	48.7	97.4
F		19,082	97.4	
G1	0.48	5506	11.5	
G2	0.48	5506	11.5	23.1
G		11,012	23.1	
H	0.13	3379	27.6	27.6
1, 4	0.10	23,893	240.0	240.0
2a, 3a	0.30	8599	28.9	
2b, 3b	0.29	11,465	40.1	97.9
2c, 3c	0.30	8599	28.9	
2, 3		28,663	97.9	

Notes for Table 1-22:

1. Deflections and forces are based on strength levels.

2. Δs are the design-level displacements from Tables 1-20 and 1-21.

Estimation of Third-Floor Level Rigidities

Shear wall rigidities at the second-floor level are estimated in the same manner as those for the roof and third floor. The calculations are summarized in Tables 1-23, 1-24, 1-25, and 1-26. A drift check is not shown.

Table 1-23. Tie-down assembly displacements at the third-floor level[1]

Wall	Tie-down Device	ASD	Strength Design						
		Uplift[2] (lb)	Uplift[2] (lb)	Tie-down Assembly Displacement					$\Delta_a^{(7)}$ (in)
				Tie-down[3] Elongation (in)	Takeup Device Elongation (in)	Shrink[4] (in)	Chord Crush[5] (in)	Bearing Plate Crush (in)	
A	Rod	576	806	0.007	0.030	0.031	0.010	0.002	0.080
B1	Rod	12,851	17,991	0.152	0.030	0.031	0.018	0.029	0.260
B2	Rod	12,851	17,991	0.152	0.030	0.031	0.018	0.029	0.260
C1	Rod	11,928	16,700	0.141	0.030	0.031	0.130	0.024	0.356
C2	Rod	11,928	16,700	0.141	0.030	0.031	0.130	0.024	0.356
E1	Rod	11,928	16,700	0.141	0.030	0.031	0.130	0.024	0.356
E2	Rod	11,928	16,700	0.141	0.030	0.031	0.130	0.024	0.356
F1	Rod	7831	10,963	0.093	0.030	0.031	0.015	0.015	0.184
F2	Rod	7831	10,963	0.093	0.030	0.031	0.015	0.015	0.184
G1	Rod	12,851	17,991	0.152	0.030	0.031	0.018	0.029	0.260
G2	Rod	12,851	17,991	0.152	0.030	0.031	0.018	0.029	0.260
H	Rod	576	864	0.007	0.030	0.031	0.010	0.002	0.080
1	None	0	0	0	0	0	0	0	0
2a	Rod	0	0	0.019	0.030	0.031	0.010	0.006	0.101
2b	Rod	0	0	0.033	0.030	0.031	0.015	0.006	0.115
2c	Rod	0	0	0.019	0.030	0.031	0.015	0.006	0.101
3a	Rod	0	0	0.019	0.030	0.031	0.010	0.006	0.101
3b	Rod	0	0	0.033	0.030	0.031	0.015	0.006	0.115
3c	Rod	0	0	0.019	0.030	0.031	0.015	0.006	0.101
4	None	0	0	0	0	0	0	0	0

Notes for Table 1-23:

1. Tie-down assembly displacements for the second-floor level are calculated for the tie-downs at the first-floor level.

2. See Table 1-15 for Footnotes 2 through 7.

Table 1-24. *Deflections of shear walls at the third-floor level in the east-west direction*

Wall	Strength v (plf)	h (ft)	A (in^2)	E (psi)	b (ft)	b_{eff} (ft)	$G_v t_v$ (psi)	Space (in)	V_n (lb)	e_n (in)	Δ_a (in)	Δ (in)
A	366	9.44	17.5	1,700,000	12.5	11.6	45,500	2	69	0.0002	0.080	0.15
B1	912	9.44	49.0	1,700,000	11.0	9.5	45,500	3	228	0.0187	0.257	0.59
B2	912	9.44	49.0	1,700,000	11.0	9.5	45,500	3	228	0.0187	0.257	0.59
B					22.0							
C1	841	9.44	49.0	1,700,000	21.5	20.0	45,500	3	210	0.0143	0.351	0.45
C2	841	9.44	49.0	1,700,000	21.5	20.0	45,500	3	210	0.0143	0.351	0.45
C					43.0							
E1	841	9.44	49.0	1,700,000	21.5	20.0	45,500	3	210	0.0143	0.351	0.45
E2	841	9.44	49.0	1,700,000	21.5	20.0	45,500	3	210	0.0143	0.351	0.45
E					43.0							
F1	601	9.44	49.0	1,700,000	21.5	20.0	45,500	2	100	0.0013	0.176	0.22
F2	601	9.44	49.0	1,700,000	21.5	20.0	45,500	2	100	0.0013	0.176	0.22
F					43.0							
G1	678	9.44	49.0	1,700,000	11.0	9.5	45,500	3	169	0.0070	0.257	0.45
G2	678	9.44	49.0	1,700,000	11.0	9.5	45,500	3	169	0.0070	0.257	0.45
G					22.0							
H	366	9.44	17.5	1,700,000	12.5	11.6	45,500	2	61	0.0002	0.080	0.15

Table 1-25. *Deflections of shear walls at the third-floor level in the north-south direction*

Wall	v (plf)	h (ft)	A (in^2)	E (psi)	b (ft)	b_{eff} (ft)	$G_v t_v$ (psi)	Space (in)	V_n (lb)	e_n (in)	d_a (in)	A_0	r	C_0	v_{max}	Δ (in)
1, 4	501	9.44	11.55	1,700,000	—		45,500	4	167	0.0067	0.00	112	0.84	0.96	523	0.15
1, 4				$\Sigma L_i = 64.5$												
2a,3a	647	9.44	77.00	1,700,000	18.0	16.0	45,500	4	216	0.0155	0.10	—	—	—	—	0.31
2b,3b	647	9.44	77.00	1,700,000	24.0	22.0	45,500	4	216	0.0155	0.12	—	—	—	—	0.29
2c,3c	647	9.44	77.00	1,700,000	18.0	16.0	45,500	4	216	0.0155	0.10	—	—	—	—	0.31
2, 3					60.0											

Table 1-26. Wall rigidities at third-floor level[1]

Wall	$\Delta^{(2)}$ (in)	F (lb)	$k_i = \dfrac{F}{\Delta}$ (k/in)	K_{total} (k/in)
A	0.15	4574	30.6	30.6
B1	0.59	10,036	17.1	
B2	0.59	10,036	17.1	34.2
B		20,071	34.2	
C1	0.45	18,080	40.5	
C2	0.45	18,080	40.5	80.9
C		36,160	80.9	
E1	0.45	18,080	40.5	
E2	0.45	18,080	40.5	80.9
E		36,160	80.9	
F1	0.25	12,914	58.1	
F2	0.25	12,914	58.1	116.1
F		25,829	116.1	
G1	0.53	7453	16.4	
G2	0.53	7453	16.4	32.9
G		14,905	32.9	
H	0.15	4574	30.6	30.6
1, 4	0.16	32,340	204.0	204.0
2a,3a	0.31	11,639	38.1	
2b,3b	0.29	15,519	52.7	
2c,3c	0.31	11,639	38.1	129.0
2, 3		38,797	129.0	

Notes for Table 1-26:

1. Deflections and forces are based on strength-force levels.

2. Δs are the design-level displacements from Tables 1-24 and 1-25.

Estimation of Second-Floor Level Rigidities

Shear wall rigidities at the second-floor level are estimated in the same manner as those for the roof, fourth floor, and third floor. The calculations are summarized in Tables 1-27, 1-28, 1-29, and 1-30. A drift check is not shown.

Table 1-27. Tie-down assembly displacements at the second-floor level[1]

Wall	Tie-Down Device	ASD	Strength Design						
		Uplift[2] (lb)	Tie-Down Assembly Displacement						$\Delta_a^{(7)}$ (in)
			Uplift[2] (lb)	Tie-Down[3] Elongation (in)	Takeup Device Elongation (in)	Shrink[4] (in)	Chord Crush[5] (in)	Bearing Plate Crush (in)	
A	Rod	1320	1848	0.016	0.030	0.031	0.015	0.003	0.095
B1	Rod	20,188	28,264	0.182	0.030	0.031	0.040	0.047	0.331
B2	Rod	20,188	28,264	0.182	0.030	0.031	0.040	0.047	0.331
C1	Rod	18,345	25,683	0.166	0.030	0.031	0.119	0.037	0.382
C2	Rod	18,345	25,683	0.166	0.030	0.031	0.119	0.037	0.382
E1	Rod	18,345	25,683	0.166	0.030	0.031	0.119	0.037	0.382
E2	Rod	18,345	25,683	0.166	0.030	0.031	0.119	0.037	0.382
F1	Rod	14,184	19,858	0.128	0.030	0.031	0.017	0.036	0.242
F2	Rod	14,184	19,858	0.128	0.030	0.031	0.017	0.036	0.242
G1	Rod	20,188	28,264	0.182	0.030	0.031	0.040	0.047	0.331
G2	Rod	20,188	28,264	0.182	0.030	0.031	0.040	0.047	0.331
H	Rod	1320	1980	0.016	0.030	0.031	0.015	0.047	0.095
1	None	0	0	0	0	0	0	0	0
2a	Rod	0	0	0.096	0.030	0.031	0.015	0.013	0.189
2b	Rod	0	0	0.109	0.030	0.031	0.024	0.013	0.207
2c	Rod	0	0	0.096	0.030	0.031	0.019	0.013	0.189
3a	Rod	0	0	0.096	0.030	0.031	0.015	0.013	0.189
3b	Rod	0	0	0.109	0.030	0.031	0.024	0.013	0.207
3c	Rod	0	0	0.096	0.030	0.031	0.019	0.013	0.189
4	None	0	0	0	0	0	0	0	0

Notes for Table 1-27:

1. Tie-down assembly displacements for the second-floor level are calculated for the tie-downs at the first-floor level.

2. See Table 1-15 for Footnotes 2 through 7.

8. Rotations of the foundation are assumed to be 0 inches. The engineer should consider possible rotational effects on shear walls due to the grade beam rotations, especially in taller structures.

Table 1-28. Deflections of shear walls at the second-floor level in the east-west direction

Wall	Strength v (plf)	h (ft)	A (in²)	E (psi)	b (ft)	b_{eff} (ft)	G_v (ft)	$G_v t_v$ (psi)	Space (in)	V_n (lb)	e_n (in)	Δ_a (in)	Δ (in)
A	414	9.44	17.5	1,700,000	12.5	11.6	12.5	45,500	2	69	0.0004	0.095	0.17
B1	1031	9.44	49.0	1,700,000	11.0	9.5	11.0	45,500	2	172	0.0074	0.327	0.60
B2	1031	9.44	49.0	1,700,000	11.0	9.5	11.0	45,500	2	172	0.0074	0.327	0.60
B					22.0		22.0						
C1	951	9.44	77.0	1,700,000	21.5	19.5	21.5	45,500	2	158	0.0057	0.377	0.42
C2	951	9.44	77.0	1,700,000	21.5	19.5	21.5	45,500	2	158	0.0057	0.377	0.42
C					43.0		43.0						
E1	951	9.44	77.0	1,700,000	21.5	19.5	21.5	45,500	2	158	0.0057	0.377	0.42
E2	951	9.44	77.0	1,700,000	21.5	19.5	21.5	45,500	2	158	0.0057	0.377	0.42
E					43.0		43.0						
F1	679	9.44	77.0	1,700,000	21.5	19.5	21.5	45,500	2	113	0.0019	0.241	0.27
F2	679	9.44	77.0	1,700,000	21.5	19.5	21.5	45,500	2	113	0.0019	0.241	0.27
F					43.0		43.0						
G1	766	9.44	49.0	1,700,000	11.0	9.5	11.0	45,500	2	128	0.0028	0.327	0.51
G2	766	9.44	49.0	1,700,000	11.0	9.5	11.0	45,500	2	128	0.0028	0.327	0.51
G					22.0		22.0						
H	414	9.44	17.5	1,700,000	12.5	11.6	12.5	45,500	2	69	0.0004	0.095	0.17

Table 1-29. Deflections of shear walls at the second-floor level in the north-south direction

Wall	v (plf)	h (ft)	A (in²)	E (psi)	b (ft)	b_{eff} (ft)	$G_v t_v$ (psi)	Space (in)	V_n (lb)	e_n (in)	d_a (in)	A_0	r	C_0	v_{max}	Δ (in)
1, 4	567	9.44	11.5	1.7E6	—		45,500	3	142	0.0039	0	112	0.84	0.96	591	0.15
1, 4				$\Sigma L_i = 64.5$												
2a,3a	731	9.44	135	1.7E6	18.0	15.3	45,500	3	183	0.0090	0.19	—	—	—	—	0.33
2b,3b	731	9.44	115	1.7E6	24.0	21.3	45,500	3	183	0.0090	0.21	—	—	—	—	0.31
2c,3c	731	9.44	135	1.7E6	18.0	15.3	45,500	3	183	0.0090	0.19	—	—	—	—	0.33
2, 3					60.0											

Table 1-30. Wall rigidities at the second-floor level[1]

Wall	$\Delta^{(2)}$ (in)	F (lb)	$k_i = \dfrac{F}{\Delta}$ (k/in)	K_{total} (k/in)
A	0.17	5171	29.8	29.8
B1	0.60	11,346	18.8	
B2	0.60	11,346	18.8	37.6
B		22,692	37.6	
C1	0.42	20,441	48.1	
C2	0.42	20,441	48.1	96.3
C		40,882	96.3	
E1	0.42	20,441	48.1	
E2	0.42	20,441	48.1	96.3
E		40,882	96.3	
F1	0.27	14,601	53.5	
F2	0.27	14,601	53.5	106.9
F		29,202	106.9	
G1	0.51	8426	16.4	
G2	0.51	8426	16.4	32.8
G		16,852	32.8	
H	0.17	5171	29.8	29.8
1, 4	0.15	36,563	238.0	238.0
2a,3a	0.33	13,159	39.4	
2b,3b	0.31	17,545	57.4	136.0
2c,3c	0.33	13,159	39.4	
2, 3		43,864	136.0	

Notes for Table 1-30:

1. Deflections and forces are based on strength-force levels.

2. Δs are the design-level displacements from Tables 1-28 and 1-29.

6.4 DISTRIBUTION OF LATERAL FORCES TO THE SHEAR WALLS USING RIGID DIAPHRAGMS   ASCE 7 §12.8.4

The base shear was distributed to the four levels in Part 2.8. In this step, the story forces are distributed to the shear walls supporting each level using the rigid diaphragm assumption. See Part 8 for a confirmation of this assumption.

For many years it has been common engineering practice to assume flexible diaphragms and to distribute loads to shear walls based on tributary areas. This has become a well-established conventional design assumption. In this design example, the rigid diaphragm assumption will be used. This is not intended to imply that seismic design of wood light-frame construction in the past should have been performed in this manner. However, recent earthquakes and testing of wood panel shear walls have indicated that drifts can be considerably higher than what was known or assumed in the past. This knowledge of the increased drifts of narrow wood-panel shear walls and the fact that the diaphragms tend to be much more rigid than the shear walls has increased the need for the engineer to consider the relative rigidities of shear walls.

ASCE 7 requires that the story force at the center of mass be displaced from the calculated center of mass (CM) a distance of five percent of the building dimension at that level perpendicular to the direction of force. This is to account for accidental torsion. ASCE 7 requires the most severe load combination to be considered and also permits the negative torsional shear to be subtracted from the direct load shear. The net effect of this is to add five percent accidental eccentricity to the calculated eccentricity.

However, lateral forces must be considered to act in each direction of the two principal axes. This design example does not consider eccentricities between the centers of mass between levels. In this design example, these eccentricities are small and are therefore deemed insignificant. The engineer must exercise good judgment in determining when those effects need to be considered.

Section 12.8.4.3 exempts structures that do not have Type 1a or Type 1b irregularities from amplifying the accidental torsional moment; the torsional amplification factor A_x has not been calculated in this design example.

The direct shear force F_v is determined from

$$F_v = F \frac{R}{\Sigma R}$$

and the torsional shear force F_t is determined from

$$F_t = T \frac{R \times d}{J}$$

where

$J = \Sigma R d_x^2 + \Sigma R d_y^2$

R = shear wall rigidity

d = distance from the lateral-resisting element (e.g., shear wall) to the center of rigidity (CR)

$T = F \times e$

F = 49,370 lb (for roof diaphragm)

e = eccentricity

Determine Center of Rigidity, Center of Mass, and Eccentricities for Roof Diaphragm

Forces in the east-west (X) direction:

$$\bar{y}_r = \frac{\Sigma k_{xx} y}{\Sigma k_{xx}} \quad \text{or} \quad \bar{y}_r \Sigma k_{xx} = \Sigma k_{xx} y$$

Using the rigidity values k from Table 1-18 and the distance y from line H to the shear wall:

$$\bar{y}_r (22.1 + 36.3 + 82 + 82 + 97 + 33.5 + 22.1) = 22.1(116) + 36.3(106) + 82(84.2) + 82(50.0) + 97(26.0)$$
$$+ 33.5(10.0) + 22.1(0)$$

Distance to calculated CR

$$\bar{y}_r = \frac{20{,}033}{374} = 53.6 \text{ ft}$$

The building is symmetrical about the X axis (Figure 1-22), and the center of mass (CM) is determined as

$$\bar{y}_m = \frac{116.0}{2} = 58.0 \text{ ft}$$

The minimum five percent accidental eccentricity for east-west forces, e_y, is computed from the length of the structure perpendicular to the applied story force:

$$e_y = (0.05 \times 116 \text{ ft}) = \pm 5.8 \text{ ft}$$

The new $\bar{y}_m$ to the displaced CM = 58.0 ft ± 5.8 ft = 63.8 ft or 52.2 ft.

The total eccentricity is the distance between the displaced center of mass and the center of rigidity:

$$y_r = 53.6 \text{ ft}$$
$$\therefore e_y = 63.8 - 53.6 = 10.2 \text{ ft} \text{ or } 52.2 - 53.6 = -1.4 \text{ ft}$$

Displacing the center of mass five percent can result in the CM being on either side of the CR and can produce added torsional shears to all walls.

The five percent may not be conservative. The contents-to-structure weight ratio can be higher in wood framing than in heavier types of construction. Also, the location of the calculated center of rigidity is less reliable than in other structural systems.

Use engineering judgment when selecting the eccentricity e.

Amplification of accidental torsional moment required in ASCE 7 Section 12.8.4.3 is exempted for structures that do not have Type 1a or Type 1b irregularities.

Forces in the North-South (*Y*) Direction

The building is symmetrical about the *y*-axis (Figure 1-42). Therefore, the distance to the CM and CR is

$$\bar{x}_m = \frac{48.0}{2} = 24.0 \text{ ft}$$

$$e'_x = (0.05)(48 \text{ ft}) = \pm 2.4 \text{ ft}$$

Because the CM and CR locations coincide,

$$e_x = e'_x$$

$$\therefore e_x = 2.4 \text{ ft} \text{ or } -2.4 \text{ ft}$$

Determine total shears on walls at roof level.

The total shears on the walls at the roof level are the direct shears, F_v, and the shears due to torsion (combined actual torsion and accidental torsion), F_t. Torsion on the roof diaphragm is computed as

$$T_x = Fe_y = 49,370 \text{ lb}(10.2 \text{ ft}) = 503,722 \text{ ft-lb for walls A, B, and C}$$

$$\text{or } T_x = 49,370 \text{ lb}(1.4 \text{ ft}) = 68,989 \text{ ft-lb for walls E, F, G, and H}$$

$$T_y = Fe_x = 49,370 \text{ lb}(2.4 \text{ ft}) = 118,492 \text{ ft-lb}$$

Because the building is symmetrical for forces in the north-south direction, the torsional forces can be subtracted for those walls located on the opposite side from the displaced CM. The critical force will then be used for the design of these walls. Table 1-32 summarizes the spreadsheet for determining combined forces on the roof-level walls.

Determine the center of rigidity, center of mass, and eccentricities for the fourth-, third- and second-floor diaphragms.

Since the walls stack with uniform nailing, it can be assumed that the center of rigidity for the third-floor and the second-floor diaphragms will coincide with the center of rigidity of the roof diaphragm.

Torsion on the fourth-floor diaphragm:

$$F = (49,370 + 55,740) = 105,110 \text{ lb}$$

$$T_x = Fe_y = 105,110 \text{ lb}(10.6 \text{ ft}) = 1,118,643 \text{ ft-lb for walls A, B, and C}$$

or 105,110 lb(1.0 ft) = 100,660 ft-lb for walls E, F, G, and H

$$T_y = Fe_x = 105,110 \text{ lb}(2.4 \text{ ft}) = 252,270 \text{ ft-lb}$$

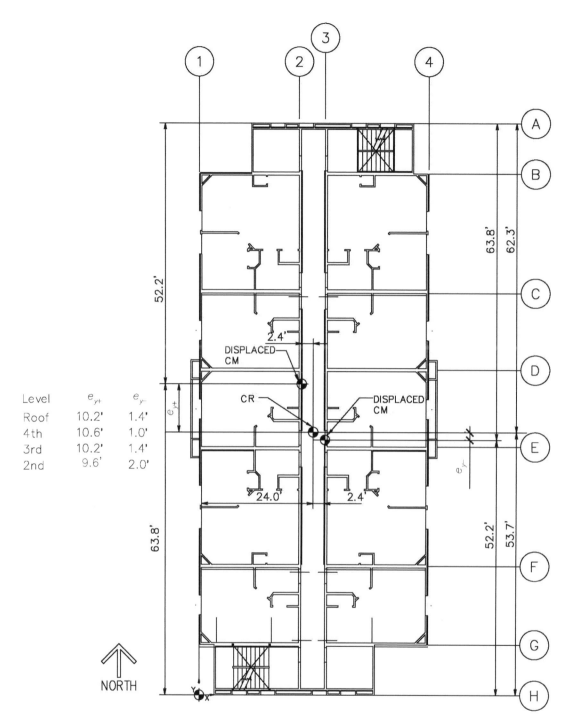

Level	e_{y+}	e_{y-}
Roof	10.2'	1.4'
4th	10.6'	1.0'
3rd	10.2'	1.4'
2nd	9.6'	2.0'

Figure 1-42. Center of rigidity and location of displaced centers of mass for second-, third-, and fourth-floor levels and roof diaphragm

Results for the fourth-floor level are summarized in Table 1-32.

Torsion on the third-floor diaphragm:

$$F = (49{,}370 + 55{,}740 + 37{,}160) = 142{,}270 \text{ lb}$$
$$T_x = Fe_y = 142{,}270 \text{ lb}(10.2 \text{ ft}) = 1{,}446{,}183 \text{ ft-lb for walls A, B, and C}$$

or 142,270 lb(1.4 ft) = 204,182 ft-lb for walls E, F, G, and H

$$T_y = Fe_x = 142{,}270 \text{ lb}(2.4 \text{ ft}) = 341{,}455 \text{ ft-lb}$$

Results for the third-floor level are summarized in Table 1-33.

Torsion on the second-floor diaphragm:

$$F = (49{,}370 + 55{,}740 + 37{,}160 + 18{,}580) = 160{,}850 \text{ lb}$$
$$T_x = Fe_y = 160{,}850 \text{ lb}(9.6 \text{ ft}) = 1{,}551{,}003 \text{ ft-lb for walls A, B, and C}$$

or 160,850 lb(2.0 ft) = 314,894 ft-lb for walls E, F, G, and H

$$T_y = Fe_x = 160{,}850 \text{ lb}(2.4 \text{ ft}) = 386{,}047 \text{ ft-lb}$$

Results for the second-floor level are summarized in Table 1-34.

Table 1-31. Distribution of forces to shear walls below the roof level

	Wall	R_x	R_y	d_x	d_y	Rd	Rd^2	Direct Force F_v	Torsional Force F_t	Total Force $F_v + F_t$
East-West	A	22.1			62.4	1379	86,054	2919	893	3812
	B	36.2			52.4	1896	99,353	4779	1227	6007
	C	81.7			28.4	2322	65,945	10,798	1503	12,301
	E	81.7			3.6	294	1058	10,798	190	10,989
	F	96.5			27.6	2664	73,524	12,752	1725	14,477
	G	33.4			43.6	1454	63,395	4406	941	5347
	H	22.1			53.6	1184	63,482	2919	767	3686
	Σ	373.8					452,811	49,372		
North-South	1		280.6	24.0		6735	161,633	15,516	1026	16,542
	2		165.8	2.5		415	1036	9170	63	9233
	3		165.8	−2.5		−415	1036	9170	−63	9106
	4		280.6	−24.0		−6735	161,633	15,516	−1026	14,491
	Σ		892.9				325,338	49,372		
	Σ						778,149			

Table 1-32. Distribution of forces to shear walls below the fourth-floor level

	Wall	R_x	R_y	d_x	d_y	Rd	Rd^2	Direct Force F_v	Torsional Force F_t	Total Force $F_v + F_t$
East-West	A	27.6			62.4	1724	107,605	8828	2763	11,591
	B	24.9			52.4	1306	68,437	7962	2093	10,055
	C	69.0			28.4	1960	55,668	22,046	3141	25,186
	E	69.0			3.6	248	893	22,046	398	22,443
	F	88.6			27.6	2445	67,466	28,300	3918	32,218
	G	23.1			43.6	1006	43,867	7373	1612	8986
	H	26.8			53.6	1436	76,959	8559	2301	10,860
	Σ	329.0					420,895	105,112		
North-South	1		239.5	24.0		5748	137,956	37,303	2077	39,381
	2		97.9	2.5		245	612	15,253	88	15,341
	3		97.9	−2.5		−245	612	15,253	−88	15,164
	4		239.5	−24.0		−5748	137,956	37,303	−2077	35,226
	Σ		674.9				277,137	105,112		
	Σ						698,032			

Table 1-33. Distribution of forces to shear walls below the third-floor level

	Wall	R_x	R_y	d_x	d_y	Rd	Rd^2	Direct Force F_v	Torsional Force F_t	Total Force $F_v + F_t$
East-West	A	30.6			62.4	1907	119,028	11,185	3760	14,946
	B	34.2			52.4	1794	94,001	12,526	3537	16,063
	C	80.9			28.4	2298	65,275	29,609	4531	34,140
	E	80.9			3.6	291	1047	29,609	574	30,183
	F	104.5			27.6	2885	79,612	38,251	5687	43,939
	G	28.0			43.6	1222	53,285	10,259	2410	12,668
	H	29.6			53.6	1587	85,041	10,833	3128	13,961
	Σ	388.8					497,289	142,273		
North-South	1		203.7	24.0		4888	117,322	43,574	2275	45,850
	2		128.8	2.5		322	805	27,562	150	27,712
	3		128.8	−2.5		−322	805	27,562	−150	27,412
	4		203.7	−24.0		−4888	117,322	43,574	−2275	41,299
	Σ		665.0				236,255	142,273		
	Σ						733,544			

Table 1-34. Distribution of forces to shear walls below second-floor level

	Wall	R_x	R_y	d_x	d_y	Rd	Rd^2	Direct Force F_v	Torsional Force F_t	Total Force $F_v + F_t$
East-West	A	29.8			62.4	1860	116,081	11,160	3587	14,748
	B	37.6			52.4	1973	103,384	14,095	3805	17,900
	C	96.3			28.4	2735	77,683	36,052	5275	41,326
	E	96.3			3.6	346	1246	36,052	668	36,720
	F	106.9			27.6	2952	81,454	40,040	5692	45,732
	G	32.8			43.6	1432	62,421	12,295	2761	15,056
	H	29.8			53.6	1598	85,633	11,160	3081	14,241
	Σ	429.7					527,902	160,853		
North-South	1		238.4	24.0		5722	137,317	51,189	2746	53,935
	2		136.2	2.5		340	851	29,238	163	29,401
	3		136.2	−2.5		−340	851	29,238	−163	29,075
	4		238.4	−24.0		−5722	137,317	51,189	−2746	48,442
	Σ		749.1				276,336	160,853		
	Σ						804,239			

6.5 COMPARISON OF LOADS ON SHEAR WALLS USING FLEXIBLE DIAPHRAGM ASSUMPTIONS VS. RIGID DIAPHRAGM ASSUMPTIONS

Table 1-31 summarizes wall forces determined under the separate flexible and rigid diaphragm analyses. Since nailing requirements were established in the flexible diaphragm analysis of Part 6.2, they must be checked for results of the rigid diaphragm analysis and adjusted if necessary (also given in Table 1-35).

Table 1-35. Comparison of loads on shear walls using flexible vs. rigid diaphragm analysis and recheck of nailing in walls

Wall	$F_{flexible}$ (lb)	F_{rigid} (lb)	Rigid/ Flexible (%)	b (ft)	$v = \dfrac{F_{max}}{1.4b}$ [7] (plf)	Plywood 1 or 2 Sides	Allowable Shear (plf) [1, 2]	Edge Nail Spacing (in)
\multicolumn{9}{c}{Roof Level}
A	1587	3812	140	12.5	218	1	340	6
B	6965	6007	−14	22.0	226	1	340	6
C	12,548	12,301	−2	43.0	208	1	340	6
E	12,548	10,989	−12	43.0	208	1	340	6
F	8963	14,477	62	43.0	240	1	340	6
G	5172	5347	3	22.0	174	1	340	6
H	1587	3686	132	12.5	211	1	340	6
1	11,223	16,542	47	64.5	183	1	340	6
2	13,463	9233	−31	60.0	160	1	340	6
3	13,463	9233	−31	60.0	160	1	340	6
4	11,223	16,542	47	64.5	183	1	340	6
\multicolumn{9}{c}{Fourth-Floor Level}
A	3379	11,594	243	12.5	663	1	665	3 [8]
B	14,829	10,054	−32	22.0	481	1	510	4
C	26,715	25,159	−6	43.0	444	1	510	4
E	26,715	22,391	−16	43.0	444	1	510	4
F	19,082	32,182	69	43.0	535	1	665	3
G	11,012	8982	−18	22.0	358	1	510	4
H	3379	11,201	231	12.5	640	1	665	3 [8]
1	23,893	39,374	65	64.5	436	1	510	4 [8]
2	28,663	15,341	−46	60.0	341	1	340	6
3	28,663	15,341	−46	60.0	341	1	340	6
4	23,893	39,374	65	64.5	436	1	510	4 [8]

(continued)

Table 1-35. Comparison of loads on shear walls using flexible vs. rigid diaphragm analysis and recheck of nailing in walls—continued

Wall	$F_{flexible}$ (lb)	F_{rigid} (lb)	Rigid Flexible (%)	b (ft)	$v = \dfrac{F_{max}}{1.4b}$ [7] (plf)	Plywood 1 or 2 sides	Allowable Shear (plf) [1,2]	Edge Nail Spacing (in)
Third-Floor Level								
A	4574	14,879	225	12.5	850	1	870	2[8]
B	20,071	15,915	−21	22.0	652	1	665	3
C	36,160	33,370	−8	43.0	601	1	665	3
E	36,160	28,978	−20	43.0	601	1	665	3
F	25,829	47,691	85	43.0	792	1	870	2[8]
G	14,905	14,643	−2	22.0	484	1	665	3
H	4574	14,291	212	12.5	817	1	870	2[8]
1	32,340	45,787	42	64.5	507	1	510	4
2	38,797	27,708	−29	60.0	462	1	510	4
3	38,797	27,708	−29	60.0	462	1	510	4
4	32,340	45,787	42	64.5	507	1	510	4
Second-Floor Level								
A	5171	14,748	185	12.5	843	1	870	2[8]
B	22,692	17,900	−21	22.0	737	1	870	2
C	40,882	41,326	1	43.0	686	1	870	2
E	40,882	36,720	−10	43.0	679	1	870	2
F	29,202	45,732	57	43.0	760	1	870	2
G	16,852	15,056	−11	22.0	547	1	870	2
H	5171	14,241	175	12.5	814	1	870	2[8]
1	36,563	53,935	48	64.5	597	1	665	3[8]
2	43,864	29,401	−33	60.0	522	1	665	3
3	43,864	29,401	−33	60.0	522	1	665	3
4	36,563	53,935	48	64.5	597	1	665	3[8]

Notes for Table 1-35:

1. In SDC D, E, or F, SDPWS Section 4.3.7.1 requires 3× nominal thickness stud framing at abutting panels or two 2× members where the required nominal shear exceeds 700 plf, or the nail spacing is 2 inches on center or less at adjoining panel edges, or 10d common nails having penetration into framing members and blocking of more than 1½ inches are 3 inches on center or less.

2. Refer to Part 7.3 in this design example for sill-plate anchorage.

3. IBC Section 1705.11 requires special inspection where the nail spacing is 4 inches on center or closer with SDC C and higher.

4. The shear wall length used for wall shears is the "out-to-out" wall length.

5. Forces are strength level and shear in wall is divided by 1.4 to convert to allowable stress design.

6. APA or TECO performance-rated Structural-I-rated wood structural panels may be either plywood or OSB. The allowable shear values are from SDPWS Table 4.3A using 10d common nails with a minimum 1½-inch penetration and $^{15}/_{32}$-inch panel thickness and divided by the ASD reduction factor of 2.0.

7. Where the force used was the higher force for the same wall at the opposite side of the structure, the higher force was used.

8. The shear forces due to the rigid diaphragm analysis exceeded the force using flexible diaphragm assumptions requiring the nailing in the wall to be increased to meet the demand. Where forces from rigid diaphragm analysis are higher than those from the flexible diaphragm analysis, wall stability and anchorage must be reevaluated. However, engineering judgment may be used to determine if a complete rigid diaphragm analysis should be repeated due to changes in wall rigidity. If rigid diaphragm loads are used, the diaphragm shears should be rechecked for total shear load for the shear walls at that line divided by diaphragm length along the individual wall lines.

6.6 DETERMINATION OF SEISMIC DRIFTS USING DIAPHRAGMS IDEALIZED AS RIGID   ASCE 7 §12.8.6

The shear wall deflections used to determine the shear wall rigidities in Tables 1-16 through 1-30 are based on strength-level seismic forces using diaphragms idealized as flexible. Since the shear wall designs are in the elastic and linear range, the seismic drifts for diaphragms idealized as rigid can be proportioned to the seismic drifts obtained from diaphragms idealized as flexible.

Table 1-36. Determination of seismic drifts using diaphragms idealized as rigid

Direction	Wall	F rigid	F flex	$\dfrac{F \text{ rigid}}{F \text{ flexible}}$	Δ flexible	Δ rigid $\left(\dfrac{F \text{ rigid}}{F \text{ flex}}\right)\Delta$ flex
				Roof Level		
East-West	A	3870	1587	2.438	0.07	0.17
	B	6083	6965	0.873	0.18	0.16
	C	12,244	12,548	0.976	0.15	0.15
	E	10,757	12,548	0.857	0.15	0.13
	F	12,906	8963	1.440	0.09	0.13
	G	4633	5172	0.896	0.15	0.13
	H	3061	1587	1.928	0.07	0.13
North-South	1	16,363	11,223	1.458	0.04	0.06
	2	9,385	13,463	0.697	0.08	0.06
	3	9,385	13,463	0.697	0.08	0.06
	4	16,363	11,223	1.458	0.04	0.06
				Fourth-Floor Level		
East-West	A	10,409	3379	3.080	0.14	0.43
	B	10,792	14,829	0.728	0.56	0.41
	C	26,060	26,715	0.975	0.38	0.37
	E	22,495	26,715	0.842	0.38	0.32
	F	29,377	19,082	1.539	0.21	0.32
	G	8064	11,012	0.732	0.45	0.33
	H	7998	3379	2.367	0.14	0.33
North-South	1	34,146	23,893	1.429	0.15	0.21
	2	20,143	28,663	0.703	0.29	0.21
	3	20,143	28,663	0.703	0.29	0.21
	4	34,146	23,893	1.429	0.15	0.21

(continued)

Table 1-36. Determination of seismic drifts using diaphragms idealized as rigid—continued

Direction	Wall	F rigid	F flex	$\dfrac{F \text{ rigid}}{F \text{ flexible}}$	Δ flexible	Δ rigid $\left(\dfrac{F \text{ rigid}}{F \text{ flex}}\right)\Delta$ flex
			Third-Foor Level			
East-West	A	11,538	4574	2.523	0.21	0.52
	B	18,326	20,071	0.913	0.55	0.50
	C	37,548	36,160	1.038	0.43	0.45
	E	32,552	36,160	0.900	0.43	0.39
	F	34,927	25,829	1.352	0.29	0.40
	G	12,109	14,905	0.812	0.49	0.40
	H	8928	4574	1.952	0.21	0.40
North-South	1	45,696	32,340	1.413	0.16	0.22
	2	28,062	38,797	0.723	0.30	0.22
	3	28,062	38,797	0.723	0.30	0.22
	4	45,696	32,340	1.413	0.16	0.22
			Second-Floor Level			
East-West	A	10,714	5171	2.072	0.26	0.54
	B	21,134	22,692	0.931	0.55	0.52
	C	46,262	40,882	1.132	0.40	0.46
	E	39,457	40,882	0.965	0.40	0.39
	F	39,005	29,202	1.336	0.30	0.40
	G	13,105	16,852	0.778	0.52	0.40
	H	8074	5171	1.561	0.26	0.41
North-South	1	48,065	36,563	1.315	0.20	0.26
	2	35,087	43,894	0.800	0.32	0.25
	3	35,087	43,864	0.800	0.32	0.25
	4	48,065	36,563	1.315	0.20	0.26

Notes for Table 1-36:

1. Values for F rigid and F flex are the forces to the respective walls from Table 1-35.

2. The Δ flexible values are from Table 1-18 for the roof level, Table 1-22 for the fourth-floor level, Table 1-26 for the third-floor level, and Table 1-30 for the second-floor level.

3. Values for Δ rigid are obtained by multiplying the ratio of F rigid/F flex times Δ flexible.

6.7 DETERMINATION IF A TORSIONAL IRREGULARITY EXISTS   SDPWS §4.2.5.1

Per ASCE 7, a Type 1a torsional irregularity exists when the maximum story drift exceeds 1.2 times the average story drift. A Type 1b torsional irregularity exists when the maximum story drift exceeds 1.4 times the average story drift (see Figure 1-43).

The ratios of the maximum to the average story drifts (see Table 1-37) are close to exceeding the limit of 1.2 times the average story drift; when they do, a Type 1a torsional irregularity exists. It is not that uncommon to exceed the limit of 1.4, and when they do, a Type 1b torsional irregularity exists.

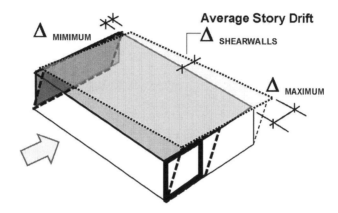

Figure 1-43. Determination of average story drift

Table 1-37. Determination of average and maximum story drifts

Level	Directions	$\Delta_{average}$	Δ_{max}	$\Delta_{max}/\Delta_{avg}$	Type 1a Exists? (> 1.2)	Type 1b Exists? (> 1.4)
Roof	East-West	0.15	0.17	1.13	No	No
	North-South	0.06	0.06	1.01	No	No
Fourth Floor	East-West	0.37	0.43	1.15	No	No
	North-South	0.21	0.21	1.01	No	No
Third Floor	East-West	0.46	0.52	1.15	No	No
	North-South	0.22	0.22	1.02	No	No
Second Floor	East-West	0.47	0.54	1.16	No	No
	North-South	0.26	0.26	1.01	No	No

Notes for Table 1-37:

1. Values for $\Delta_{average}$ are the average story drifts obtained from Table 1-36.

Per ASCE 7 Section 12.3.3.1:

For a Type 1a torsional irregularity:
  • Does not exist with flexible diaphragms
  • Applies only to rigid or semirigid diaphragms

For a Type 1b extreme torsional irregularity:
  • Does not exist with flexible diaphragms
  • Applies only to rigid or semirigid diaphragms
  • Shall not be permitted in Seismic Design Category E or F

The tests for diaphragm irregularity in ASCE 7 pertain to diaphragms classified as semirigid or idealized as rigid. For diaphragms idealized as flexible, these requirements do not apply since distribution is by tributary area, and the diaphragms are not able to distribute torsional forces. Refer to Section 3 in this design example for further discussion on the use of diaphragms idealized as flexible.

ASCE 7 requires structures with Type 1a or Type 1b horizontal irregularities to be amplified per the equation below:

$$A_x = \left(\frac{\delta_{max}}{1.2\delta_{avg}} \right)^2$$

δ_{max} = maximum displacement using $A_x = 1.0$

δ_{avg} = average displacement at the extreme points using $A_x = 1.0$

where the amplification factor A_x is multiplied by the accidental torsion length, e (see Section 6.4).

Torsional irregularity can potentially be a cause for failure in an earthquake. In structures classified as torsionally irregular, SDPWS now has added special requirements that must be met in order for the structure to have a better performance. These include limits on diaphragm materials, diaphragm aspect ratios, and building drift.

Per SDPWS Section 4.2.5.1

Where a torsional irregularity exists in structures assigned in Seismic Design Categories B, C, D, E, and F, diaphragms shall meet the following requirements:

1. The diaphragm conforms to Sections 4.2.7.1, 4.2.7.2, and 4.2.7.3.

2. The L/W ratio is not greater than 1.5:1 when sheathed in conformance to Section 4.2.7.1 or not greater than 1:1 when sheathed in conformance to Section 4.2.7.2 or 4.2.7.3.

3. The maximum story drift at each edge of the structure shall not exceed the ASCE 7 allowable story drift when subject to seismic design forces, including torsion and accidental torsion.

Checks:

1. The diaphragm assemblies used in this design example are constructed with wood structural panels; therefore, requirement 1 is met.

2. The maximum L/W ratio in this design example (see Figure 1-2):

$$\frac{L}{W} = \left(\frac{32.0 \text{ ft}}{48.0 \text{ ft}} \right) = 0.67 < 1.5$$

Therefore, requirement 2 is met.

3. Building drifts will be checked in Section 6.8.

6.8 DETERMINATION OF BUILDING DRIFTS

ASCE 7

Drift Checks

To establish drift, the story drift, δ_x, must be determined as follows:

§12.8.6

$$\delta_x = \left(\frac{C_d \Delta_{xe}}{I} \right)$$

where

$$C_d = 4.0$$
$$I = 1.0$$
$$\delta_x = \frac{4.0\Delta}{I} = 4.0\Delta$$

The calculated story drift using δ_x shall not exceed the maximum Δ_a, which is 0.025 times the story height. The drift check is summarized in Table 1-38.

Per ASCE 7 Section 12.8.6

Story drifts shall be computed as the difference of the deflections at the centers of mass (or a vertical projection where the centers of mass do not align).

In Seismic Design Categories C through F having Type 1a or 1b horizontal irregularity, the design story drift shall be the largest difference of the deflections of vertically aligned points along any of the edges of the structure.

Table 1-38. Drift check at each level

	Wall	Δ (in)	Height (ft)	δ_x (in)	Max. Δ_a (in)	Status
			Roof Level			
East-West	A	0.17	8.21	0.67	2.46	ok
	B	0.16	8.21	0.64	2.46	ok
	C	0.15	8.21	0.58	2.46	ok
	E	0.13	8.21	0.51	2.46	ok
	F	0.13	8.21	0.52	2.46	ok
	G	0.13	8.21	0.52	2.46	ok
	H	0.13	8.21	0.53	2.46	ok
North-South	1, 4	0.06	8.21	0.23	2.46	ok
	2a, 3a	0.06	8.21	0.23	2.46	ok
	2b, 3b	0.06	8.21	0.23	2.46	ok
	2c, 3c	0.06	8.21	0.23	2.46	ok
			Fourth-Floor Level			
East-West	A	0.43	9.44	1.72	2.83	ok
	B	0.41	9.44	1.64	2.83	ok
	C	0.37	9.44	1.47	2.83	ok
	E	0.32	9.44	1.27	2.83	ok
	F	0.32	9.44	1.29	2.83	ok
	G	0.33	9.44	1.31	2.83	ok
	H	0.33	9.44	1.32	2.83	ok
North-South	1, 4	0.21	9.44	0.85	2.83	ok
	2a, 3a	0.21	9.44	0.85	2.83	ok
	2b, 3b	0.21	9.44	0.83	2.83	ok
	2c, 3c	0.21	9.44	0.83	2.83	ok

(continued)

Table 1-38. Drift check at each level—continued

	Wall	Δ (in)	Height (ft)	δ_x (in)	Max. Δ_a (in)	Status
Third-Floor Level						
East-West	A	0.52	9.44	2.09	2.83	ok
	B	0.50	9.44	2.00	2.83	ok
	C	0.45	9.44	1.80	2.83	ok
	E	0.39	9.44	1.56	2.83	ok
	F	0.40	9.44	1.59	2.83	ok
	G	0.40	9.44	1.61	2.83	ok
	H	0.40	9.44	1.62	2.83	ok
North-South	1, 4	0.22	9.44	0.90	2.83	ok
	2a, 3a	0.22	9.44	0.90	2.83	ok
	2b, 3b	0.22	9.44	0.86	2.83	ok
	2c, 3c	0.22	9.44	0.86	2.83	ok
Second-Floor Level						
East-West	A	0.54	9.44	2.16	2.83	ok
	B	0.52	9.44	2.06	2.83	ok
	C	0.46	9.44	1.83	2.83	ok
	E	0.39	9.44	1.56	2.83	ok
	F	0.40	9.44	1.59	2.83	ok
	G	0.40	9.44	1.62	2.83	ok
	H	0.41	9.44	1.63	2.83	ok
North-South	1, 4	0.26	9.44	1.04	2.83	ok
	2a, 3a	0.26	9.44	1.04	2.83	ok
	2b, 3b	0.25	9.44	1.01	2.83	ok
	2c, 3c	0.25	9.44	1.01	2.83	ok

7. Design and Detailing of Shear Wall at Line C

7.1 DETAIL OF SHEAR TRANSFER AT ROOF

Edge nailing from the roof sheathing to the collector truss may need to be closer than the roof sheathing edge nailing or "field nailing" because of shears being collected from each side of the truss. It is also common to use a double collector truss at these locations. The 2 × 4 braces at the top of the shear wall need to be designed for compression or to provide tension bracing on each side of the wall (Figure 1-44).

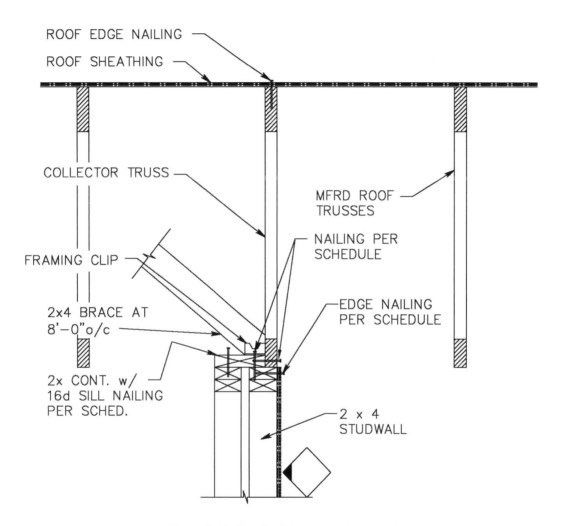

Figure 1-44. Detail of shear transfer at roof

7.2 DETAIL OF SHEAR TRANSFER AT SECOND FLOOR

This detail uses the double top plates at the underside of the floor sheathing (Figure 1-45). This is advantageous for shear transfer. Another often-used detail is to bear the floor joists directly on the top plates. However, when the floor joists are on top of the top plates, shear transfer is required through the glue joint in the webs and heavy nailing from the joist chord to the top plate.

The nailers for the drywall ceiling need to be installed after the wall sheathing and gypsum board have been installed.

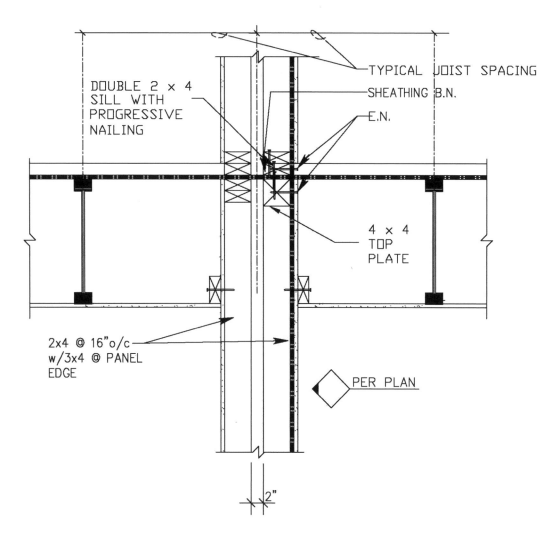

Figure 1-45. Detail of shear transfer at second-floor level

7.3 DESIGN SHEAR TRANSFER AT FOUNDATION SILL PLATE

Sill-Plate Anchorage for Shear Walls

Washer Plates

The SDPWS requires the 3-inch × 3-inch × 0.229-inch plate washers to within ½ inch of the edge of the bottom plate on the side(s) with sheathing where the nominal shear capacity is greater than 400 plf for both wind and seismic forces. The SDPWS has an exception to the 3-inch × 3-inch × 0.229-inch plate washers. Section 4.3.6.4.3 permits standard-cut washers in individual full-height shear wall segments (Section 4.3.5.1) when three conditions are met:

1. The shear wall anchorage at the wall ends used to resist overturning is designed neglecting all dead loads for overturning resistance.

2. The shear wall aspect ratio is a maximum of 2:1.

3. The ASD seismic demand is a maximum of 490 plf.

The most significant issue with sill-plate anchorage is the requirement of having the washer extend to within ½ inch of the bottom plate edge on the side of the sheathing.

1. For a 4-inch-nominal-wide sill plate and using 3-inch × 3-inch × 0.229-inch washer plates, this presents no problem.

2. For 6-inch-nominal and larger sill plates, this will require the anchor bolts to be offset from the center of the sill plate when 3-inch × 3-inch × 0.229-inch washer plates are used. It is also possible to use a larger rectangular plate.

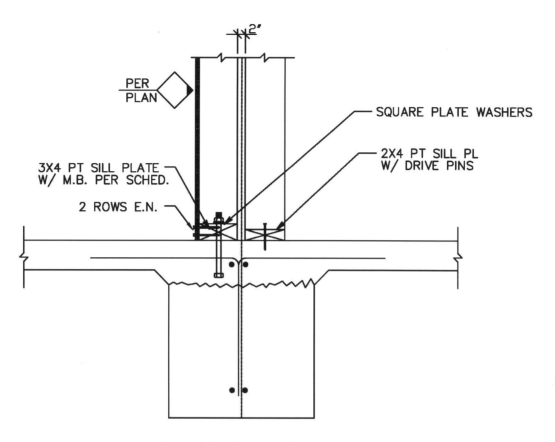

Figure 1-46. Shear transfer at the foundation

Anchor Bolts

IBC Section 1905.1.8 exempts ACI 318 Chapter 17 requirements on anchor bolts in wood sill plates. The lateral design strength is determined using the values specified in NDS Table 12E, provided that the anchor bolts comply with all of the following conditions:

1. Allowable in-plane shear strength is determined in accordance with NDS Table 12E.

2. The anchor bolts must be a maximum of ⅝-inch diameter.

3. The anchor bolts are embedded a minimum of 7 inches into concrete.

4. The anchor bolts are located a minimum of 1¾ inches from the concrete edge that is parallel to the sill plate.

5. The anchor bolt is located a minimum of 15 anchor diameters from a concrete edge that is perpendicular to the sill plate.

6. The sill plate is of 2-inch or 3-inch nominal thickness

It is the opinion of the SEAOC Seismology Committee that ¾-inch-diameter bolts can be included in those conditions, and the Committee is working on code change proposals for this. Outside of California, the designer still has to meet the requirements of ACI 318 Chapter 17. In Section 17.2.3.5, there is a provision for stud bearing walls. It is the opinion of the SEAOC Seismology Committee that additional code changes need to be implemented into ACI allowing the exemption of ACI 318 Chapter 17 for sill plate bolts.

Design Sill Plate Anchor Bolts

See the discussion about fasteners for preservative-treated wood.

From Table 1-36:

$$V = 806 \text{ plf}$$

For a side member, thickness = 2.5 inches in Hem-Fir wood (note that designing for Hem-Fir will require a tighter nail and bolt spacing) and using a ⅝-inch bolt:

$$Z_{\|} = 1070 \text{ lb / bolt}$$

$$\text{Required spacing} = \frac{Z_{\|} C_D}{v} = \frac{1070 \times 1.6}{806} = 2.12 \text{ ft} = 25.5 \text{ in}$$

Use ⅝-inch-diameter anchor bolts at 24-inch spacing.

Corrosion of Fasteners in Treated Sill Plates

With the EPA removing CCA as a wood preservative, the chemicals that are now used for wood preservatives contain higher levels of copper. This higher level of copper in the preservative-treated lumber has a dissimilar metals reaction with carbon steel. IBC Section 2304.10.5.1 requires fasteners in contact with preservative-treated wood to be hot-dipped zinc-coated galvanized steel, stainless steel, silicon bronze, or copper. This requirement applies to not only the anchor bolts but to the washers and nails. Even the toe nails from the stud to the sill plate would require the protection. The nailing of the shear-wall sheathing to the sill plate would need to meet this requirement. Most nail guns used by carpenters cannot use galvanized nails, meaning that the carpenter needs to either hand nail the nails from the sheathing to the sill plate or change nail guns to make these fastenings. Electrogalvanized nails (silver shiny nails) do not meet the above requirements. The IBC does give an exception to the above requirements when two conditions are met:

1. The preservative-treatment process uses SBX/DOT or zinc borate.

2. Fasteners are used in an interior, dry environment.

Many of the preservative-treatment plants do not use the above processes, so depending on the location of the project, this type of treated wood may not be available. There can be no excuse that the framer/carpenter did not know which type of preservative treatment was used for the lumber purchased; these are stated on a label that is stapled onto the ends of each piece of lumber. Many of these labels will have statements "Corrosive to Fasteners" or similar wording.

Species of Preservative-Treated Wood

An additional caution for sill plates is the type of wood used. The most common species used on the west coast for pressure treatment is Hem-Fir, which has lower fastener values (specific gravity $G = 0.43$) for nails and bolts than Douglas Fir-Larch. A tighter nail spacing to the sill plate may be necessary, depending on the loads.

Gap at Bottom of Sheathing

Investigations into wood-frame construction have found that plywood or OSB sheathing that bears on concrete at perimeter exterior edges can wick up moisture from the concrete and cause corrosion of the fasteners and rotting in the sheathing. To help prevent this problem, the sheathing can be placed with a gap above the concrete surface. A ¼-inch gap is recommended for a 3× sill plate, and a ⅛-inch gap is recommended for a 2× sill plate (Figure 1-47).

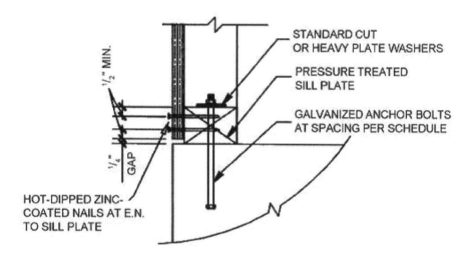

Figure 1-47. Sill plate at the foundation edge

The SDPWS only requires a minimum edge distance of ⅜ inch for nails in sheathing. Tests have shown that sheathing with greater edge distances has performed better. In addition, the ¼-inch gap shown at the bottom of the sheathing should be a minimum. Recent cyclic testing has shown that when this gap is ½ inch, the shear wall has performed better.

8. Diaphragm Deflections to Determine if the Diaphragm Is Flexible

This step is shown only as a reference for how to calculate horizontal diaphragm deflections. Since the shear wall forces were determined using both flexible and rigid diaphragm idealization, there is no requirement to verify the diaphragm is actually rigid or flexible.

The roof diaphragm has been selected to illustrate the methodology. The design seismic force in the roof diaphragm using ASCE 7 Equation 12.10-1 must first be determined. The design seismic force is then divided by the diaphragm area to determine the horizontal loading in pounds per square foot. These values are used for determining diaphragm shears (and also collector forces). The design seismic force shall be not less than $0.2S_{DS}Iw_{px}$ nor greater than $0.4S_{DS}Iw_{px}$.

8.1 ROOF DIAPHRAGM CHECK

The roof diaphragm will be checked in two steps. First, the shear in the diaphragm will be determined and compared to allowable. Next, the diaphragm deflection will be calculated. In Part 7b, the diaphragm deflection is used to determine whether the diaphragm is flexible or rigid.

Check Diaphragm Shear

The roof diaphragm consists of $^{15}\!/_{32}$-inch-thick sheathing nailed with 10d common nails at 6 inches on center, and panel edges are unblocked. Loading on the segment between lines C and E, where

$$v = \frac{(8.31) \times 48.0 \text{ ft} \times (32.0 \text{ ft}) \times 0.7}{48.0 \text{ ft} \times 2} = 93 \text{ plf}$$

Diaphragm span = 32.0 ft

Diaphragm depth = 48.0 ft

Diaphragm shears are converted to allowable stress design by multiplying by 0.7.

From SDPWS Table 4.2C, the allowable shear of 380/2 = 190 plf is based on $^{15}\!/_{32}$-inch APA or TECO performance-rated wood structural panels with unblocked edges and 10d common nails spaced at 6 inches on center at boundaries and supported panel edges. APA or TECO performance-rated wood structural panels may be either plywood or OSB. However, this design example will use plywood with five plys.

Check Diaphragm Deflection

The code specifies that the deflection is calculated on a unit load basis. In other words, the diaphragm deflection should be based on the same load as the load used for the lateral-resisting elements, not F_{px} total force at the level considered. Since the code requires building drifts to be determined by the strength-level forces specified in Section 12.8, strength loads on the building diaphragm must be determined.

The basic equation to determine seismic forces on a diaphragm is

$$F_{px} = \frac{\sum_{i=x}^{n} F_t}{\sum_{i=x}^{n} w_i} w_{px}$$

ASCE 7 Eq 12.10-1

$$f_{proof} = \frac{(43.92 \times 165.67)}{165.67} = 43.92 \text{ kips}$$

For simplicity, the wall weights parallel to the direction of loading are included in w_{px}.

For the uppermost level, the above calculation will always produce the same force as computed in ASCE 7 Equation 12.8-11. Then divide by the area of the diaphragm to find the equivalent uniform force.

$$f_{proof} = \frac{43.92 \times 1000}{5288} = 8.31 \text{ psf}$$

In this example, the roof and floor diaphragms spanning between lines C and E will be used to illustrate the method. The basic SDPWS equation to determine the deflection of a diaphragm is

$$\Delta = \frac{5vL^3}{8EAW} + \frac{0.25vL}{1000G_a} + \frac{\Sigma(x\Delta_C)}{2W}$$

SDPWS Eq 4.2-1

For the purpose of this design example, the diaphragm is assumed to be a simple span supported at lines C and E (refer to Figure 2-4). In reality, with continuity, the actual deflection will be less.

With nails at 6 inches on center, the strength load per nail is $93 \times 1.4(6/12) = 65$ lb/nail $= V_n$. Other terms in the deflection equation are

$v = 93$ plf

$L = 32.0$ ft

$W = 48.0$ ft

$G_a = 10 \times 1.2 = 12.0$ kips/in   SDPWS T4.2C

$E = 1,700,000$ psi

$A_{2\times4 \text{ chords}} = 5.25 \text{ in}^2 \times 2 = 10.50 \text{ in}^2$

Assume a chord splice at the mid-span of the diaphragm that will be nailed. The allowable loads for fasteners are based on limit state design. In other words, the deformation is set at a limit rather than the strength of the fastener. The deformation limit is 0.05 diameters of the fastener. For a 16d common nail, a conservative slippage of 0.01 inch will be used.

Using strength-level diaphragm shear:

$$\Sigma(\Delta_C X) = (0.01)16.0 \text{ ft}(2) = 0.32 \text{ in-ft}$$

$$\Delta = \frac{5(93 \times 1.4)32.0^3}{8(1.7E6)10.50(48.0)} + \frac{0.25 \times (93 \times 1.4) \times (32.0)}{1000 \times 12.0} + \frac{0.32}{2(48.0)} = 0.09 \text{ in}$$

From Table 1-21, the shear wall deflection at line C and line E is 0.33 inch. For flexible diaphragm assumptions (one of three methods), the SDPWS and ASCE 7 require the diaphragm to deflect twice as much as the lateral-resisting elements, or in other words, to be considered flexible the diaphragm would need to deflect $0.33 \times 2 = 0.66$ inch. By the definition in the code, the diaphragm is considered to be rigid.

9. Discontinuous System Considerations and the Overstrength (Ω_0) Factor

9.1 ANCHOR FORCES TO PODIUM SLAB

For over 20 years, the building codes have had requirements to use amplified seismic forces in the design of elements supporting discontinuous systems. Earlier editions of the codes used the term 3Rw/8, while current codes use the term Ω_0. ASCE 7 Section 12.3.3.3 requires amplification of seismic loads in the design of structural elements supporting discontinuous walls. Previous editions of the IBC and the 1997 Uniform Building Code exempted concrete slabs supporting light-frame construction from these requirements. However, ASCE 7 does not have this exception, thus adding slabs to the list of elements needing the design strength to resist the maximum axial force that can be delivered per the load combinations with the overstrength factor (Ω_0) in ASCE 7 Section 12.4.3.2.

This means that the shear wall boundary overturning forces (axial uplift and axial compression) need to have the Ω factor of 3.0 applied to the supporting slab design. Footnote g of ASCE 7 Table 12.2-1 states that for structures with flexible diaphragms, this value may be 2.5. The overstrength factor does not need to be applied to the shear wall's connections. ASCE 7 Section 12.3.3.3 states that the connections of the discontinuous wall to the supporting element need only be adequate to resist the forces for which the discontinuous wall was designed. The expanded commentary (3rd printing of ASCE 7-10) of Section 12.3.3.3 provides further explanation:

"For wood light-frame shear wall construction, the final sentence of §12.3.3.3 results in the shear and overturning connections at the base of a discontinued shear wall (i.e., shear fasteners and tie-downs) being designed using the load combinations of §2.3 or 2.4 rather than the load combinations with overstrength factor of §12.4.3."

However, Chapter 17 of ACI 318, Building Code Requirements for Structural Concrete, does apply a factor similar to an overstrength factor to brittle concrete breakout failure modes if they govern the anchorage design. It is common to have anchorage to the podium slab not fall within the scope of Chapter 17 because of edge distances or available embedment lengths. Other means of bolt anchorage commonly used include through bolting or sleeves for post-installed through-bolts, embeding plates with welded studs, bearing plate washers at the bolt nut, or special steel reinforcing bars used in conjunction with the anchor bolts/ bearing plates. Recent testing has shown that adding reinforcing cages at the tie-down rods increase the strength significantly.

As discussed in ASCE 7 Section 12.4.3.1, one possible route to reduce the calculated overstrength load occurs when it can be shown that yielding of other elements (tie-down rod, shear wall, diaphragm, collector, etc.) will occur below the overstrength-level forces. When this is the case, the seismic load effects including overstrength can be reduced to a lower value. ASCE 7's commentary on Section 12.4.3 provides further explanation:

"The standard permits the seismic load effects, including overstrength factor, to be taken as less than the amount computed by applying Ω_0 to the design seismic forces where it can be determined that yielding of other elements in the structure limits the amount of load that can be delivered to the element and, therefore, the amount of force that can develop in the element."

10. Special Inspection and Structural Observation

Special Inspections

IBC Section 1705.12.2 requires special inspection when the nail spacing is 4 inches on center or closer with SDC C and higher.

Currently, IBC Section 1705.12.2 is not clear on how far up the load path to go with the special inspections. The IBC states: "periodic special inspection shall be required for nailing, bolting, anchoring and other fastening of elements of the seismic force-resisting system, including wood shear walls, wood diaphragms, drag struts, braces, shear panels and hold-downs." The code then exempts special inspection requirements for the above items when the fastener spacing to the sheathing is *more than* 4 inches on center.

The code also exempts special inspections when either the S_{DS} does not exceed 0.5 and the building height of the structure does not exceed 35 feet. In the case of this design example, the value of S_{DS} exceeds 0.5, and the height exceeds 35 feet.

An itemized list of special inspection items placed on the structural drawings can help the process of which items should be inspected, but from experience, the items that the engineer of record and the building official agree to being placed on the permit set of plans often gets either ignored or amended by the city inspector at the site.

Structural Observations

The code has been amended to indicate a structural observation as follows due to the building official at the end of the work, not prior to calling for each inspection:

1704.6.1 Structural observations for structures. Structural observations shall be provided for those structures where one or more of the following conditions exist:

1. The structure is classified as Risk Category IV.

2. The structure is a high-rise building.

3. Such observation is required by the registered design professional responsible for the structural design.

4. Such observation is specifically required by the building official.

1704.6.2 Structural observations for seismic resistance. Structural observations shall be provided for those structures assigned to Seismic Design Category D, E or F where one or more of the following conditions exist:

1. The structure is classified as Risk Category III or IV.

2. The structure is assigned to Seismic Design Category E, is classified as Risk Category I or II, and is greater than two stories above the grade plane.

11. Items Not Addressed in This Example

The following items are not addressed in this example but are nevertheless necessary for a complete design of the seismic-load-resisting system:

- Comparison of wind and seismic forces.

- Anchorage to concrete for tie-down bolts.

- Building separations.

- Design of foundations.

- Rotational effects of foundations (if any) on shear wall deflections.

- Design of the vertical load-carrying system, including bearing studs.

- Design of load-bearing walls to meet 1-hour fire-rating requirements.

- Shear transfer at roof trusses to interior corridor walls.

- Determination of redundancy factor ρ.

- Verification of shear wall drifts at all levels.

Design Example 2
Flexible Diaphragm Design

OVERVIEW

This example illustrates the design of a large flexible diaphragm in a big-box retail store subjected to lateral seismic loading. The roof structure consists of a panelized hybrid roof system, which is very common in large-diaphragm roofs in the seismically active western United States. This roof system comprises structural wood-panel sheathing with light dimensional lumber supports, resting on open-web steel joists and joist girders. While this example illustrates the design of a wood diaphragm, a similar methodology is applicable to untopped steel deck diaphragms.

OUTLINE

1. Building Geometry and Loads

2. Roof Diaphragm Lateral Loading

3. Shear Nailing of the Roof Diaphragm (North-South)

4. Considerations for Plan Irregularities

5. Diaphragm Chords (North-South)

6. Diaphragm Collectors

7. Diaphragm Deflection

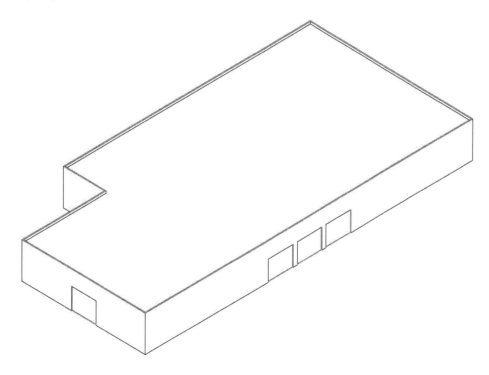

Figure 2-1. Typical building with flexible diaphragm

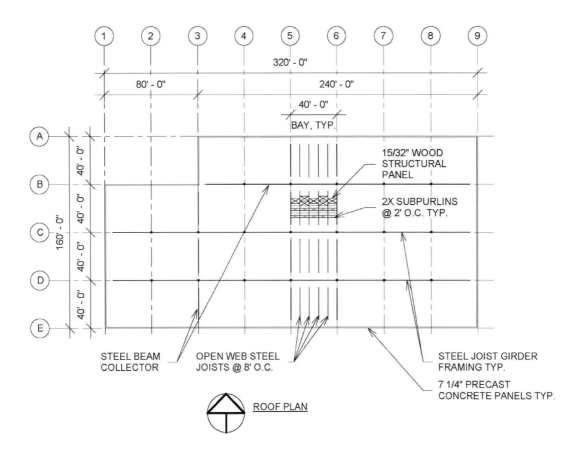

Figure 2-2. Example's roof plan

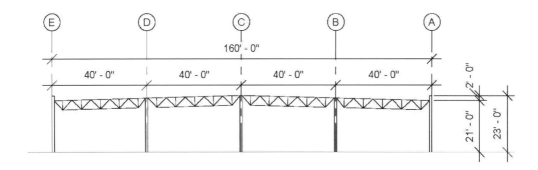

Figure 2-3. Example's building section

1. Building Geometry and Loads   ASCE 7

1.1 GIVEN INFORMATION

Seismic-Force-Resisting System

Bearing-wall system consisting of intermediate precast concrete shear walls supporting a flexible diaphragm of wood structural panel.

Seismic and Site Data

Mapped spectral accelerations for the site $S_s = 1.5$ (short period) $S_1 = 0.6$ (1-second period)
Risk Category II (Occupancy)
Site Class D
Seismic response coefficient $R = 4$ (T 12.2-1)
Overstrength factor $\Omega_0 = 2.5$ (T 12.2-1)
$C_S = 0.25$ (ASCE 7 Section 12.8.8.1)
$V = 0.25W$ (ASCE 7 Section 12.8.1)
Seismic Design Category D
$S_{DS} = 1.0$

Wind

> Assumed not to govern

Roof

> Dead load = 14 psf
> Live load (roof) = 20 psf (reducible) (IBC Table 1607.1)

Walls

> Thickness = 7.25 inches of concrete
> Height = 23 feet
> Normal weight concrete = 150 pcf

Roof Structure

> Structural-I sheathing (oriented strand board wood structural panel)
> Pre-engineered/premanufactured open-web steel joists and joist girders with full-width wood nailers
> All wood is Douglas Fir-Larch

2. Roof Diaphragm Lateral Loading   ASCE 7

2.1 ROOF DIAPHRAGM SHEAR COEFFICIENT

The roof diaphragm must be designed to resist seismic forces in each direction. The following formula is used to determine the total seismic force F_{px} on the diaphragm at a given level of a building.

$$F_{px} = \frac{\sum_{i=x}^{n} F_i}{\sum_{i=x}^{n} w_i} w_{px}$$ Eq 12.10-1

As given, the base shear for this building is $V = 0.25W$. Because it is a one-story building, Equation 12.10-1 simply becomes the following:

$$F_{px} = 0.25w_{px}$$

F_{px} shall be not less than

$$0.2S_{DS}I_e w_{px} = 0.2(1.0)(1.0)w_{px} = 0.2w_{px} \qquad \text{Eq 12.10-2}$$

but need not exceed

$$0.4S_{DS}I_e w_{px} = 0.4(1.0)(1.0)w_{px} = 0.4w_{px} \qquad \text{Eq 12.10-3}$$

Based on the criteria given in Section 12.10.1.1, $F_{px} = 0.25w_{px}$.

Alternatively, instead of designing a diaphragm (including chords and collectors) to Sections 12.10.1 and 12.10.2, ASCE 7-16 introduced Section 12.10.3 as an alternative methodology, which considers unique diaphragm design force reduction factors, R_s, and a diaphragm design acceleration coefficient, C_{px}. The seismic force on the diaphragm at any given level of a building is:

$$F_{px} = \frac{C_{px}}{R_s} w_{px} \qquad \text{Eq 12.10-4}$$

For a one-story building ($N = 1$), Figure 12.10-2 indicates $C_{px} = C_{pn}$, where

$$C_{pn} = \sqrt{(\Gamma_{m1}\Omega_0 C_s)^2 + (\Gamma_{m2}C_{s2})^2} \qquad \text{Eq 12.10-7}$$

For a one-story building ($\Gamma_{m1} = 1.0$, $\Gamma_{m2} = 0$, $C_{s2} = 0$), C_{pn} becomes

$$C_{pn} = \Omega_0 C_s = 2.5(0.25) = 0.625 \quad \text{(Note: Footnote b to Table 12.2-1 shall not apply.)}$$

However, C_{pn} shall be not less than C_{pi}, where C_{pi} is the greater of

$$C_{pi} = 0.8C_{po} = 0.8(0.4S_{DS}I_e) = 0.8(0.4)(1.0)(1.0) = 0.32 < 0.625 \; \ldots \; \text{OK}$$

and

$$C_{pi} = 0.9\Gamma_{m1}\Omega_0 C_s = 0.9(1.0)(2.5)(0.25) = 0.5625 < 0.625 \; \ldots \; \text{OK}$$

In practice, C_{pi} will never control the value of C_{pn} for one-story buildings, thus making this check irrelevant.

Therefore, $C_{px} = 0.625$.

The diaphragm design force factor, R_s, is 3.0 per Table 12.10-1. Therefore

$$F_{px} = \frac{C_{px}}{R_s} w_{px} = \frac{0.625}{3.0} w_{px} = 0.208w_{px} \qquad \text{Eq 12.10-4}$$

But F_{px} shall be not less than

$$F_{px} = 0.2S_{DS}I_e w_{px} = 0.2(1.0)(1.0)w_{px} = 0.2w_{px} \qquad \text{Eq 12.10-5}$$

Thus, when using Section 12.10.3

$$F_{px} = 0.208w_{px},$$ in conjunction with using $\Omega_0 = 2.5$

Alternatively, when using Sections 12.10.1 and 12.10.2

$$F_{px} = 0.25w_{px},$$ in conjunction with using $\Omega_0 = 2.5 - 0.5 = 2.0$ (Footnote b to Table 12.2-1)

This example will use ASCE 7 Section 12.10.3.

Therefore, for diaphragm design use $F_p = 0.208w_p$.

2.2 ROOF DIAPHRAGM SHEARS

The wood structural panel roof system is permitted to be idealized as a flexible diaphragm per ASCE 7 Section 12.3.1.1 or SDPWS Section 4.2.5. Seismic forces for the roof are computed from the tributary weight of the roof and the walls oriented perpendicular to the direction of the seismic forces. Walls parallel to the direction of seismic forces do not load the flexible diaphragm. The distributed lateral loading to the diaphragm will be computed in each orthogonal direction.

East-west direction

Because the panelized wood roof diaphragm in this building is idealized as flexible, lines A, B, and E are considered lines of resistance for the east-west seismic forces. A collector is needed along line B to drag the tributary east-west diaphragm forces into the shear wall on line B. The loading and shear diagrams are shown in Figure 2-4.

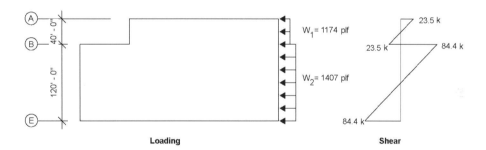

Figure 2-4. East-west diaphragm loading

The uniform loads W_1 and W_2 in the east-west direction are computed using the diaphragm lengths and wall heights.

Roof dead load = 14 psf

Wall dead load $= \dfrac{7.25}{12} 150 \text{ pcf} = 90.6 \text{ psf}$

Roof height = 21 feet average
Parapet height = 2 feet average

$$W_1 = 0.208(14 \text{ psf})(240 \text{ ft}) + \left[0.208(90.6 \text{ psf})(23)\left(\frac{23}{2}\right)\frac{1}{21} \right]2 = 1174 \text{ plf}$$

$$W_2 = 0.208(14 \text{ psf})(320 \text{ ft}) + \left[0.208(90.6 \text{ psf})(23)\left(\frac{23}{2}\right)\frac{1}{21} \right]2 = 1407 \text{ plf}$$

In this example, the effect of any wall openings reducing the wall weight has been neglected. This is considered an acceptable simplification because the openings usually occur in the bottom half of the wall. In addition, significant changes in parapet height should also be considered if they occur due to significant roof slope.

Diaphragm shear at line A and on the north side of line B is

$$\frac{23,500 \text{ lb}}{240 \text{ ft}} = 97.9 \text{ plf}$$

Diaphragm shear at the south side of line B and at line E is

$$\frac{84,400 \text{ lb}}{320 \text{ ft}} = 264 \text{ plf}$$

North-south direction

Diaphragm forces for the north-south direction are computed using the same procedure and assumptions as the east-west direction and are shown in Figure 2-5.

$$W_3 = 0.208(14 \text{ psf})(120 \text{ ft}) + \left[0.208(90.6 \text{ psf})(23)\left(\frac{23}{2}\right)\frac{1}{21} \right]2$$

$$W_3 = 824 \text{ plf}$$

$$W_4 = 0.208(14 \text{ psf})(160 \text{ ft}) + \left[0.208(90.6 \text{ psf})(23)\left(\frac{23}{2}\right)\frac{1}{21} \right]2$$

$$W_4 = 941 \text{ plf}$$

Diaphragm unit shear at line 1 and the west side of line 3 is

$$\frac{33,000 \text{ lb}}{120 \text{ ft}} = 275 \text{ plf}$$

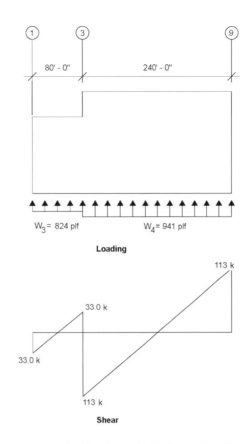

Figure 2-5. North-south diaphragm loading

Diaphragm unit shear at the east side of line 3 and at line 9 is

$$\frac{113{,}000 \text{ lb}}{160 \text{ ft}} = 706 \text{ plf}$$

3. Shear Nailing of the Roof Diaphragm (North-South)   SDPWS

The diaphragm loaded in the north-south direction has been selected to illustrate the design of a wood structural panel roof diaphragm. A similar design is required in the other orthogonal direction, east-west, but is not illustrated here. Allowable stress design (ASD) will be used. The basic loading combinations are given in IBC Section 1605.3.1, and those involving earthquake loading have been simplified in ASCE 7 Section 2.4.5.

The governing seismic load combination for allowable stress design is (8)

$$1.0D + 0.7E_v + 0.7E_h \hspace{4cm} \text{§2.4.5}$$

where $E_h = \rho Q_E$

When designing the structural diaphragm, the engineer need not consider the vertical loading in conjunction with the lateral diaphragm shear stresses. Therefore, the dead load $D = 0$ and the vertical earthquake effect $E_v = 0$ in this load combination.

For diaphragms of buildings in Seismic Design Category D, E, or F, the redundancy factor ρ is required within the seismic-load combination, but is typically set to ρ = 1.0 for diaphragm loads per Section 12.10.3 Item 3. In unique multistory situations where the diaphragm is acting to transfer forces horizontally due to vertical system offsets or due to changes in vertical element stiffnesses, the redundancy factor ρ will conform to Sections 12.3.4 and 12.10.3.3. In this example, ρ = 1.0 for the diaphragm design. Thus, the applicable basic load combination reduces to simply $0.7Q_E$.

Assume the diaphragm is to be constructed with $^{15}/_{32}$-inch Structural-I OSB sheathing (wood structural panels) with all edges supported (blocked). Refer to the 2015 AWC SDPWS Table 4.2A for nailing requirements. The sheathing arrangement (shown in Figure 2-2) for north-south seismic forces is Case 3 with the long panel direction parallel to the supports.

Because open-web steel joist purlins in a hybrid roof structure have full-width wood nailers, the continuous sheathing edges loaded in this north-south direction are supported by framing greater than a 3-inch nominal width, allowing nail spacings of 2½ inches or less at adjoining panel edges (AWC SDPWS Section 4.2.7.1.1). However, in the east-west direction, the sheathing edges are supported by only 2× subpurlin framing, and the strength is therefore limited by the nail spacings associated with 2-inch nominal framing width. Although not applicable in this example, 3× framing is required where adjoining panel edges are fastened with 10d common nails at 3-inch spacing if the nail penetration is greater than 1½ inches. In these large panelized roof systems, the nailing contractor is often instructed to order custom 2-inch length nails to obtain the 1½-inch penetration, allowing 2× framing in certain locations.

Various nail spacings at sheathing panel edges and their respective seismic shear capacities for Case 3 (north-south seismic loading) are given in Table 2-1. Minimum intermediate (field) nailing is 10d common nails at 12-inch spacing, and 10d common nails require 1½-inch member penetration. A similar calculation (not shown) must be done for east-west seismic forces.

Table 2-1. Allowable diaphragm shear capacities

Zone	Boundary and North-South Edge Nailing[1, 3]	East-West Edge Nailing[2, 3]	Nominal Unit Shear Capacity (plf)	ASD Allowable Shear (plf)
A	10d @ 2½ in o.c.	10d @ 4 in o.c.	1280	640
B	10d @ 4 in o.c.	10d @ 6 in o.c.	850	425
C	10d @ 6 in o.c.	10d @ 6 in o.c.	640	320

Notes for Table 2-1:

1. The north-south running sheet edges are the "continuous panel edges parallel to load" mentioned in SDPWS Table 4.2A.

2. The east-west sheet edges are the "other panel edges" in SDPWS Table 4.2A. The nailing for east-west running diaphragm boundaries is per the tighter boundary spacing.

3. Nails are common smooth-shank nails (10d = 0.148-inch diameter). Screw-shank nails (deformed shank) are often used in some regions of the country where special concerns exist of nails backing out in withdrawal due to wind uplift loads or framing member drying shrinkage.

The diaphragm boundaries at lines 3 and 9 have a shear demand of $v = 706$ plf (see Part 2.2). Converting to allowable stress design, $v_{ASD} = 0.7(706) = 494$ plf, which is less than nailing zone A's allowable stress of 640 plf.

At a particular location across the diaphragm, nailing zone B (425 plf) will become acceptable as the diaphragm shears reduce farther from the diaphragm boundary. The demarcation between nailing zones A and B may be located as follows using allowable stress design:

Shear demand (ASD) ≤ Shear capacity (ASD)

$0.7[113,000 \text{ lb} - (941 \text{ plf})x] \le 425 \text{ plf} (160 \text{ ft})$

where

x = the demarcation distance from the diaphragm boundary

Solving for x obtains

$x = 16.9 \text{ ft}$

Because a panelized wood roof system typically consists of 8-foot-wide panel modules, the demarcation is increased to the next 8-foot increment or to $x = 24$ feet.

A similar process is undertaken to determine the demarcation between zones B and C. In this situation, $x = 42.4$ feet, and the demarcation is increased to 48 feet from the diaphragm boundary. The resulting diaphragm shears at these demarcation boundaries are shown in Table 2-2.

Table 2-2. Evaluation of nailing zone distances

Nailing Zone	Distance from Boundary	Maximum Shear (plf)	ASD Shear (plf)	Allowable Shear Capacity (plf)
A	0 feet	$v_{max} = 706$	$v_{ASD} = 494$	640
B	24 feet	$v_{max} = 565$	$v_{ASD} = 396$	425
C	48 feet	$v_{max} = 424$	$v_{ASD} = 297$	320

The resulting nailing zones for the north-south loading are shown in Figure 2-6.

These demarcation calculations assume the full depth of the diaphragm is available for shear capacity. However, typical warehouse construction often contains skylights and smoke vents that can substantially perforate the structural diaphragm. In these situations, the designer must account for these diaphragm interruptions, resulting in larger shear stresses.

Commentary

Plywood and other wood structural panels are common diaphragm materials in the west and parts of the south. Other parts of the United States commonly use steel deck for diaphragms in conjunction with steel roof framing. Steel-deck diaphragms are approached in the same manner with a similar diaphragm table assigning various deck gauges and attachments to specific diaphragm zones, depending on the shear demands. In this example, the wood structural panel edge will coincide with the collector line. For a metal-deck diaphragm, this might not be the case. Therefore, special details will be required to define adequate shear transfer between the steel deck and the collector lines.

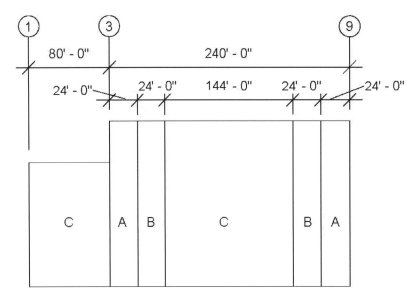

Figure 2-6. Illustration of nailing zone locations

This wood diaphragm resisting seismic forces must have its aspect ratio checked against the limitations in SDPWS Table 4.2.4. For blocked diaphragms using wood structural panels, the maximum aspect ratio is $L/W = 4:1$.

For this example, $L/W = 240/160 = 1.5 < 4$ ... OK

Commentary

Aspect ratio limitations for metal-deck diaphragms are found under the specific deck manufacturer's ICC-ES Evaluation Report. Within these reports, a table titled "Diaphragm Flexibility Limitation" provides guidance on limiting diaphragm flexibility in conjunction with diaphragm aspect ratios.

4. Considerations for Plan Irregularities   ASCE 7

Because there is a reentrant corner at the intersection of lines B and 3, a check for Type 2 horizontal structural irregularity must be made. Requirements for horizontal structural irregularities are given in ASCE 7 Table 12.3-1. The building projections beyond the reentrant corner are checked dimensionally against a 15 percent plan dimension criteria.

East-west direction check:

> 0.15×320 ft = 48 ft
>
> 80 ft projection > 48 ft

North-south direction check:

> 0.15×160 ft = 24 ft
>
> 40 ft projection > 24 ft

Because both projections are greater than 15 percent of the plan dimension in the direction considered and the structure is SDC D or higher, a Type 2 horizontal structural irregularity exists. ASCE 7 Section 12.10.3.3 directs the design engineer to the requirements of Section 12.3.3.4, resulting in a 25 percent increase in seismic forces for connections of diaphragms to the vertical elements, connections of diaphragms to collectors, and the collectors themselves.

According to AWC, the 25 percent force increase is not intended to require increased diaphragm sheathing nailing. Instead, Section 12.3.3.4 increases the forces for the shear transfer from ledgers and wood nailers to shear walls and collectors. The design of this shear transfer is not a part of this example. This horizontal plan irregularity also affects the collector design, as will be shown in Part 6. The 25 percent force increase is not applied to out-of-plane wall anchorage forces connected to the diaphragms.

5. Diaphragm Chords (North-South)   ASCE 7

Chords are required to carry the tension forces developed by the in-plane bending moments in the diaphragm. In this building, the chords are continuous reinforcement located in the wall panels at or near the roof level as shown in Figure 2-7. In this example, the chord reinforcement is below the roof ledger to facilitate the chord splice connection at the wall panel joints.

Note: Wall anchorage is a very important aspect of design when concrete or masonry walls interface with wood diaphragms. The necessary members and connections for anchorage are not shown in Figure 2-7 for simplicity, and the design of wall anchorage is illustrated in Design Example 5 of this publication.

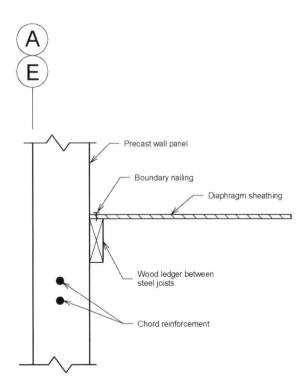

Figure 2-7. Interface of diaphragm at wall

The north-south diaphragm spans between lines 1 and 3 and lines 3 and 9. The diaphragm is idealized as flexible, and the moments in segments 1-3 and 3-9 can be computed independently, assuming a simple span for each segment. In this example, the chord reinforcement between lines 3 and 9 will be determined for an applied distributed load *w* onto the diaphragm. This reinforcement is embedded in the wall panels on lines A and E.

$w = 941$ plf from Part 2.2

$$M = \frac{wl^2}{8} = \frac{0.941 \text{ klf}(240)^2}{8} = 6775 \text{ kip-ft}$$

The chord forces are computed from

$$P_u = \frac{6775 \text{ k-ft}}{160 \text{ ft}} = 42.3 \text{ kips}$$

The chord will be designed using strength design with ASTM A706 Grade 60 reinforcing steel. A706 reinforcing is used here in anticipation that the chord steel will be welded at the splice between wall panels (see ACI Section 26.6.4.1). The load factor is 1.0 for seismic forces (ASCE 7 §2.3.6).

$$A_s = \frac{P_u}{\emptyset f_y} = \frac{42.3 \text{ kips}}{0.9(60 \text{ ksi})} = 0.783 \text{ in}^2$$

Therefore, use a minimum of two #6 reinforcing bars, $A_s = 0.88 \text{ in}^2 > 0.783 \text{ in}^2$ ... OK

The chord designed above consists of two #6 bars. These must be spliced at the joint between adjacent wall panels, typically using details that are highly dependent on the accuracy in placing the bars and the quality of the field welding. The welded reinforcing splice connection must develop at least 125 percent f_y per ACI 318 Section 25.5.7.1.

Chords can also be combined with the ledger where steel channels or angles are used. Where steel shapes are used, wood nailers can be bolted to the ledgers to provide a wood substrate for the diaphragm nailing. Alternatively, the structural wood panel may be directly fastened to the steel ledger/chord with proprietary pneumatically driven steel pin fasteners (see manufacturer's ICC-ES evaluation reports for requirements and design values).

In some cases, concrete wall panel shrinkage and any thermal expansion/contraction should be considered in the chord detailing, but is not a part of this design example.

6. Diaphragm Collectors   ASCE 7

Collectors (or struts) are provided in diaphragms to transmit the diaphragm reactions to vertical lateral-resisting elements such as shear walls or frames. Where the entire diaphragm's length parallel to the lateral load is uniformly attached to a shear wall, the diaphragm shears simply transfer uniformly into the shear wall. However, where the supporting shear walls are shorter in length than the diaphragm, or where a frame is placed for lateral diaphragm support, the shears must be collected and then transmitted to the shear wall or frame. The collector is a critical member in the load path and is thus subjected to an additional design consideration in Seismic Design Categories C, D, E, and F (ASCE 7 Section 12.10.3.4).

6.1 DESIGN THE COLLECTOR ALONG LINE 3 BETWEEN LINES B AND C

The collector and shear wall ledger along line 3 carry one-half of the north-south roof diaphragm seismic force. The force in the collector is "collected" from the tributary shear length between lines B and E and transmitted to the shear wall on line 3.

6.2 DETERMINE THE COLLECTOR FORCE IN THE STEEL BEAM COLLECTOR

From the diaphragm shear diagram for north-south seismic forces (Figure 2-5), the accumulating unit shear entering the collector on line 3 is calculated:

$$q = \frac{33.0 \text{ k}}{120 \text{ ft}} + \frac{113 \text{ k}}{160 \text{ ft}} = 0.981 \text{ klf}$$

On a hybrid roof system, lightly loaded collectors can utilize the steel joists and joist girders if properly designed by the joist manufacturer. For heavier-loaded collectors, rolled steel beams are more common. In this example, a W18 × 50 with wood nailer is assumed to be the collector and assumed adequate to support dead and live loads. ASTM A992, $F_y = 50$ ksi will be used in design. Not knowing whether the mode of failure would be yielding of the cross-section or buckling at mid-span, the engineer will evaluate the design collector force at the highest magnitude along its length.

$$P = ql = 0.981 \text{ klf}(120 \text{ ft}) = 118 \text{ kips tension or compression in beam}$$

6.3 DETERMINE THE WOOD NAILER ATTACHMENT ON THE STEEL BEAM COLLECTOR

In a hybrid roof system, the wood structural panel diaphragm is fastened to the steel roof framing with the use of flat wood nailers attached to the top chords of the steel joists and the top flanges of the steel beam collectors. The attachment can be in the form of steel bolting or threaded weld studs.

To prevent a conflict with the wood structural panels' placement and the weld studs' nutting, the wood nailers are countersunk so the nuts recess below the wood structural panel. In this example, ¾-inch-diameter threaded weld studs will be assumed to be welded to the collector's top flange and bolted to a 4× wood nailer with 1-inch-deep countersunk recesses.

The connection shear capacity of the wood nailer fastened with threaded weld studs is based on the 2018 NDS. The threaded weld studs have a fixed end support on the steel flange, and the reference design shear value could be calculated by applying the yield limit equations of NDS Table 12.3.1A. A simpler and slightly conservative method is for the designer to use the values associated with bolts that are fixed in concrete found in NDS Table 12E. It is important to note that these threaded fasteners have a reduced diameter D_r compared with standard wood bolts, and this reduction will affect their design shear value (NDS Section 12.3.7). Using NDS Appendix L, a fully threaded ¾-inch shank will effectively have a $D_r = 0.627$ inch, which is approximately ⅝ inch.

For a ¾-inch-diameter fully threaded dowel shank (~⅝-inch diameter unthreaded) in 2½ inches of net wood thickness

$$Z'_{\parallel} = 1180 \text{ lb (ASD)}$$

Applying the adjustment factors of NDS Table 11.3.1:

$$Z'_\parallel = 1180 \text{ lb} \times C_D \times C_M \times C_t \times C_g \times C_\Delta \times C_{eg} \times C_{di} \times C_{tn}$$

$C_D = 1.6$	NDS §11.3.2
$C_M = 1.0$	NDS §11.3.3
$C_t = 1.0$	NDS §11.3.4
$C_g = 1.0$	NDS §11.3.6
$C_\Delta = 1.0$	NDS §12.5.1
$C_{eg} = 1.0$	NDS §12.5.2
$C_{di} = 1.0$	NDS §12.5.3
$C_{tn} = 1.0$	NDS §12.5.4

$$Z'_\parallel = 1180 \text{ lb} \times 1.6 = 1888 \text{ lb/stud (ASD)}$$

The shear demand under allowable stress design is $q_a = 0.7(0.981 \times 1.25) = 0.858$ klf, where the 1.25 factor is per Section 12.3.3.4 as directed by Section 12.10.3.3. The required weld stud spacing is

$$s = 1.88/0.858 = 2.19 \text{ ft/stud}$$

Thus, the designer should provide ¾-inch-diameter × 3½-inch-long fully threaded weld studs at 24-inch spacing with nuts countersunk 1 inch.

6.4 CHECK STEEL BEAM COLLECTOR AS REQUIRED BY SECTION 12.10.3.4   ASCE 7

The governing seismic load combination for LRFD under Section 2.3.6 is

$$(6)\ 1.2D + E_v + E_h + L + 0.2S$$

For this example, $L = 0$, $S = 0$, $E_v = 0.2S_{DS}D$, $E_h = \rho Q_E$, and $S_{DS} = 1.0$. Because collectors are considered a part of the diaphragm system, the redundancy factor $\rho = 1.0$, as was discussed previously in Part 3. Thus, the applicable basic load combination for LRFD reduces to the following:

$$(6)\ 1.4D + Q_E$$

The unfactored distributed gravity load and bending moment are as follows:

$$w_D = 8 \text{ ft}(14 \text{ psf}) + 50 \text{ plf} = 162 \text{ plf}$$

$$M_D = \frac{162 \text{ plf}(40 \text{ ft})^2}{8} = 32{,}400 \text{ lb-ft or } 32.4 \text{ kip-ft}$$

As shown in Part 4, this building contains a Type 2 horizontal structural irregularity, and the requirements of Section 12.3.3.4 apply. This results in a 25 percent increase in seismic forces for collectors and their connections. The collector's axial seismic force becomes $Q_E = 1.25 \times 118$ kips = 148 kips. Additionally, collectors in SDC C through F require a 1.5 multiplier per Section 12.10.3.4 because of their critical role.

Thus, $Q_E = 1.5 \times 148$ kips = 222 kips.

AISC 360 Section H1 contains the equations for combined axial compression and bending. Because the bending is not biaxial, it is advantageous for the engineer to use Section H1.3 by checking failure about each axis independently. In this example, the collector's top flange is continuously supported with closely spaced diaphragm nailing, thus preventing lateral-torsional buckling. The collector's bottom flange will be laterally braced at the member's equal third points with use of an angle brace (design not shown), resulting in an unbraced length of $L_y = 40/3 = 13.33$ ft. The strong axis unbraced length is simply the span $L_x = 40$ ft.

As a condition of AISC 360 Section H1.3, the effective lateral-torsional buckling length L_{cz} must be less than the effective out-of-plane weak-axis buckling length L_{cy}, and this is confirmed.

$$L_{cz} \le L_{cy}$$
$$0 \text{ ft} \le 13.33 \text{ ft}$$

Failure will be checked separately about each axis per Section H1.3.

X-axis limit state (in-plane instability)

AISC 360 Section H1.3(a) provides the approach to check in-plane stability of the loaded W18 × 50 collector. First, the designer must compute the available in-plane strengths P_{cx} and M_{cx} for use in Equation H1-1. P_{cx} is the available axial strength and is a function of the collector's strong-axis unbraced length.

$$\frac{L_{cx}}{r_x} = \frac{KL_x}{r_x} = \frac{1.0(40.0)12}{7.38} = 65.0 \qquad \text{§E3}$$

$$F_{ex} = \frac{\pi^2 E}{\dfrac{L_{cx}}{r_x}} = \frac{\pi^2 (29 \times 10^3)}{(65.0)^2} = 67.7 \text{ ksi} \qquad \text{Eq E3-4}$$

Because $F_y/F_e \le 2.25$, Equation E3-2 is applicable.

$$F_{cr} = \left(0.658^{\frac{F_y}{F_e}}\right) F_y = \left(0.658^{\frac{50}{67.7}}\right) 50 = 36.7 \text{ ksi} \qquad \text{Eq E3-2}$$

$$P_{nx} = F_{cr} A_g = 36.7(14.7) = 539 \text{ kips} \qquad \text{Eq E3-1}$$

$$P_{cx} = \phi_c P_{nx} = 0.90(539) = 485 \text{ kips} \qquad \text{§E1}$$

M_{cx} is the available flexural strength for in-plane bending.

$$M_{cx} = \varnothing_b M_n = \varnothing_b F_y Z_x = 0.90(50 \text{ ksi})(101) = 4545 \text{ kip-in}$$
$$M_{cx} = 379 \text{ kip-ft}$$

Second, the designer must determine the required axial and flexural strengths P_r and M_r using the basic LRFD load combination (6) $1.4D + Q_E$:

$$P_r = Q_E = 222 \text{ kips (includes the 1.25 increase for plan irregularity and the 1.5 increase for collector)}$$
$$M_r = 1.4M_D = 1.4(32.4) = 45.4 \text{ kip-ft}$$

Per Section H1.3(a), the in-plane stability check uses Equation H1-1. P_{cx} is the appropriate in-plane buckling strength.

$$\frac{P_r}{P_{cx}} = \frac{222}{485} = 0.46 \geq 0.20$$

Therefore, Equation H1-1a is applicable for checking combined forces.

$$\frac{P_r}{P_{cx}} + \frac{8}{9}\left(\frac{M_r}{M_{cx}}\right) = 0.46 + \frac{8}{9}\left(\frac{45.4}{379}\right) = 0.57 \leq 1.0 \quad \ldots \quad \text{OK}$$

Y-axis limit state (out-of-plane buckling and lateral-torsional buckling)

AISC 360 Section H1.3(b) provides the approach to check out-of-plane buckling and lateral-torsional buckling of the loaded collector. First, the designer must compute the available out-of-plane strength P_{cy} and lateral-torsional buckling strength M_{cx} for use in Equation H1-3. P_{cy} is the available axial strength and is a function of the collector's weak-axis unbraced length.

$$\frac{L_{cy}}{r_y} = \frac{KL_y}{r_y} = \frac{1.0(13.33)12}{1.65} = 96.9 \qquad \text{§E3}$$

$$F_{ey} = \frac{\pi^2 E}{\dfrac{L_{cy}}{r_y}} = \frac{\pi^2(29 \times 10^3)}{(96.9)^2} = 30.5 \text{ ksi} \qquad \text{Eq E3-4}$$

Because $F_y/F_e \leq 2.25$, AISC Equation E3-2 is applicable.

$$F_{cr} = \left(0.658^{\frac{F_y}{F_c}}\right)F_y = \left(0.658^{\frac{50}{30.5}}\right)50 = 25.2 \text{ ksi} \qquad \text{Eq E3-2}$$
$$P_{ny} = F_{cr}A_g = 25.2(14.7) = 370 \text{ kips} \qquad \text{Eq E3-1}$$
$$P_{cy} = \phi_c P_{ny} = 0.90(370) = 333 \text{ kips} \qquad \text{§E1}$$

With the top flange fully supported laterally:

$$M_{cx} = \varnothing_b M_n = \varnothing_b F_y Z_x = 0.90(50 \text{ ksi})(101) = 4545 \text{ kip-in}$$
$$M_{cx} = 379 \text{ kip-ft}$$

Per AISC Section H1.3(b), the out-of-plane buckling check uses Equation H1-3.

$$\frac{P_r}{P_{cy}}\left(1.5 - 0.5\frac{P_r}{P_{cy}}\right) + \left(\frac{M_{rx}}{C_b M_{cx}}\right)^2 = \frac{222}{333}\left(1.5 - 0.5\frac{222}{333}\right) + \left(\frac{45.4}{(1.0)379}\right)^2 = 0.79$$
$$0.79 \leq 1.0 \quad \ldots \quad \text{OK}$$

Thus, the W18 × 50 collector is adequate for combined axial compression and bending.

Evaluating the W18 × 50 collector for combined axial tension and bending per Section H1.2 is not necessary because axial strength P_c is less for compression and thus more critical than for tension. Evaluating the W18 × 50 collector under a load combination with overstrength (Section 12.10.2.1) is not necessary because the alternative design provisions of Section 12.10.3 were followed instead.

6.5 COLLECTOR CONNECTION TO SHEAR WALL

The design of the connection of the steel beam to the shear wall on line 3 is not given, but the unfactored force is calculated as $F_p = 0.981$ klf $\times$ 120 ft = 118 kips. This is an important connection because it is the sole avenue to transfer the large "collected" seismic force into the shear wall. The connection must be designed to carry the gravity and seismic forces from the collector beam, including the 1.5 multiplier on axial loads per ASCE 7 Section 12.10.3.4 in Seismic Design Categories C, D, E, and F. As shown in Part 4, this building has a Type 2 horizontal structural irregularity, and thus the collector connection forces increase by 25 percent in addition to the 1.5 multiplier.

Because there is also a collector along line B, there is similarly an important connection of the girder between lines 3 and 4 to the shear wall on line B. Having to carry two large tension and/or compression forces through the intersection of lines B and 3 (but not simultaneously) requires careful design consideration.

7. Diaphragm Deflection   ASCE 7

Diaphragm deflections are estimated to determine the displacements imposed on attached structural and nonstructural elements, and to evaluate the significance of the *P*-delta effects. Under ASCE 7 Section 12.12.2, diaphragm deflections are limited to the amount that will permit the attached elements to maintain structural integrity and to continue supporting their prescribed loads. For structural elements, the intent here is to ensure structural stability by avoiding formation of collapse mechanisms in the vertical support system and avoiding excessive *P*-delta loading effects. For nonstructural elements, the intent of this section is to prevent failure of connections or self-integrity that could result in a localized falling hazard.

Traditionally, in-plane diaphragm deflections are typically evaluated simply by comparing the span-to-width ratio *L/b* to the acceptable code limits. For this example, SDPWS Table 4.2.4 limits the span-to-width ratio for blocked wood structural panel diaphragms to a maximum of four, which is greater than the diaphragms contained in this building. Nevertheless, there are important reasons to estimate the actual diaphragm deflections, such as to determine whether a diaphragm may be idealized as flexible or not and when determining building setbacks from property lines or other adjacent buildings. Another important reason that will be illustrated next is to evaluate excessive *P*-delta loading effects.

For the purpose of evaluating horizontal diaphragm deflections, the diaphragm loading used is that associated with the seismic story force F_x of Section 12.8.3 instead of the diaphragm design force F_{px} from Section 12.10.1 or 12.10.3. It is important that both the vertical seismic-force-resisting system's displacement and horizontal diaphragm displacements share the same basis of F_x, allowing both displacements to be directly added together for computing the total structure's maximum displacement. Additionally, when evaluating whether a diaphragm is flexible by calculation (Section 12.2.1.3), it is appropriate that the displacements of both the vertical and horizontal systems also share the same basis F_x. For a one-story building, $F_x = C_s W$, and thus in this example building the diaphragm deflection is evaluated under loading $F_x = 0.25W$.

7.1 DEFLECTION OF NORTH-SOUTH DIAPHRAGM   SDPWS

An acceptable method of determining the horizontal deflection of a blocked wood structural panel diaphragm under lateral forces is given in SDPWS Section 4.2.2.

$$\delta_{dia} = \frac{5vL^3}{8EAW} + \frac{0.25vL}{1000G_a} + \frac{\Sigma(x\Delta_c)}{2W}$$ Eq 4.2-1

This example will compute the deflection of the OSB diaphragm spanning between lines 3 and 9. Values for each of the parameters in Equation 4.2-1 are given here:

$v = 706$ plf for strength design (see Part 2.2)

$v = 706 \times 0.25/0.208 = 849$ plf for deflection evaluation

$L = 240$ ft

$E = 29 \times 10^6$ psi

$A = 2$ #6 bars $= 2 \times 0.44 = 0.88$ in^2

$W = 160$ ft

$G_a = 20.0$ k/in Zone A (see Part 3 for nailing zones)   T 4.2A

        15.0 k/in Zone B

        24.0 k/in Zone C

$\Delta_c = 0$ (Assume no slip in steel chord connections)

The flexural deformation portion of the equation $\dfrac{5vL^3}{8EAW}$ assumes a uniformly loaded diaphragm and is computed as follows:

$$\delta_{\text{diaphragm flexure}} = \frac{5vL^3}{8EAW} = \frac{5(849 \text{ plf})(240 \text{ ft})^3}{8(29 \times 10^6 \text{ psi})0.88(160 \text{ ft})} = 1.80 \text{ in}$$

The shear deformation portion of the equation $\dfrac{0.25vL}{1000G_a}$ is derived from a uniformly loaded diaphragm with uniform shear stiffness. Because this example has various nailing zones, and the apparent shear stiffness G_a varies by nailing zone, this portion of the equation must be modified. Using virtual work methods, the shear deformation of a uniformly loaded diaphragm with various shear stiffness zones is

$$\delta_{\text{diaphragm shear}} = \frac{0.5v_{i \text{ ave}}L_i}{1000G_{ai}}$$

where

$v_{i \text{ ave}}$ = the average diaphragm shear within each shear stiffness zone based on F_x, not F_{px}

L_i = the length of each stiffness zone measured perpendicular to the loading direction

G_{ai} = the apparent shear stiffness of each shear stiffness zone being considered

Working across the diaphragm from grid 3 to 9, Table 2-3 is helpful using information from Part 3.

Table 2-3. Worksheet computing shear deformation

Zone	v_{left}	v_{right}	$v_{i\,\text{ave}}$	L_i	G_a	$\dfrac{0.5 v_{i\,\text{ave}} L_i}{1000 G_{ai}}$
A	849	679	764	24 ft	20	0.46 in
B	679	509	594	24 ft	15	0.48 in
C	509	0	255	72 ft	24	0.38 in
C	0	509	255	72 ft	24	0.38 in
B	509	679	594	24 ft	15	0.48 in
A	679	849	764	24 ft	20	0.46 in
						$\Sigma = 2.64$ in

$\delta_{\text{diaphragm shear}} = 2.64$ in

Because the chord reinforcing bars are directly welded together at their splice, no chord slip is assumed to occur:

$$\delta_{\text{chord slip}} = \frac{\Sigma(x \Delta_c)}{2W} = 0.00 \text{ in}$$

$$\delta_{\text{diaph}} = \delta_{\text{diaph flexure}} = \delta_{\text{diaph shear}} + \delta_{\text{chord slip}} = 1.80 + 2.64 + 0.00 = 4.44 \text{ in}$$

To compute the maximum expected diaphragm deflection δ_x, ASCE 7 Equation 12.8-15 is used:

$$\delta_x = \frac{C_d \delta_{xe}}{I_e} \qquad\qquad \text{Eq 12.8-15}$$

$\delta_{xe} = 4.44$ in (using an elastic analysis under strength forces, δ_{diaph})

$C_d = 4$ T 12.2-1

$$\delta_x = \frac{4(4.44)}{1.0} = 17.8 \text{ in}$$

Note: The deflection amplification factor C_d from ASCE 7-16 Table 12.2-1 is primarily associated with reversing the effects of applied response modification coefficient R used in determining the base shear $V = 0.25W$.

Instead of using SDPWS Equation 4.2-1 to compute the elastic deflection, the designer could use Equation C4.2.2-1 in the SDPWS *Commentary*. Although this method is a little more complex, it will be more accurate if properly applied. Additional information is available in Lawson, 2019, and Skaggs, 2004.

7.2 LIMITS ON DIAPHRAGM DEFLECTION   ASCE 7

Limits are placed on diaphragm deflection primarily for two reasons. The first is to separate the building from adjacent structures and property lines in accordance with Section 12.12.3. In this situation, δ_x is computed for the diaphragm and then added to the displacement contribution of the vertical lateral-force-resisting system (shear walls, frames, etc.) to obtain the total maximum building displacement δ_M. Buildings at property lines are usually set back a distance of δ_M in accordance with Section 12.12.3. Adjacent structures shall be separated from each other by a distance δ_{MT} in accordance with Equation 12.12-2 where δ_{M1} and δ_{M2} are the maximum structural displacements for structure 1 and structure 2 at their adjacent edges.

$$\delta_{MT} = \sqrt{(\delta_{M1})^2 + (\delta_{M2})^2}$$

The second reason for limiting diaphragm deflection is to maintain structural integrity under design load conditions. Diaphragm deflections are limited by Section 12.12.2, and for wood diaphragms, SDPWS Section 4.2.1:

> Permissible deflection shall be that deflection that will permit the diaphragm and any attached elements to maintain their structural integrity and continue to support their prescribed loads as determined by the applicable building code or standard.

The language of this section is intentionally not well defined, with the approach left much to the engineer's own rational judgment.

The diaphragm's deflection results in the columns and perpendicular walls rotating about their bases because of the diaphragm's translation at the top (see Figure 2-8). Assuming the columns and walls were modeled with pinned bases during their individual design, this base rotation is permitted to occur even if some unintentional fixity exists.

Unintentional fixity may be the result of standard column base plate anchorage or wall-to-slab anchorage. The assumption of plastic hinges forming at the base may be acceptable, provided that these hinges do not result in loss of support. Research conducted by Kong et al. (2019) provides several design approaches for HSS columns subject to large drift.

A possible source of instability is the *P*-delta effect resulting in added diaphragm loading due to a horizontal thrust component from the leaning axially loaded gravity columns and walls.

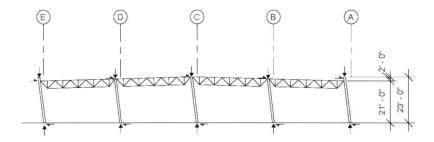

Figure 2-8. Building section with diaphragm deformation

Although it was not originally intended to be used to evaluate diaphragm deformations, Section 12.8.7 can be used as a guide to investigate stability of the roof system under diaphragm *P*-delta effects. The stability coefficient θ is defined as

$$\theta = \frac{P_x \Delta I_e}{V_x h_{sx} C_d}$$

Eq 12.8-16

P_x is the vertical load acting on the translating system and has two components in this example. $P_{x\,roof}$ is the translating roof load, and because load combination 6 of Section 2.3.6 is applicable, no roof live load is considered. $P_{x\,wall}$ is the translating concrete wall dead load and comprises the upper half of the wall plus parapet. Load factors need not exceed 1.0.

$$P_{x\,roof} = 14 \text{ psf}(240 \text{ ft})(160 \text{ ft}) = 538 \text{ kips}$$

$$P_{x\,wall} = \frac{7.25 \text{ in}}{12}(150 \text{ pcf})\left(\frac{21 \text{ ft}}{2} + 2 \text{ ft}\right)240 \text{ ft}(2 \text{ sides}) = 544 \text{ kips}$$

$$P_x = P_{x\,roof} + P_{x\,wall} = 538 + 544 = 1082 \text{ kips}$$

Δ = the average horizontal story drift

Because this is a flexible diaphragm with an approximately parabolic deflected shape, the average translation is

$$\frac{2}{3}\delta_x = \frac{2}{3}(17.8) = 11.9 \text{ in}$$

V_x = the seismic shear force acting on the translating system under consideration

Recall that diaphragm deflections are computed with $F_x = 0.25W$, not $F_{px} = 0.208W$. Thus,

$$V_x = (941 \text{ plf} \times 0.25/0.208)(240 \text{ ft}) = 271 \text{ kips}$$

$$h_{sx} = 21 \text{ ft} \times 12 = 252 \text{ in}$$

$$C_d = 4$$

T 12.2-1

Therefore:

$$\theta = \frac{1082(11.9)1.0}{271(252)4} = 0.047 < 0.10$$

Thus, *P*-delta effects on story shears, moments, and story drifts are not required to be considered.

Note: The story drift limitations of Section 12.12.1 are not intended to apply to flexible diaphragm deflections, but instead are intended to apply to the acting lateral-resisting wall or frame systems. These limitations on building drift were primarily developed for the classic flexible frame system with rigid diaphragm. Story drift limits are designed to ensure that the frames and walls do not excessively distort in plane. Similarly, the *P*-delta limitations of Section 12.8.7 are also intended to restrict in-plane movements of the vertical seismic-resisting system, especially in flexible frames resisting vertical and lateral forces together while subjected to potentially large secondary moments. Stiff concrete and masonry shear wall buildings generally are not impacted by secondary moments from in-plane *P*-delta effects.

7.3 DEFORMATION COMPATIBILITY ISSUES

This example building provides a very simple illustration to design a flexible diaphragm. While flexible diaphragm analysis is very straightforward on simple buildings, the analysis can become quite difficult to accurately model more complex building shapes. Often small changes in the outline of a building can create significant deformation compatibility issues. Small offsets or jogs along wall lines introduce stiff elements that are not long enough to act as shear walls, yet will inadvertently resist diaphragm movement due to their stiffness.

These elements are not a part of the lateral-force-resisting systems, but depending on where they are located within a building, they may be required to translate at the diaphragm level or else the diaphragm may tear away from the element. This concept of deformation compatibility must be considered by the engineer when designing buildings with flexible diaphragms.

Design Example 3
Three-Story Light-Frame Multifamily Building Design Using Cold-Formed-Steel Wall Framing and Wood Floor and Roof Framing

OVERVIEW

This example will be reviewing the design of a three-story apartment building sitting on a raised structural reinforced concrete podium deck, with one level of subterranean parking.

1. The design of this example will be limited to the lateral design of one of the three-story apartment buildings and does not investigate the design of the raised first-floor structural concrete podium deck that the three-story apartment buildings sit on.

2. The adequacy of the building's gravity system also is not evaluated except where required as part of the building's lateral-force-resisting system.

OUTLINE

1. Building Geometry and Seismic Criteria

2. Roof and Floor Gravity Loads

3. Lateral Loading: Seismic

4. Diaphragm Flexibility

5. Flexible Diaphragm Condition

6. Building Classification: Regular or Irregular

7. Redundancy Factor

8. Redundancy Check for Building B

9. Selected Analytical Procedure

10. Distribution of Seismic Forces to Shear Walls

11. Sheathed CFS-Stud Shear Walls: Framing Materials

12. Shear Wall Design Example: Building B

13. Shear Wall Deflection

14. Discussion: Framing with Cold-Formed Steel

15. Discussion: Seismic Joints

16. Discussion: Elevators

17. Items Not Addressed in This Example

18. References

DESIGN EXAMPLE BUILDING

Figures 3-1 through 3-5 illustrate the apartment building complex's front elevation, first floor, second floor, third floor, and roof plans used in this design example. Figure 3-6 shows an elevation cut through the building of stacked cold-formed steel (CFS) framed shear walls. The building complex is cut into a sloping grade, which is very common for these types of buildings. The first floor, podium level, is an elevated reinforced concrete structural slab over the partial subterranean parking level. There are two light-frame three-story buildings that sit on this podium deck: Buildings A and B. Building A has a single-story community room wing, which has a green roof. This roof, as well as the direction of the decorative wood slat siding on the exterior walls of the building, can be seen in the front elevation of Figure 3-1.

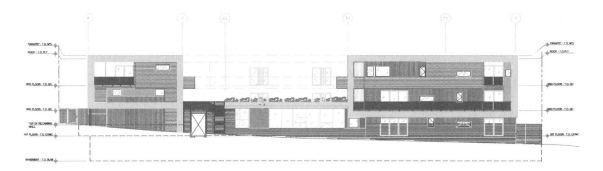

Figure 3-1. Apartment complex front elevation

The two three-story Buildings A and B are interconnected by a pedestrian bridge that has a seismic joint (see Figures 3-3 and 3-4). Access to the residential units is by means of exterior stairs and cantilever walkways. The walls of the residential units at each floor level stack vertically, so there are no horizontal offsets of the load-bearing walls and shear walls between floor levels. Engineered wood I-joists are used for the floor system, and prefabricated metal-plate-connected wood trusses are used for the roof members. Rated wood structural panel (WSP) sheathing is used for the floor and roof diaphragms.

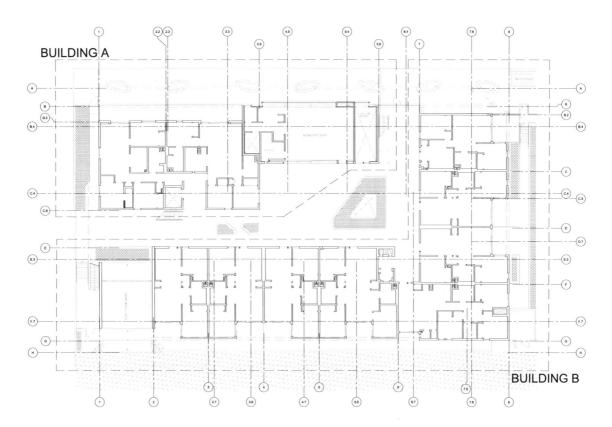

Figure 3-2. First-floor plan—Buildings A and B sitting on a common podium deck

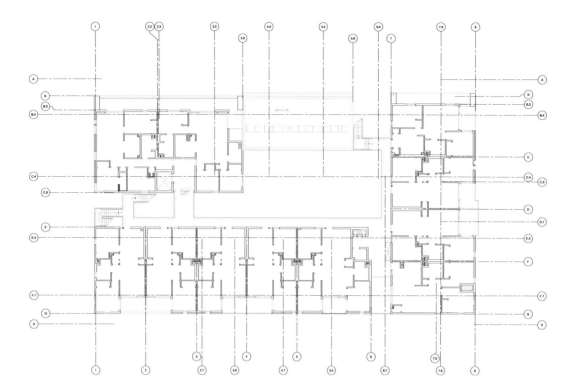

Figure 3-3. Second-floor plan

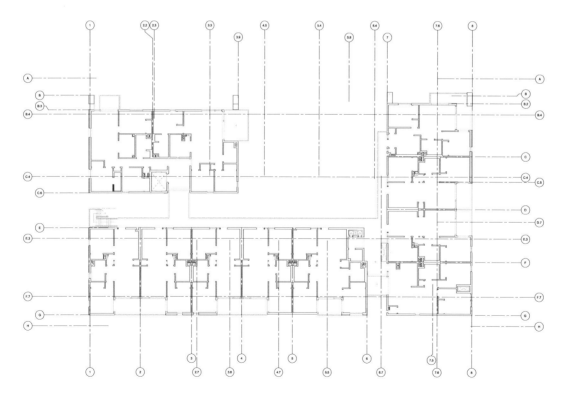

Figure 3-4. Third-floor plan

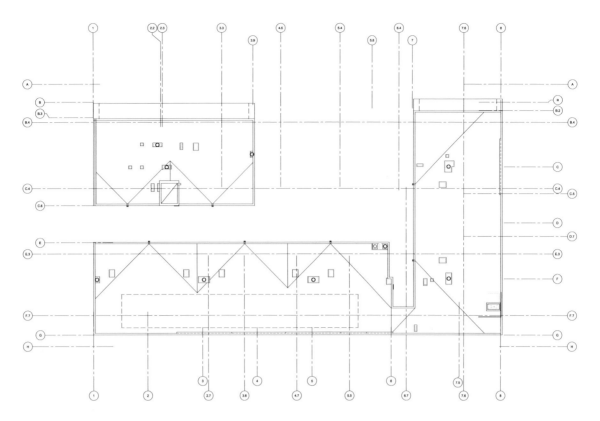

Figure 3-5. Roof plan

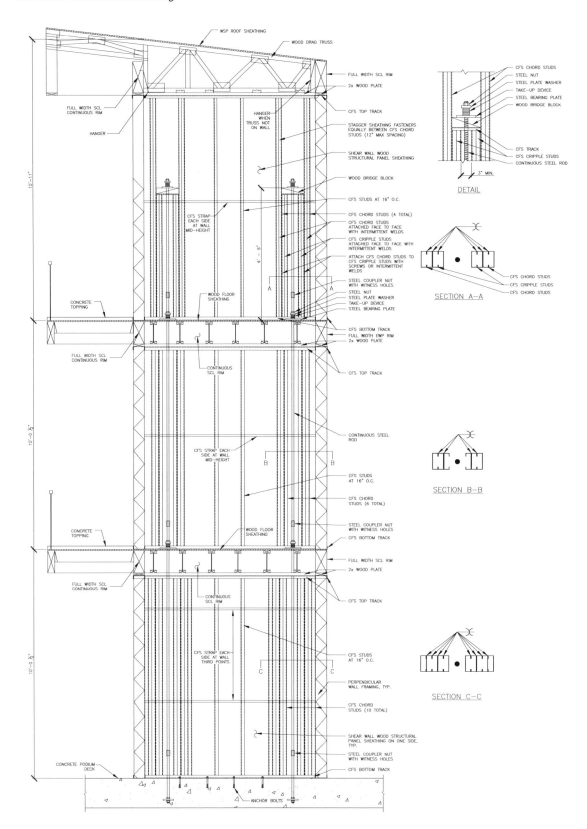

Figure 3-6. Shear wall elevation using mixed framing materials—cold-formed steel (CFS) light-frame shear wall and wood-frame floor and roof

The unique aspect of this building is that CFS wall framing is used for the building's wall gravity and lateral framing (wood structural panel-sheathed shear walls), while the roof and floor system is framed with wood members. The use of continuous wood rim joists along the top of CFS stud bearing walls in wood floor and roof framing systems allows for flexibility in the floor- and roof-joist layout, regardless of where the CFS studs align. The wood floor and roof framing is supported by hangers from the wood rim joist, which acts as the vertical load distribution member to the CFS studs. If the floor or roof framing is to bear directly on the wall, then the CFS stud wall top track or wood top plates must be designed for flexure and shear to support the wood I-joist reactions and transfer them to the CFS studs.

Where CFS floor joists and metal-plate-connected wood roof trusses are used with CFS-framed bearing walls, the alignment of the CFS studs within the wall with the CFS floor joists and wood roof trusses is much more critical. Regardless of the floor system selected, CFS floor framing or wood floor framing, the design of the CFS stud walls' top track or wood double plate, or combination of both, must be designed to transfer the floor gravity loads to the wall studs.

MIXED-USE, MULTIFAMILY, MULTISTORY PROJECTS

The apartment complex is no longer just a relatively simple structure built from wood or CFS studs sitting on a concrete slab-on-grade with continuous and isolated reinforced concrete pad footings.

The apartment building is now typically just one component of a larger mixed-use, multifamily, multistory complex that includes retail spaces, office spaces, loading docks, and above- and below-grade parking in addition to the apartment units. The apartment/rental units typically occupy the space above the uppermost podium deck, while the concrete podium structure contains the parking, retail, delivery, and commercial functions. The concrete podium deck can occur at grade level over multiple levels of subterranean parking or be several stories tall above grade. These mixed-use projects commonly contain anywhere from just five or six individual rental units to several hundred apartment/rental units, and the supporting concrete podium footprint can extend for hundreds of feet in each direction.

Apartment buildings constructed during the 60s, 70s, and 80s typically were smaller, and the designer only worried about the street-front appearance since the sides were obscured by adjacent buildings, and not much emphasis was placed on the alley elevations. These larger mixed-use projects often take up the majority of the block, stretching from street to adjacent street, to taking up the entire block, requiring very elaborate street-front appearances on all exterior elevations of the building complex as opposed to just the single street-front elevation of the apartment building of past years.

FIRE-RESISTIVE CONSTRUCTION

The demand for residential housing (apartment rentals/condominiums) since the 1980s has led to an increase in the typical number of residential floors being provided in these residential projects from three stories and less, to typically four and five stories, and in some jurisdictions to six stories using light-frame construction. Along with increasing the number of floor levels being utilized in residential housing have come additional building code requirements regarding use of noncombustible construction framing members (CFS studs, fire-treated lumber, etc.). Light-frame buildings that are three stories or less typically fall into the category of Type V construction, but once the designer goes above three stories, the building may now fall into the category of Type III construction, which has more stringent fire-rating requirements. In Type III construction, the fire rating of the exterior wall assembly has now become more important, often dictating the direction of the floor framing to minimize exterior wall fire-rating requirements, depending on whether the exterior wall is a bearing wall or a nonbearing wall.

For light-frame structures five stories and taller, it is recommended that the designer review the requirements of Type IIIA or B construction provided in the *International Building Code* (IBC) Chapter 6, since they significantly impact framing-design requirements. This would include the engineer being familiar with fire-separation distances, since they impact the required fire rating of the exterior walls. Since the building example being presented here is just three stories in height, the requirements of Type IIIA or B construction will not be discussed.

TERMINOLOGY

The light-frame multifamily building structure above the structural reinforced concrete podium deck at the first-floor level will typically be referred to as the "superstructure" for discussion purposes. The definition is to divide the building vertically into two zones: the light-frame structure above the podium deck (superstructure zone) and the first-floor podium deck down to the lowest parking level (substructure zone).

DESIGN EXAMPLE OUTLINE—CODES

This design example follows the provisions of the 2018 IBC and the applicable standards referenced in IBC Chapter 35. These include ACI 318-14, AWC NDS 2018, AWC SDPWS-2015, AISC 360-16, AISI S201-17, AISI S240-15, AISI S400-15/S1-16, ASCE 7-16, and applicable ASTM standards. Some groups offer their electronic standards for free, such as AISI through CFSEI. AISI S240 Commentary Section A2 references AISI S201 Section A1, which defines cold-formed steel light-frame construction as that where the CFS member thickness is between 0.0179 inch (25 gauge) and 0.118 inch (10 gauge). IBC Section 2211 requires the design of CFS light-frame construction to be in accordance with AISI S240 and that seismic-force-resisting systems shall be in accordance with AISI S400.

While Chapter 22 of the 2018 IBC references S100-16 for CFS design, for CFS light-frame construction, it references S240-15 and S400-15/S1-16, which in turn reference the previous CFS specification edition, S100-12. The authors recommend using S100-16 along with its supplement S1-18 as it represents the latest CFS research and understanding. Note that the sections in S100-16 and supplement S1-18 are reorganized and some content was added/deleted. S100-16 contains a chapter/section cross reference back to the S100-12 edition to assist in understanding the changes.

The AISI standards consist of the following:

> AISI S100-16: Specification
>
> AISI S201-17: Product Standard
>
> AISI S202-15: Code of Standard Practice
>
> AISI S220-15: Nonstructural Members
>
> AISI S230-15: Prescriptive Method for One- and Two-Family Dwellings
>
> AISI S240-15: Structural Framing
>
> AISI S310-16: Profiled Steel Diaphragm Panels
>
> AISI S400-15/S1-16: Seismic Design of Cold-Formed Steel Structural Systems

The following has been updated since the adoption by the 2018 IBC and the authors recommend that it be considered as it contains updated/deleted information:

> AISI S100-16/S1-18: Supplement

Where standards are referenced in the following design example, such as AISI S400, the author's expectation is the reader will be using the adopted or latest supplement to that standard (example: AISI 400-15/S1-16) where it occurs.

Only Building B is being evaluated in this design example since the design approach for Building A would be similar.

1. Building Geometry and Seismic Criteria

1.1 GIVEN INFORMATION

1. The building framing consists of light-frame construction utilizing CFS-framed bearing walls, wood structural panel (WSP) sheathing, engineered wood I-joists and structural composite lumber (SCL) beams for the floor, and engineered metal-plate-connected wood trusses for the roof. The superstructure's type of construction is considered to be Type V-A, R-2 (apartment building).

2. The floor heights are (finish floor to finish floor)

   a. first to second floor: 10 ft (actual = 10 ft ½ in)

   b. second to third floor: 10 ft (actual = 10 ft ½ in)

   c. third floor to roof: 11 ft (actual = 10 ft 11 in)

3. Building Seismic Design Category (SDC): D

4. Building Risk Category: II

5. Building superstructure's lateral-resisting system: Bearing Wall System (ASCE 7 Table 12.2-1):

   a. Shear walls: light-frame (cold-formed steel) walls sheathed with steel sheets or wood structural panels rated for shear resistance

   b. $R = 6.5$, $\Omega_0 = 3.0$, $C_d = 4.0$

      i. If diaphragm is considered to be flexible, then $\Omega_0 = 2.5$ (Footnote b, ASCE 7 Table 12.2-1)

   c. Maximum allowed building height: SDC D = 65 ft

      i. Architectural and fire requirements may reduce allowable building height. Building occupancy is R-2.

      ii. Fire sprinklers are required by the building code, type of fire sprinklers impacts height limits
         • IBC Table 504.3: Type V-A construction: Standard sprinkler (S) = 70 ft (S13R sprinklers = 60 ft)
         • IBC Table 504.4: Type V-A construction: Standard sprinkler (S) or (S13R sprinklers) = 4 story levels maximum above podium

      iii. 65 ft > 60 ft > building height = (10 ft + 10 ft + 11 ft) = 31 ft

6. Selected analytical procedure: To be determined

7. Floor and roof diaphragms are constructed of WSP sheathing and are blocked

8. Soils report: Soil Site Class D

2. Roof and Floor Gravity Loads

The following is a description of the building superstructure's dead loads and the superimposed live loads for the roof, third-, and second-floor levels of the building. The applicable live loads to use for this design example are defined in the building code, depending on the function of the space (roof, living unit, balcony, corridor, parking, public access, etc.).

The gravity loads are divided between horizontal framing elements (floors) and vertical framing elements (walls). The gravity loads are also used in calculating the design seismic forces for the building structure.

2.1 ROOF LOADING

Live load: 20 psf   Dead load: 16.0 psf

Table 3-1. Roof dead-load materials

Materials	Weight (psf)
Roofing	2.0
½-inch or ⅝-inch plywood/OSB span-rated sheathing	2.0
Wood roof trusses at 24 inches on center	2.0
Two layers of ½-inch gypsum board[1] ceiling	5.0
Sprinklers	1.0
Insulation	1.0
Miscellaneous (ducts, conduits, pipes)	3.0
Total:	16.0

Note for Table 3-1:

    1. Gypsum board, Gyprock, Sheetrock, plasterboard, wallboard and drywall are all words used to describe the same product.

Additional roof dead loads:

1. Some designers include the weight for a future re-roof where new roofing is placed over the existing roofing material. This can be a good design practice to account for a future re-roof, but including the re-roof weight also impacts the seismic design of the building. It is assumed for this example that when new roofing is required, the existing roofing will be removed down to the existing wood roof sheathing, and thus the weight of a re-roof is not included.

2. Roof sheathing thickness varies, depending on project-design requirements. The thicker the roof sheathing, the fewer issues with the de-bonding of the roofing material adhesives from the wood sheathing as a result of maintenance people or others walking on the roof over the years. A two-ply roofing membrane system is assumed for this project.

3. Rooftop air-conditioning/heating units are not being used on this project, and a custom air-conditioning unit has been installed in individual units.

4. Solar panels: The owner would like the roof to accommodate future solar panels in predesignated areas. An additional 8.0 psf of dead load will be considered in those designated areas for the weight of the solar panels and framing. The future solar panel design will have to work within these dead-load limits.

5. No roof areas for the three-story buildings are designated to be green roof areas requiring additional dead load for rooftop landscape. Only the single-story wing has a green roof, but it is not part of the three-story building chosen for the design example, and thus the additional weight is not accounted for in the roof dead-load materials table.

2.2 THIRD-FLOOR AND SECOND-FLOOR DEAD LOAD AND SUPERIMPOSED LIVE LOADS

The live loads at the second and third floors are limited to use within the unit and walking along corridors or stairs to get to individual units. The live load used within the units accounts for a normal expected furniture and cabinetry floor layout. The designer still must review whether special floor framing will be required under any special permanent fixtures to be located within the unit. An example might be a heavy spa tub.

Table 3-2. Third- and second-floor live loads

Live-Load Requirements by Location	Design Load (psf)
Within units	40.0
Balconies[1]	60.0
Corridors	100.0
Exterior stairs	100.0

Note for Table 3-2:

1. Balcony live load (per ASCE 7 Table 4.3-1) is a minimum of 1.5 times the unit served live load, but is not required to exceed 100 psf.

Table 3-3. Third- and second-floor dead loads

Floor Dead-Load Material	2nd- and 3rd-Floor Weight (psf)	1st-Floor (podium level) Weight (psf)
Finish flooring (carpet/linoleum)	1.0	1.0
1½-inch lightweight concrete (120 pcf)	15.0	—
⅝-inch or ¾-inch plywood/OSB span-rated floor sheathing	2.5	—
Wood floor joists at 16 inches on center	2.5	—
Sprinklers	1.0	1.0
Miscellaneous (ducts, conduits, pipes)	3.0	3.0
2 layers of ½-inch gypsum board ceiling	5.0	—
12-inch-thick reinforced concrete structural slab	—	150.0
6-inch exterior concrete topping slab (where occurs)	—	0.0/75.0
Subtotal	30.0	155/230.0
Interior partitions (see partition calculation)	14.0/15.0	14.0
Total	44.0/45.0	169.0/244.0

Additional floor dead loads:

1. The type of finish flooring being used should be verified with the architect/owner to see if it is going to be stone/masonry tile, wood, linoleum tile, or carpet. For this example, the finish floor is assumed to be carpet throughout the building and linoleum in the kitchen and bathrooms with a weight of 1.0 psf.

2. The thickness of the concrete topping over the floor joists, where provided, ranges from ¾, 1, or 1½ inches within the unit, and can be in the range of 3 inches in corridor transition zones from interior to exterior locations along the corridor, which has a significant impact on the floor weight. The concrete topping weight, depending on thickness and density, typically varies between 8.0 psf to 15.0 psf within the individual units. For this building example, the weight is assumed to be 15.0 psf.

3. The required thickness of the WSP floor sheathing can be dependent on the required sound transmission control (STC) rating. This design example assumes that ¾-inch WSP sheathing will be used along with two layers of ½-inch gypsum board on the bottom of the joists.

4. The floor wood I-joist weight will vary, depending on actual I-joist depth, span, spacing, and the size of I-joist flanges and webs. The weight of commercially available floor wood I-joists 9½ inches to 14 inches deep typically ranges between 2.3 to 4.2 pounds per linear foot of joist. The average multifamily, multistory project will typically use one wood I-joists "depth" throughout the project, but will likely include three or four different types of wood I-joists for the selected joist depth to address different joist-span conditions. Since different types of wood I-joists and wood I-joist spacings often occur throughout a floor level of the building, an "average" floor joist weight is used. The average floor joist weight for this design example is assumed as 2.5 psf when spaced at 16 inches on center.

5. The first-floor (podium level) weights are included for completeness of the building weight. There are often additional concrete topping slabs on the podium deck for waterproofing. Additional loads for planters, cantilever masonry security walls, and other permanent architectural features (shade structures, trellis, colonnades, etc.) must be included in the concrete podium design.

2.3 INTERIOR PARTITION WALL LOADS (GRAVITY DESIGN)

The interior partition walls include both bearing walls and nonbearing walls, some of which are shear walls. IBC Section 1607.5 requires floors on which partitions can be rearranged or moved to use a minimum partition live load of 15 psf. Often people have used 20 psf for the partition gravity load in commercial buildings that are considered to have moveable walls, and a lesser amount in residential buildings. Since the residential-unit walls are considered fixed, the actual average partition wall weight will be used. The individual unit demising walls often have WSP sheathing or steel sheets, but this is not typical for the units' interior walls. The upper floor shear walls will typically have only WSP sheathing or steel sheets on one side, while the lower floors are likely to have WSP sheathing or steel sheets on both sides.

Table 3-4. Partition dead-load material

Material	Non-shear Wall Weight (psf)	Shear Wall Weight (psf)
$^{15}/_{32}$-inch WSP sheathing (conservatively assume both faces)	0.0	3.0
½-inch gypsum board each face	5.0	5.0
4-inch or 6-inch CFS studs at 16 inches on center	1.5	1.5
Miscellaneous (pipes, conduits)	1.5	1.5
Total	8.0	11.0

The average partition floor load was determined by summing up the the wall weight of all the walls within an individual unit (length of walls × height of walls × wall weight psf) and then dividing the total weight by the square footage of the individual unit. This was done for several units, resulting in average partition wall weights of 12+ and 13+ psf of floor area.

The floor-to-floor height is typically 10 feet ½ inch. Wall clear height is about 9 feet 0 inches at the first and second floor, and it is about 9 feet 6 inches from the third floor to the underside of the roof framing.

For this design example, a partition gravity load of 14 psf (conservatively used since it exceeds 13+ psf found for some units) shall be used uniformly across the floor at the second floor, while a 15 psf partition gravity load is used at the third floor due to the taller wall height to the roof.

2.4 EXTERIOR WALL WEIGHTS

The exterior wall weight needs to be accounted for when determining the building's gravity loads imposed on the first floor structural concrete podium. The wall weight is important as well for calculation of the building's seismic base shear. The exterior wall weight calculation should also include interior corridor wall weights if they were not included in the partition loading. The wall heights typically used are the floor-to-floor height, since this will account for the weight of rim joist and blocking in the wall that is not included in the normal floor dead loads. Some designers choose to define the wall height as the clear height between the top of the floor sheathing and the top of the platform wall construction (underside of floor or roof joist), in which case the weight of the floor line rim joist and blocking are included as part of the floor joist framing weight.

Table 3-5 summarizes the exterior wall material and its representative weight based on the wall vertical surface area. Wall weights are typically determined based on vertical surface area.

Table 3-5. Exterior wall dead-load material

Material	Wall Surface Area Weight (psf)
Wall siding or ⅞-inch-thick stucco	10.0
½-inch plywood (assume plywood both faces)	3.0
½-inch gypsum board (interior face)	2.5
6-inch CFS studs at 16 inches on center	1.5
Insulation	0.5
Miscellaneous (pipes, conduit)	1.5
Total	19.0

2.5 EXTERIOR WALL AND INTERIOR WALL PARTITION GRAVITY AND LATERAL LOADS

The exterior wall and interior wall partition weight is accounted for differently, depending on the purpose of the wall weight calculation:

1. Building seismic lateral calculations.

2. First-floor concrete podium imposed design loads.

Thus, two different wall weight calculations are typically done.

Exterior Walls: Building Seismic Lateral Calculations

The building's exterior wall weight for this design example is summed based on a floor-to-floor analysis.

Exterior wall weight = (individual wall length) × (wall height) × (wall weight in psf)

All exterior wall weights in the building are then summed together for each floor level, and this total weight is used in calculating the building's seismic base shear. For simplicity of design, door and window openings are often omitted, and the walls are considered solid. Some designers may account for openings by actually calculating the area of the openings or subtracting some portion of the exterior wall weight to account for the openings.

Since the building walls span between floor levels, half of the wall weight is distributed to the floor level above and half is distributed to the floor level below. This division is used to determine the tributary mass for each building floor level. At the upper most floor level of the building, the upper half of that floor level's wall weight is associated with the tributary roof mass. If the floor-to-floor heights vary, then the tributary wall weight associated with each floor level will vary over the building height.

This total weight for each floor level may then be divided by the total floor area for that particular level of the building. This can be helpful in accounting for the average weight or mass associated with each floor level of the building footprint when calculating the seismic design force distribution over the height of the building.

Exterior Walls: First-Floor Concrete Podium Imposed Design Loads

The design of the concrete podium is not part of this design example, but the superstructure design loads are shown for completeness to demonstrate how they would be calculated and implemented in the concrete podium design.

The design loads imposed on the podium are typically divided among:

1. Uniform surface loads (example: live loads).

2. Line loads (example: wall loads).

3. Point loads (example: column reactions).

Current design practice utilizes finite element analysis software to evaluate the elevated structural concrete podium and determine the resulting design forces based on the imposed design loads. The design engineer determines how they want to apply the design loads. Some design practitioners just sum up all of the vertical loads and apply this as a uniform surface load over the slab, while others use a more refined approach to consider all the uniform, line, and point loads separately. The appropriateness of different design approaches used for applying loads (surface, line, point) for podium design is left to the design engineer.

Podium-imposed wall design loads are generally accounted for individually. The vertical wall loads are usually calculated on a per-foot-length-of-wall basis to make them easier to enter into the podium analysis software.

Exterior wall weight (per foot) = [(total wall height) × (wall weight in psf)] + [individual floor tributary loads to exterior wall (per foot of wall length)]

The same approach would be used for calculating interior bearing wall loads to be imposed on the podium deck as well.

3. Lateral Loading: Seismic   ASCE 7

3.1 LATITUDE AND LONGITUDE

The seismic spectral response accelerations S_s and S_1 for use specifically with the IBC and ASCE 7 are obtained from the United States Geological Survey (USGS) based on the latitude and longitude coordinates of the building site (https://earthquake.usgs.gov/hazards/designmaps/usdesign.php) using third-party web GUIs from:

1. ASCE: https://asce7hazardtool.online/

2. SEAOC/OSHPD: https://seismicmaps.org/

3. ATC: https://hazards.atcouncil.org/

USGS previously provided online tools to determine S_s and S_1, but it has now discontinued this service. USGS still provides the seismic data that third-party software developers retrieve in determining the S_s and S_1 values for a given location.

There are programs available on the internet that allow for the conversion of the building's street address to latitude and longitude coordinates. A good program will check several different internet sources to determine the latitude and longitude coordinates for a given address since each internet source calculates the latitude and longitude coordinates differently. For example, a good program would check several search engines like Google, Tamu, Geocoder, Yahoo, and Virtual Earth. Generally, the reported latitude and longitude results for the building site from each source are very close to each other. The three third-party web GUIs referenced earlier give the user the option of using either latitude and longitude or the street address of the building site.

If the project site is large, or if the engineer wants a general idea of the seismicity around the project site, they may want to check several different latitudes and longitudes across the project site or surrounding area by varying the program latitude and longitude coordinates in increments of 1/100th degree plus or minus.

Latitude: 1/100th degree = 0.6 minutes = 36 sec = 36 (~100 ft/sec) = 3600 ft
Longitude (at latitude = 30°): 1/100th degree = 0.6 minutes = 36 sec = 36 (~88 ft/sec) = 3168 ft

This gives the engineer a sense of the variation in S_s and S_1 across the area surrounding the building site.

3.2 BUILDING SITE SEISMIC DATA

The apartment building complex is located in Los Angeles, which is a high seismic region. The following design information was determined based on the latitude and longitude entered into the SEAOC/OSHPD seismic design maps website program for the building site. The geotechnical report for the building site should include some of this information as well to confirm the engineer's initial design assumptions regarding site soil properties used to determine soil site class, S_s, and S_1.

Near-Fault Sites   **§11.4.1**

Site is not a near-fault site (per soils report)

1. Site is located farther than 9.5 miles from a surface projection of a known active fault capable of producing M_w7 or larger events.

2. Site is located farther than 6.5 miles from the surface projection of a known active fault capable of producing M_w6 or larger events.

Table 3-6. Spectral accelerations (from SEAOC/OSHPD program)

Period (seconds)	S_a (g)
0.2	1.675 (S_s)
1.0	0.600 (S_1)

Spectral Response Accelerations Based on Site-Specific Soil Classifications

Site soil properties: Site Class D—stiff soil (confirmed in the project's soils report)

Long-period transition period $T_L = 8.0$ sec   F 22-14

Site coefficient: $F_a = 1.0$ (1.0 per soils report; otherwise, $F_a = 1.2$. by default per §11.4.4)   T 11.4-1

Site coefficient: $F_v = 1.7$ (also see §11.4.8 that follows)   T 11.4-2

$S_{DS} = 2/3\ S_{MS} = 2/3\ F_aS_s = 1.117$g   §11.4-1 and §11.4-3
$S_{D1} = 2/3\ S_{M1} = 2/3\ F_vS_1 = 0.680$g   §11.4-2 and §11.4-4

Site-Specific Ground Motion Procedures   **§11.4.8**

Per Item 3 of this section, a ground motion hazard analysis shall be performed in accordance with Section 21.2 for structures located on either Soil Site Class D or E where S_1 is greater than or equal to 0.2. The ground motion hazard analysis is not required for structures located on Soil Site Class D when the following are satisfied:

1. C_s (per equation 12.8-2): Use $1.0 \times C_s$ (when $T \leq 1.5T_s$) where $T_s = S_{D1}/S_{DS} = 0.680/1.117 = 0.609$

2. C_s (per equation 12.8-3): Use $1.5 \times C_s$ (when $T_L \geq T > 1.5T_s$)

3. C_s (per equation 12.8-4): Use $1.5 \times C_s$ (when $T > T_L$)

A response spectrum analysis is not required for this building structure.   T 12.6-1
The equivalent lateral force procedure shall be used for this analysis.

3.3 BUILDINGS A AND B—SEISMIC DESIGN REQUIREMENTS

Structural system: Light-frame CFS walls sheathed with wood structural panels

    Number of floors: 3

    Building height (above the podium level) = h_n = 31 ft

    Risk Category: II   IBC T 1604.5 and T 1.5-1

    Soil Site Class: D—stiff soil   From Soils Report

    Seismic Design Category (SDC): D   T 11.6-1 and T 11.6-2

    Importance factor: I_e = 1.0   T 11.5-2

    Building response modification coefficient: R = 6.5   T 12.2-1

Building period determination:

    Approximate period parameter, C_t = 0.02   T 12.8-2

    Approximate period parameter, x = 0.75   T 12.8-2

    Approximate fundamental period $T_a = C_t h_n^x$ = 0.263 sec   T 12.8-7

    Coefficient C_u = 1.4   T 12.8-1

    Building period (T) used = $C_u(T_a) = 1.4 \times 0.263 = 0.37$ sec $< 1.5T_s = 1.5(0.609)$
                                                     ASCE 7 §11.4.8 (Exception 2)

Note: Seismic Design Category E is not required since S_1 is less than 0.75.   ASCE 7 §11.6

Seismic Lateral Loads

    $V = C_s W$ Eq 12.8-1

Base shear (V) equation checks (using No Ground Motion Hazard study) T & T_s per ASCE 7 §11.4.8:

    V (when $T < 1.5T_s$) = $(S_{DS}I_e/R)W = [(1.117)(1.0)/(6.5)]W = 0.172W$ Eq 12.8-1 and Eq 12.8-2

    V (when $1.5T_s < T < T_L$) = $(S_{D1}I_e/RT)W = [(0.68)(1.0)]/[(6.5)(0.37)](1.5)W = 0.424W$ Eq 12.8-3

    V (when $T > T_L$) = $(S_{D1}I_eT_L/RT^2)W = [(0.68)(1.0)(8.0)]/[(6.5)(0.37)^2](1.5)W = 9.17W$ Eq 12.8-4

    V_{min} = $0.044S_{DS}I_eW = [(0.044)(1.117)(1.0)]W = 0.049W \geq 0.01W$ Eq 12.8-5

    V_{min} = $(0.5S_1I_e/R)W = [(0.5)(0.60)(1.0)]/(6.5)W = 0.046W$ Eq 12.8-6

Therefore, use $V = 0.172W$.

Vertical distribution coefficient, $k = 1.0$ §12.8.3

Author's Discussion: Equations 12.8-3 and 12.8-4 are shown for completeness, as designers often use a generic spreadsheet showing all three base shear Equations 12.8-2, 12.8-3, and 12.8-4 so they can use the spreadsheet for every project. Since the calculated building period (T) is less than $1.5T_s$, Equations 12.8-3 and 12.8-4 do not need to actually be checked for this design example. If the building period (T) was longer than $1.5T_s$, then Equations 12.8-3 and 12.8-4 would need to be evaluated, as appropriate.

If a soils report has not been provided, then by default $V = 0.172 \times 1.2W = 0.206W$ as $F_a = 1.2$ instead of 1.0. For longer period (T) buildings, a ground hazard analysis would likely be performed by a geotechnical engineer as the 1.5 multiplier for C_s is a large penalty for the building base shear (V). Since a soils report was performed, this would include the Site-Specific Ground Motion Procedures per Sections 11.4.8 and 21.2; thus, the multiplier for $C_s = 1.0$ for Equations 12.8-3 and 12.8-4 instead of 1.5 when no site-specific ground motion procedures are checked.

Maximum S_{DS} Value in Determination of C_s and E_v ASCE 7 §12.8.1.3

The building code allows C_s to be calculated using a value of S_{DS} equal to 1.0, but not less than 70 percent of S_{DS}, as defined in ASCE 7 Section 11.4.5, when the following occurs:

1. The building does not have irregularities, as defined in Section 12.3.2.

2. The building is five stories or less above the lower of the base or grade plane, as defined in Section 11.2. Where present, each mezzanine level shall be considered a story for the purpose of this limit.

3. The building period (T) is 0.5 second or less, as determined using Section 12.8.2.

4. The structure meets the requirements necessary for the redundancy factor, ρ, to be permitted to be taken as 1.0, in accordance with Section 12.3.4.2.

5. The site soil properties are not classified as Site Class E or F, as defined in Section 11.4.3.

6. The structure is classified as Risk Category I or II, as defined in Section 1.5.1.

As will be demonstrated later in this design example, Building B due to its "L-shaped" plan configuration is classified as "Irregular", and therefore is not permitted to use the S_{DS} limit. S_{DS} used in this design example shall remain $S_{DS} = 1.117$.

Author's Discussion: The number of stories is measured from the grade plane, so for purposes of determining S_{DS}, this building would be considered as being four stories (one level of podium and three levels of light-frame construction), which is less than the five-story limit.

3.4 BUILDING MASS

Generic Building Footprint/Layout of Buildings

The schematic outlines of the two three-story buildings on the first floor podium are shown in Figure 3-7. As noted previously, only the seismic forces for Building B are being calculated.

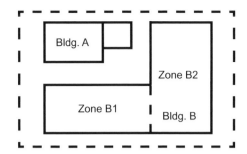

Figure 3-7. Layout of Buildings A and B on larger podium deck

Building B

The floor area for each floor level will be determined utilizing a summation of rectangular areas that are slightly larger than the actual floor footprint. Floor openings, such as stairs or duct/pipe chases, will not be subtracted out and will be considered as being solid. Recesses and notches along the perimeter of the building will be considered as nonexistent.

Building B is divided into two rectangles for calculating the building weight, Zones B1 and B2. This is to account for additional point loads/masses at the floor and roof levels and the fact that Roof Zones B1 and B2 are almost essentially detached from each other, as can be seen in Figure 3-5, "Roof plan."

Though there is some conservatism in this approach, using a more accurate floor area calculation does not usually lead to a significant decrease in the seismic mass at each floor level of the building. If the openings are significantly large in the floor or roof, then the designer may want to account for these openings in reducing the mass associated with that floor level. The other reason to use a slightly larger footprint is to account for potential adjustments in the building footprint by the architect as the construction documents are developed. It is always better for the designer to be conservative on the weight of the building than to discover later that the building weight/mass has been underestimated.

Two Surface Areas (B1, B2) and Lineal Feet of Exterior Wall

As noted above, the actual building dimensions have been increased slightly for calculating the floor and roof areas.

Second- and third-floor areas:

$$B1 = 45 \times 135 = 6075 \text{ ft}^2$$
$$B2 = 45 \times 96 = 4320 \text{ ft}^2$$

Roof area:

$$B1 = 40 \times 135 = 5400 \text{ ft}^2$$
$$B2 = 40 \times 96 = 3840 \text{ ft}^2$$

The calculated building area is larger at the floors than the roof to account for the exterior cantilever walkways.

Perimeter wall lengths (second and third):

$$B1 = 40 + 135 + 40 + 135 = 350 \text{ lineal feet}$$
$$B2 = 40 + 96 + 40 + 96 = 272 \text{ lineal feet}$$

Perimeter wall lengths (roof):

$$B1 = 40 + 135 + 40 + 135 = 350 \text{ lineal feet}$$
$$B2 = 40 + 96 + 40 + 96 = 272 \text{ lineal feet}$$

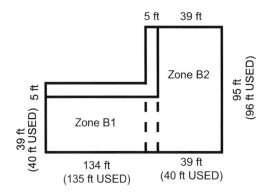

Figure 3-8. Building B footprint

3.5 SEISMIC WEIGHT

The weights/mass associated with each floor level of the building are determined and are used to calculate the building seismic base shear.

The partition wall weights for seismic design are distributed half to the floor level above and half to the floor level below. The contribution of half of the partition wall weight to the roof mass needs to be considered.

Table 3-7. Building B weights for building base shear (V) calculations

Level	Zone	Area (ft²)	Floor Weight (psf)	Total Floor Weight (lb)	Wall Length (ft)	Tributary Wall Height (ft)	Wall Weight (psf)	Total Wall Weight (lb)
Roof	B1	5400	(16 + 7.5)	126,900	350	7.0	19.0	46,550
	B2	3840	(16 + 7.5)	90,240	272	7.0	19.0	36,176
Total		9240		217,140	622			82,726
3rd	B1	6075	(30 + 14.5)	270,338	350	5.5 + 5.0	19.0	69,825
	B2	4320	(30 + 14.5)	192,240	272	5.5 + 5.0	19.0	54,264
Total		10,395		462,578	622			124,089
2nd	B1	6075	(30 + 14.0)	267,300	350	5.0 + 5.0	19.0	66,500
	B2	4320	(30 + 14.0)	190,080	272	5.0 + 5.0	19.0	51,680
Total		10,395		457,380	622			118,180

1. Half of the third-floor partition load (15/2 = 7.5 psf) and half of the third-floor exterior wall weight (19.0 psf) is distributed to the roof level.

2. The height of the third floor is 10 feet 11 inches, and half the wall height is 5 feet 5½ inches, which is rounded to 5.5 feet. The parapet height is 1 foot 6 inches, so the total wall height tributary to the roof is 5.5 + 1.5 = 7.0 feet.

3. The tributary partition wall load at the third floor is (15.0 + 14.0)/2 = 14.5 psf to account for the different floor heights. The tributary partition wall load at the second floor is 14.0 psf.

4. The wall height for each of second and third floors is 10 feet ½ inch. Half of this wall height is 5 feet ¼ inch, which is rounded to 5.0 feet.

Additional Weights/Masses to Consider

Often there are additional individual masses that should be accounted for in the building design that do not fit into a floor surface area or are limited to certain areas of the building. These loads are often added in as additional floor loads at the floor level where they occur.

1. Solar panels.
   A portion of Building B's roof will support solar panels in the future. The weight of the individual solar panels (often ranging between 2.0 to 3.5 psf) and the support framing above the roof is assumed to equal 8.0 psf.
   The future roof area for solar panels is 14 feet × 100 feet = 1400 square feet.
   The assumed weight for the solar panels is $1400 \times 8.0 = 11,200$ pounds.

2. Rooftop equipment.
   Individual rooftop units typically range in weight between 100 to 500 pounds. The rooftop equipment weight should also include weight for the curb or housekeeping pad the equipment sits on. There are often other lighter weight fans and other miscellaneous equipment on the roof as well. Some designers will add an additional 1.0 psf to the roof-weight load to account for mechanical units; others will assume a number of rooftop units of a given weight range and add it to the roof weight.

   There are no rooftop units on this building, and the miscellaneous roof dead-load weight of 3.0 psf can be considered to cover the weight of the few pieces of mechanical equipment that are installed on the roof.

3. Exterior stairs/walkways.
   The majority of exterior stairs are integral with buildings, unless there is a seismic joint, and therefore their mass is added. Half of the stair weight between floors will be added to the floor above, and half will be added to the floor below. The stair weight needs to include the guard-rail weight, which can often be very heavy. The dead load of a stair considering a combination of concrete infill treads, stringers, concrete-filled pans, guard rails and stanchions, and infill steel pickets can be extremely heavy. When the total stair dead load is divided by the footprint of a flight of stairs between floor levels, the weight can often range between 50 to 100 psf.

   The added stair weight at the second floor is 9 feet × 12 feet × 75 psf × 2 stairs = 16,200 pounds. The added weight at the third floor is half of the second floor = 16,200/2 = 8100 pounds.

4. Elevated walkway/bridge between buildings.
   Since there is a seismic joint, the mass of the bridge needs to be included with the mass of the anchor building from which it is cantilevering. When the bridge moves in a direction parallel to the bridge span, it induces a load on the anchor building by trying to pull away or push into the anchor building. When the bridge moves perpendicular to the bridge span, an independent lateral-resisting system probably should be provided (such as moment frames at the end where the seismic joint occurs) or some other system created that ties the bridge back into the anchor building.

   The added mass for Building B at the third floor and second floor to account for the bridge is 13 feet × 8 feet × 50 psf (assumed bridge dead load) = 5200 pounds.

5. Planters.
   With green building codes and stormwater retention systems being required in these building projects, there are often planters on upper floor levels to provide green space as well as temporarily store rainwater to be released at a later date into the public storm drain systems.

   There are no planters on Building B in this design example. There is a planter/stormwater retention system that is part of Building A that would have to be addressed in the design of Building A.

Summary of Building B Weights:

Roof area B1 = 126,900 + 46,550 + 11,200 =	184,650 pounds	= 184.7 kips
Third-floor area B1 = 270,338 + 69,825 + 8100 + 5200 =	353,463 pounds	= 353.5 kips
Second-floor area B1 = 267,300 + 66,500 + 16,200 + 5200 =	355,200 pounds	= 355.2 kips
Total =	893,313 pounds	= 893.4 kips
Roof area B2 = 90,240 + 36,176 =	126,416 pounds	= 126.5 kips
Third-floor area B2 = 192,240 + 54,264 + 8100 =	254,604 pounds	= 254.6 kips
Second-floor area B2 = 190,080 + 51,680 + 16,200 =	257,960 pounds	= 258.0 kips
Total =	638,040 pounds	= 639.1 kips

3.6 BUILDING BASE SHEAR (*V*)—STRENGTH LEVEL

Building B1 = $0.172W = 0.172(893.4) = 153.7$ kips.　　Use 160.0 kips.

Building B2 = $0.172W = 0.172(639.1) = 109.9$ kips　　Use 116.0 kips.

To help simplify the math, the numbers are rounded up to an even number and increased slightly to provide a small buffer for future small items that might be added during the design stages of the building. Thus, the engineer will not have to go back and check the lateral analysis. In this case the author has added a cushion of about 5 percent to the calculated building base shear. The building code does not require this round-off, and the designer can use the calculated base shear if they wish.

Building B1: $V = 153.7 \times 1.05 = 161.4$ kips, which is approximately 160 kips.

Building B2: $V = 109.9 \times 1.05 = 115.4$ kips, which is approximately 116 kips.

3.7 VERTICAL DISTRIBUTION OF SEISMIC DESIGN FORCES, STORY SHEARS, AND DIAPHRAGM FORCES

Tables 3-8 and 3-9 show the distribution of design forces, story shears, and diaphragm design forces for the two zones of Building B.

Table 3-8.　Building zone B1

Level	Story						Diaphragm					
	W_x (kips)	H_x (ft)	$W_x H_x^k$	% V	F_x (kips)	Story V (kips)	W_{px} (kips)	ΣW_i (kips)	$\dfrac{W_{px}}{\Sigma W_i}$	ΣF_i (kips)	F_{px} (kips)	F_{px} (min) (kips)
Roof	184.7	31	5725.7	0.350	56.0	56.0	184.7	184.7	1.0	56.0	56.0*	41.3
3rd	353.5	20	7070.0	0.433	69.3	125.3	353.5	538.2	0.657	125.3	82.4*	79.0
2nd	355.2	10	3552.0	0.217	34.7	160.0	355.2	893.4	0.398	160.0	63.6	79.4*
Σ check	893.4		16,347.7	1.000	160.0							

Summation check (*V*) = 160, same as 160 hand calculation, therefore okay.

Table 3-9. Building zone B2

Level	Story						Diaphragm					
	W_x (kips)	H_x (ft)	$W_x H_x^{\ k}$	% V	F_x (kips)	Story V (kips)	W_{px} (kips)	ΣW_i (kips)	$\dfrac{W_{px}}{\Sigma W_i}$	ΣF_i (kips)	F_{px} (kips)	F_{px} (min) (kips)
Roof	125.5	31	3890.5	0.337	39.1	39.1	125.5	125.5	1.0	39.1	39.1*	28.1
3rd	254.6	20	5092.0	0.440	51.1	90.2	254.6	380.1	0.670	90.2	60.4*	56.9
2nd	258.0	10	2580.0	0.233	27.0	117.2	258.0	638.1	0.405	117.2	47.5	57.7*
Σ check	638.1		11,562.5	1.010	117.2							

Summation check (V) = 117.2 > 116.0 hand calculation, therefore okay.

Notes for Tables 3-8 and 3-9:

1. % $V = C_{vx} = W_x H_x^{\ k}/\Sigma(W_x H_x^{\ k})$ and $k = 1.0$ (ASCE 7 Section 12.8.3).

2. $F_{px} = \Sigma F_i (W_{px}/\Sigma W_i)$.

3. Diaphragm limits (ASCE 7 Section 12.10.1.1):
   a. F_{px} need not exceed $0.4 S_{DS} I_e W_{px} = 0.4(1.117)(1.0)W_{px} = 0.447 W_{px}$ Eq 12.10-3
   b. F_{px} shall not be less than $0.2 S_{DS} I_e W_{px} = 0.2(1.117)(1.0)W_{px} = 0.223 W_{px}$ Eq 12.10-2

4. For simplicity, the weight tributary to the diaphragm at each level, W_{px}, and the weight tributary to the level, W_i, are considered equal in the two orthogonal directions of the building. The weight of shear walls in the direction under consideration could be subtracted from the diaphragm weight, but this refinement is typically not warranted in light-frame construction. However, in some cases, such as a long narrow building with a large number of shear walls in the building's transverse direction, the designer may want to consider the refinement to reduce diaphragm design forces.

As noted by the symbol (*) in Tables 3-8 and 3-9 for Buildings B1 and B2, the diaphragm design force at the second floor is governed by the building code minimum design requirements.

4. Diaphragm Flexibility

ASCE 7 Section 12.3.1 requires that the structural analysis for all buildings include the relative stiffness of the floor and roof diaphragms and the vertical elements of the seismic-force-resisting system, which is light-frame shear walls in this design example. If the diaphragm cannot be idealized as being either flexible or rigid, the structural analysis is to explicitly include consideration of the stiffness of the diaphragm as being semirigid.

The commentary for ASCE 7-05 Section C12.8.4.1 "Inherent Torsion" stated the following:

> Most diaphragms of light-frame construction are somewhere between rigid and flexible for analysis purposes, that is, semirigid. Such diaphragm behavior is difficult to analyze when considering torsion of the structure. As a result, it is believed that consideration of amplification of the torsional moment is a refinement that is not warranted for light-frame construction.

The commentary for ASCE 7-16 Section C12.3.1 "Diaphragm Flexibility" states:

> The diaphragm in most buildings braced by wood light-frame shear walls are semirigid. Because semirigid diaphragm modeling is beyond the capabilities of available software for wood light-frame buildings, it is anticipated that this requirement will be met by evaluating force distribution using both rigid and flexible diaphragm models and taking the worse case of the two.

Section C12.3.1.1 "Flexible Diaphragm Condition" notes that compliance with story drift limits along each line of shear walls is intended as an indicator that the shear walls are substantial enough to share load on a tributary area basis and not require torsional force redistribution.

ASCE 7 Section C12.8.4.1 "Inherent Torsion" states that for structures with flexible diaphragms, vertical elements of the seismic-force-resisting system are assumed to resist the inertial forces from the mass that is tributary to the elements with no explicitly computed torsion.

Therefore, the wood diaphragm in light-frame construction is considered a semirigid diaphragm, even if the common practice has been traditionally to consider it as flexible. The semirigid diaphragm classification is a result of a large number of interior nonseismic bearing and nonbearing wall partitions, as well as interior and exterior perimeter seismic shear walls contributing to the stiffness of the diaphragm. These partitions and walls form a honeycomb grid of cross walls that interlock the adjacent floor diaphragms together over multiple levels of the building, so the building structure behaves more as a rigid box structure than a collection of stiff vertical lateral-resisting elements with a flexible diaphragm spanning between them.

This semirigid diaphragm behavior has led some light frame designers to use an envelope method for the design of the diaphragms, which is discussed in ASCE 7-16 Section C12.3.1 as noted previously.

1. First, consider the diaphragms as flexible and determine the distribution of lateral forces to the shear walls.

2. Second, consider the diaphragms as rigid and determine the distribution of lateral forces to the shear walls.

3. Third, the actual individual shear wall design will then be based on the diaphragm analysis that produces the larger design forces.

The envelope method results in some of the individual shear wall designs using the forces from the flexible diaphragm analysis, while the other shear walls are designed using the forces from the rigid diaphragm analysis. Checking both extremes of idealized diaphragm behavior, rigid and flexible, provides bounds that will encompass the maximum shear wall design forces, as if a semirigid diaphragm analysis approach was utilized. The envelope method has now been included as an alternative method to semirigid horizontal analysis for horizontal distribution of shear to shear walls in Section 4.2.5, AWC SDPWS 2015. (Note that the authors recommend referring to the 2018 SDPWS as it is the most recent published standard even though it will not be adopted until the 2021 IBC.)

Due to the generally good performance of one- to four-story light-frame buildings sheathed with WSP, ASCE 7 has allowed for a few prescriptive design requirements which, if satisfied, allow the diaphragm to be idealized as flexible for design purposes, while the actual behavior is more likely between semirigid and rigid in behavior. If the prescriptive section requirements cannot be met, then the building code allows for a more rigorous approach to determine if the diaphragm behavior is flexible. Building designers typically prefer the "flexible diaphragm" approach since less design time is required for the building design than for a rigid diaphragm approach. There are some design offices though that have automated electronic spreadsheets for doing a rigid diaphragm analysis with torsion and use that for the shear wall designs, and do not consider the flexible diaphragm approach. So it is left up to the designer as to the design approach they want to take and to determine the rigidity of the diaphragm.

5. Flexible Diaphragm Condition

Building B is an L-shaped building, and the roof diaphragm is not continuous around the intersection of the two roofs. A flexible diaphragm will be assumed for distribution of seismic forces to the various shear walls at each floor level of Building B. This is permissible since per ASCE 7 Section 12.3.1.1(c):

1. For light-frame construction where the vertical seismic-force-resisting system elements comply with the allowable story drift in Table 12.12-1 and the nonstructural concrete, or similar material, floor topping thickness over the wood structural panel diaphragm does not exceed 1.5 inches.

   a. A possible exception might include that topping slab thickness can increase to 2.5 inches along edges where topping slopes down to 1.5 inches or less at floor drainage systems at breezeways and balconies since they represent a relatively minor area of the building's total square footage.

Since the floor and roof diaphragms are considered to be flexible by definition of Section 12.3.1.1(c), the additional "calculated" flexible diaphragm condition (ASCE 7 Section 12.3.1.3) is not required to be checked. This section requires the in-plane deflections of the horizontal diaphragm between shear walls be compared to the top of shear wall deflections. If the average horizontal diaphragm deflection exceeds two times the top of shear wall deflection, then the horizontal diaphragm is considered to be flexible.

6. Building Classification: Regular or Irregular

Building B needs to be classified as being either a regular or irregular building based on whether there are horizontal and/or vertical structural irregularities present within the building.

1. Regular building: No horizontal or vertical irregularities.

2. Irregular building: One or more horizontal or vertical irregularities.

Horizontal Irregularity Check   **ASCE 7 §12.3.2.1**

Horizontal structural irregularities are defined in ASCE 7 Table 12.3-1. Table 3-10 indicates how these horizontal irregularities apply to Building B.

Table 3-10. Applicability of horizontal structural irregularities to Building B

ASCE 7 Table 12.3-1—Horizontal Structural Irregularities		
Type	Description	Design Check for Building B
1a	Torsional Irregularity	N.A.—Flexible floor and roof diaphragms
1b	Extreme Torsional Irregularity	N.A.—Flexible floor and roof diaphragms
2	Reentrant Corner Irregularity	Detailed check required—See below
3	Diaphragm Discontinuity Irregularity	OK—No large diaphragm openings
4	Out-of-Plane Offset Irregularity	OK—Shear walls stack
5	Nonparallel System Irregularity	OK—Shear walls oriented orthogonal to each other and parallel to building axis

1. N.A.: Not Applicable—No check required (for reason stated).

2. OK: Building does not meet conditions of noted irregularities requiring a detailed evaluation (for reason stated).

The only horizontal irregularity that requires a detailed check for Building B is "Type 2—reentrant corner irregularity," since Building B is L-shaped and in SDC D. The reentrant corner is considered to be a potential horizontal irregularity where the two legs of the building come together. The projection of the reentrant corner in the direction being considered cannot be more than 15 percent of the overall building length in that direction to avoid a horizontal irregularity.

Roofs:

B1: 5 ft/(134 ft + 5 ft) = 3.6% < 15%
B1: 6 ft/39 ft = 15.4% ~ 15% (say OK)

B2: 5 ft/(39 ft + 5 ft) = 11.4% < 15%
B2: 6 ft/95 ft = 6.3% < 15%

Roof: Considered regular since the roofs are essentially separate.

Floors:

B2: (95 ft − 39 ft − 5 ft)/95 ft = 53.7% > 15%
B1: 134 ft/(134 ft + 5 ft + 39 ft) = 75.3% > 15%

Floors: Have Type 2 irregularity (reentrant corner)

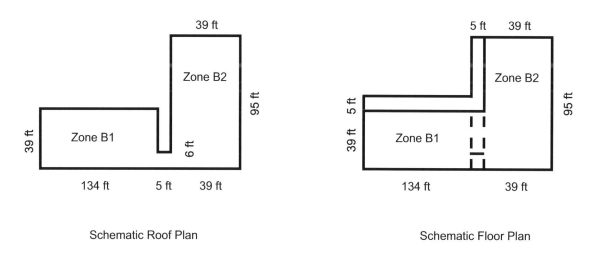

Figure 3-9. Building B schematic plans for reentrant corner detail check

When a Table 12.3.-1 Type 2 horizontal irregularity occurs, then the design forces for the framing elements of the floor diaphragm (example: collectors and collector connections must be increased 25 percent per ASCE 7 Section 12.3.3.4). In this case, Building B's second- and third-floor diaphragm framing element design forces would have to be increased 25 percent, but the diaphragm framing element design forces would not have to be increased at the roof. This design force increase is in addition to any redundancy design requirements.

Vertical Irregularity Check   **ASCE 7 §12.3.2.2**

Vertical structural irregularities are defined in ASCE 7 Table 12.3-2. Table 3-11 indicates how these vertical irregularities apply to Building B.

Table 3-11. Applicability of vertical structural irregularities to Building B

ASCE 7 Table 12.3-2—Vertical Structural Irregularities		
Type	Description	Design Check for Building B
1a	Stiffness—Soft-story irregularity	OK. Shear walls stack; lateral stiffness of shear walls at each floor level is more than 70% of shear walls at floor level above.
1b	Stiffness—Extreme soft-story irregularity	OK. Shear walls stack; lateral stiffness of shear walls at each floor level is more than 60% of shear walls at floor level above.
2	Weight (mass) irregularity	OK. Weight of any floor level is not more than 150% of floor level above or below.
3	Vertical geometric irregularity	OK. Shear walls stack; individual shear wall lengths at a given floor level are not more than 130% of that in the adjacent story.
4	In-plane discontinuity in vertical lateral-force-resisting element irregularity	OK. Shear walls stack; there are no in-plane offsets between shear walls of adjacent floor levels in the same line that are more than the length of the shear wall above.
5a	Discontinuity in lateral strength—Weak-story irregularity	OK. Shear walls stack; story lateral strength is more than 80% of floor level above.
5b	Discontinuity in lateral strength—Extreme weak-story irregularity	OK. Shear wall strength exceeds 65% of the lateral strength at the adjacent floor above.

1. OK: Building does not meet conditions of noted irregularities requiring a detailed evaluation (for reason stated).

2. Mass irregularity exception: When a roof is lighter than the floor below it, it need not be considered for mass irregularity.

When a vertical irregularity occurs per Table 12.3-2, then the building design must satisfy the requirements of the applicable referenced sections in Table 12.3-2. The design example for Building B illustrates three different shear wall configurations that could occur along a given wall line. In the case of shear wall configuration options 1 and 3, there is no vertical irregularity. Shear wall configuration option 2 is considered to have a Type 4 vertical irregularity since the shear wall is shorter at the first floor than at the floor level above and would have to be further evaluated per the requirements of Table 12.3-2.

7. Redundancy Factor

The concept of redundancy in building seismic-force-resisting systems is to provide enough elements resisting lateral forces so catastrophic failure of the building does not occur if one element is overloaded or fails. The redundancy factor, ρ, imposes a penalty on the design of certain components of the lateral-force-resisting system by requiring design for higher forces when adequate redundancy is not provided. Redundancy is typically provided in buildings by the use of multiple lateral-force-resisting elements

ASCE 7 Section 12.3.4 requires that a redundancy factor be assigned to the building's seismic-force-resisting system in each of the two orthogonal directions relative to the building's footprint. A value of ρ equal to 1.3 is used unless the conditions of either Section 12.3.4.1 or 12.3.4.2 are satisfied, in which case the value of $\rho = 1.0$ may be used.

Conditions Where Value of ρ Is 1.0   **ASCE 7 §12.3.4.1**

ASCE 7 Section 12.3.4.1 is a general catchall section that recognizes that it is not appropriate for the engineer to automatically apply a redundancy factor greater than 1.0 to all seismic regions (seismic design categories) or aspects of the seismic lateral-force-resisting system evaluation and component design. A value of ρ equal to 1.0 may be used for the six design conditions related to light-frame construction listed below. The six individual design conditions have been sorted according to application instead of listing them individually, as occurs in Section 12.3.4.1. There are three other conditions not included as they are not generally applicable to light-frame building construction.

1. Seismic Design Category

    a. Building structures assigned to Seismic Design Categories (SDC) B, C.

        i. Structures assigned to SDC A do not require consideration of seismic forces, so the redundancy factor, ρ, does not apply.

2. Building Displacements

    a. Drift calculations and *P*-delta effects.

3. Building Component Design

    a. Design of nonstructural components.

    b. Design of collector elements, splices, and their connections when the overstrength factor, Ω_0, is included in the seismic load combination being used for design of the element.

    c. Design of seismic-force-resisting system members or connections where the seismic load combinations require the overstrength factor, Ω_0, be included.

    d. Diaphragm inertial loads derived from using Equation 12.10-1 for distribution of diaphragm seismic forces to the various floor/roof levels of the building.
    [Note: ρ = 1.3 is required for forces transferred through a diaphragm due to an offset of the lateral-force-resisting system between floor levels (example: out-of-plane offset of shear walls between floor levels)].

Redundancy Factor, ρ, for Seismic Design Categories D through F   **ASCE 7 §12.3.4.2**

ASCE 7 Section 12.3.4.2 specifically addresses Seismic Design Categories (SDC) D, E and F and requires ρ equal to 1.3 for the design of the seismic-force-resisting system unless the conditions in either Section 12.3.4.2.a or 12.3.4.2b are satisfied, in which case a value of ρ equal to 1.0 may be used.

ASCE 7 Section 12.3.4.2a

For each story level resisting more than 35 percent of the building base shear in the direction under consideration, the seismic-force-resisting system complies with ASCE 7 Table 12.3-3 "Requirements for Each Story Resisting More Than 35% of the Base Shear."

Table 12.3-3 provides requirements for different types of lateral force-resisting elements. The category of interest for most light-frame buildings is "shear walls or wall piers with a height-to-length ratio of greater than 1.0." The requirements to be evaluated are

1. Removal of either a shear wall or wall pier with a height-to-length ratio greater than 1.0 within any story level or collector connections thereto would not result in more than a 33 percent reduction in story strength.

2. Removal of a shear wall or pier does not result in an extreme torsional irregularity (Type 1b horizontal irregularity).

ASCE 7 Section 12.3.4.2b

Section 12.3.4.2b also applies to each story level resisting more than 35 percent of the building base shear, and is summarized as follows:

1. Structure is "regular" in plan at all floor levels.

2. Seismic-force-resisting system requirements:

   a. At least two bays, at the perimeter, on each side of the building.

   b. Seismic-force-resisting systems are orthogonal to each other.

A single bay is commonly denoted as the distance between two adjacent columns of a moment frame or braced frame. Since shear wall behavior is different from a moment frame or braced frame, an equivalent definition for shear wall "bay" has been developed. The number of shear wall bays is defined as follows for the various wall construction materials:

- Concrete, masonry, or steel shear wall bay quantity: wall length/story height.

- Light-frame shear wall bay quantity: $(2) \times$ (wall length/story height).

Therefore, a single long shear wall could be equivalent to one or more shear wall bays, whereas a single short shear wall could be equivalent to less than one bay. The sum of all shear wall bays along the building's perimeter, on each side of the building, must exceed two in order to use $\rho = 1.0$.

Author's Discussion—Equivalent Shear Wall Bays

Light-frame shear walls typically have openings such as doors, windows, and ducts. The decision of which wall lengths should be used in calculating the number of equivalent shear wall bays is left to the engineer, but two options are discussed here for consideration.

Option 1: Shear wall length defined from vertical edge of opening to vertical edge of opening.

> Conservatively, the engineer might use only the shear wall lengths on each side of the wall openings. This would be appropriate where the opening is a door that interrupts the perimeter boundary edge of the shear wall.

Option 2: Shear wall elements designed to transfer design forces around the opening in the shear wall.

> In the author's opinion, a wall opening length (window, duct, etc.) can be ignored and the wall considered as being one single longer wall that includes the length of the opening and the shear wall elements on each side of the wall opening, if the shear wall has been designed to transfer the wall design forces around the opening.

Some engineering judgment should be applied when using this option, and the following criteria are suggested.

1. The length of the wall opening shall not exceed 30 percent of the sum of the individual shear wall lengths on each side of the opening; otherwise, this condition should be treated as separate individual shear walls on each side of the opening.

2. The width of a wall pier in a shear wall on either side of an opening shall be not less than 24 inches (AISI S240-15 Section B5.2.2.1 "Type I Shear Walls"), half the height of the opening, or half the length of the opening, whichever is more; otherwise, this condition should be treated as separate individual shear walls on each side of the opening.

8. Redundancy Check for Building B

Components of the seismic-force-resisting-system in this design example will be evaluated using a redundancy factor, ρ, equal to 1.0 based on the conditions noted in ASCE 7 Section 12.3.4.2 and diaphragm Section 12.10.1.1

ASCE 7 Section 12.3.4.1 (applicable conditions where $\rho = 1.0$ in Building B)

1. Drift calculations: The shear wall drifts and diaphragm drifts would be evaluated using $\rho = 1.0$ since $\rho = 1.3$ is not applicable to drift calculations and *P*-delta effects.

2. Diaphragms: The design of the floor and roof diaphragms shall use $\rho = 1.0$ as the diaphragm forces are distributed to the various floors and roof per Equation 12.10-1.

   a. In accordance with Section 12.10.1.1, diaphragm design, ρ applies to diaphragm design in SDC D, E, and F, and since the inertial forces were calculated in accordance with Equation 12.10-1, the value of $\rho = 1.0$ is permissible for diaphragm design.

   b. In accordance with Section 12.3.3.4, if there is a horizontal or vertical offset irregularity, then the design forces shall be increased 25 percent for the following seismic-force-resisting elements:

      i. Diaphragm connection to collector ($1.25 \times$ diaphragm design force at collector)

      ii. Collector members

      iii. Collector member connections

3. Collectors (collector elements, splices, and collector splices)

   a. ASCE 7 Section 12.10.2.1 has an exemption for structures braced entirely by light-frame shear walls. The collector elements and collector connections for buildings in SDC C, D, E, and F need to be designed only to resist forces for Section 12.4.2.3 seismic load combinations when diaphragm design forces are calculated per Section 12.10.1.1. Since Section 12.4.3.2 load combinations with overstrength factor Ω_0 are not required to be included, ρ used for the structure is required for collector design (equal to 1.0 in this design example).

b. ASCE 7 Section 12.10.1.1 requires the value of ρ for elements transferring forces between vertical elements above and below the diaphragm (example: collectors at an in-plane offset— Type 4 vertical irregularity) be the same as for the overall building system. If the requirements of either Section 12.3.4.2a or 12.3.4.2b cannot be met, then ρ = 1.3 would be required for the structure and therefore also for the collector design.

c. The value of ρ for collector design for this example is 1.0 in accordance with Section 12.3.4.2, and this determination is shown below.

ASCE 7 Section 12.3.4.2 (Building B redundancy factor)

Since the building in this design example is located in SDC D, the requirement of Section 12.3.4.2 has to be evaluated. Either AISC 7 Section 12.3.4.2a or 12.3.4.2b must be satisfied to allow for ρ = 1.0 for the design of the seismic-force-resisting system components. For completeness of the design problem, both sections shall be checked.

ASCE 7 Section 12.3.4.2a

Determination of where story level shear exceeds 35 percent of the base shear is based on calculations for the complete building footprint.

Table 3-12. Building B story shear summation check

Floor Level	Zone B1 Story Shear (kips)	Zone B2 Story Shear (kips)	Building B Story Shears (kips)	Percent Story Shear per Floor Level (V)	Summation Percent Story Shear (V)
3rd	56.0	39.1	95.1	0.345	0.345 < 0.35
2nd	69.3	51.1	120.4	0.436	0.781 > 0.35
1st	34.7	27.0	61.7	0.223	1.004 > 0.35
Σ	160.0	117.2	277.2	1.004	

At the first and second stories where the shear exceeds 35 percent of the building base shear, there are sufficient numbers of shear walls in each orthogonal direction, so that:

1. Removal of a shear wall or wall pier with a height-to-length ratio greater than 1.0 does not result in a 33 percent reduction in story strength at each floor level. In the event all of the shear walls have a height-to-length ratio less than 1.0, then the lateral-force-resisting element noted as "Other" in ASCE 7 Table 12.3-3 would be used. In this case, there are no requirements, so the building would be deemed to satisfy this section without further investigation.

2. Removal of a shear wall does not result in extreme torsional Type 1b horizontal irregularity, which does not apply where the floor and roof diaphragm are idealized as being flexible, as is the case for Building B.

Therefore, ρ = 1.0 is permissible for the light-frame shear wall seismic-force-resisting system in this design example because the condition in Section 12.3.4.2a is satisfied.

ASCE 7 Section 12.3.4.2b

This section would not normally be checked if the building successfully complied with Section 12.3.4.2a for allowing ρ = 1.0. However, for completeness, the required checks are discussed. Also, in some cases this may be a quicker check than can be performed visually, so Section 12.3.4.2b may be checked before Section 12.3.4.2a.

The shear exceeds 35 percent of the building base shear at the first and second stories. The redundancy factor ρ = 1.0 is allowed based on the following requirements:

1. Have the equivalent of at least two bays of light-frame shear walls at all perimeter sides of the building at each floor level of the building.

2. Shear wall seismic-force-resisting systems are orthogonal to each other.

However, the redundancy factor, ρ, would have to be increased to 1.3 since the building is not regular in plan as it has a Type 2 horizontal irregularity and therefore does not satisfy the requirements of Section 12.3.4.2.b.

This section cannot be used to permit ρ = 1.0 since the building is not regular in plan. As noted previously, the requirement of Section 12.3.4.2 is to satisfy either Section 12.3.4.2a or 12.3.4.2b, and they are considered to be independent checks. Since Building B passed the requirements of Section 12.3.4.2a, ρ = 1.0 is permissible for the design of Building B.

Author's Discussion

A redundancy factor of ρ = 1.0 is commonly used for many multistory, light-frame, shear wall structures per Section 12.3.4.2a due to the large number of individual shear walls that occur in these buildings. However, in the event a structure does not satisfy the requirements of Section 12.3.4.2a, it seems likely a redundancy factor of ρ = 1.3 would be required for many multistory, light-frame, shear wall buildings per Section 12.3.4.2b as these buildings often are not "regular" in plan and have irregularities noted in ASCE 7 Tables 12.3-1 and 12.3-2.

One weakness of Section 12.3.4.2a is that it does not take into account the layout of the shear walls in plan when the engineer encounters a flexible diaphragm, since the engineer does not have to consider building torsion. Section 12.3.4.2b, on the other hand, specifically addresses the requirement of shear walls on the perimeter of the building. While some engineers have designed light-frame multistory structures using just the interior corridor walls for the shear resistance in one direction of the building without any parallel building perimeter shear walls, the SEAOC Seismology Light-Frame Committee has stated "this practice is not recommended without explicitly considering building performance, including the control of localized horizontal diaphragm deflections that could lead to instability," and "limitations on cantilever spans, diaphragm deflections at building corners and the corresponding methods of structural analysis are under investigation by the Structural Engineers Association of California (SEAOC) and the American Wood Council (AWC)." The desired seismic performance of the building is expected to be achieved where there are perimeter exterior shear walls. If perimeter light-frame shear walls are not included in the direction under consideration in the building design, then consideration should be given to using ρ = 1.3.

Even if the engineer satisfies Section 12.3.4.2a and uses $\rho = 1.0$, it is common in light-frame multistory buildings to have vertical irregularities such as out-of-plane and in-plane offsets of shear walls from story to story. It is left to the designer to determine the number of acceptable out-of-plane or in-plane offsets after which the redundancy factor of $\rho = 1.3$ might be used for the light-frame shear wall system. The in-plane offsets and out-of-plane offsets of light-frame shear walls do result in design penalties for connecting and supporting framing members, but the building's overall stiffness is still less than when the light-frame shear walls stack from floor to floor. The increase of $\rho = 1.3$ becomes a seismic brute strength approach to address that the building has structural irregularities and is not considered to be regular in plan.

By the same token, just because an irregularity does occur once in a light-frame multistory building, the entire building should not necessarily be penalized by a strict interpretation of the building code. It would be inappropriately penalizing a large multistory light-frame building that has many shear walls to require $\rho = 1.3$ just because only one or two shear walls do not stack or are offset at one floor level.

The suggested number of in-plane and out-of-plane shear wall offsets between floor levels should not exceed the following when the engineer is using a flexible diaphragm and $\rho = 1.0$, after which consideration should be given to using a value of $\rho = 1.3$:

1. 15 percent of the total number of shear walls in that direction for that floor level.

2. 20 percent of the total number of shear walls in that direction for all floor levels of the building.

3. 20 percent of the total number of shear walls for both orthogonal directions for all floor levels of the building.

It is also recommended that $\rho = 1.3$ if a minimum of two light-frame shear walls are not being provided along or near each perimeter face of the building.

9. Selected Analytical Procedure

ASCE 7 Table 12.6-1 lists the permitted analytical procedures that can be used to evaluate the building. The equivalent lateral force procedure per ASCE 7 Section 12.8 is permitted to be used since the structural characteristic of the building superstructure is light-frame construction.

10. Distribution of Seismic Forces to Shear Walls

Seismic design forces are distributed to the individual shear walls based on their tributary area since the floor and roof diaphragms are considered to be flexible. In this design example, since $\rho = 1.0$, the calculated seismic design forces do not have to be adjusted related to redundancy issues.

1. Redundancy factor, $\rho = 1.0$.

2. Inherent torsion considerations are omitted per flexible diaphragm assumptions, so the designer does not have to consider building torsion.

Table 3-13. Building B vertical seismic-force-resisting system seismic story forces (pounds per square foot)

Level	Zone	Area (ft²)	Seismic Design Force (F_x) (kips)	(F_x/Area) (psf)	Zone	Area (ft²)	Seismic Design Force (F_x) (kips)	(F_x/Area) (psf)
Roof		5400	56.0	10.4		3840	39.1	10.2
3rd	B1	6075	69.3	11.4	B2	4320	51.1	11.8
2nd		6075	34.7	5.7		4320	27.0	6.3
Σ			160.0				117.2	

Discussion

The distribution of the seismic forces between the two zones of Building B are similar, and to further simplify the lateral force design, it is suggested to use the larger design forces of the two building wings for the entire building.

If the seismic design forces were significantly different between the two building wings (zones), then the designer may want to use these design forces for the two different building zone designs. Since the building is L-shaped, it is suggested the shear wall design forces for those walls located at the vertex zone (intersection) of the two building wings should be the larger of the two zone design forces.

So for this design example, the vertex zone seismic design forces would be:

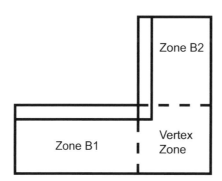

Figure 3-10. Building B zones (plain view)

Table 3-14. Vertex zone seismic design forces

Level	Controlling Zone	Design Force (psf)
Roof	B2*	10.2
3rd	B2	11.8
2nd	B2	6.3

*Zone B2 governs at the roof since the roof diaphragms are separate; if they were connected, then Zone B1 would have governed the vertex zone seismic design forces.

11. Sheathed CFS-Stud Shear Walls: Framing Materials

The following is a brief review of the framing materials utilized for CFS-framed sheathed shear walls, as well as minimum building code design requirements. The gravity load of the building is supported by CFS bearing studs, which are sheathed with a structural material to provide lateral stability for the building. The primary elements of the shear wall construction include sheathing screws, CFS studs, CFS tracks, CFS blocking/bridging, shear transfer fasteners at the top and bottom of walls, an overturning restraint (hold-down) system, and structural sheathing.

The American Iron and Steel Institute (AISI) publishes the *North American Specification for the Design of Cold-Formed Steel Structural Members* (AISI S100), a series of standards for cold-formed steel framing (AISI S201, S240, S400), as well as the *Cold-Formed Steel Design Manual* (D100). These publications cover the design requirements for CFS member, connection, and system design.

11.1 SCREW DESIGN   AISI S100, S240, S400

The design requirements for screws used in CFS materials are covered in

1. AISI S100 *North American Specification for the Design of Cold-Formed Steel Structural Members*, Section E4 and Appendix A.

2. AISI S240 *North American Standard for Cold-Formed Steel Structural Framing*, Sections B1.5.1, B5.2.2.3.2, and B5.2.2.3.3.

3. AISI S400 *North American Standard for Seismic Design of Cold-Formed Steel Structural Systems* (with Supplement 1).

Screw Sizes

Some of the typical screw sizes used for attaching CFS studs to CFS studs or structural steel are shown in Table 3-15 (AISI S240 Tables C-B1.5.1.1-1 and C-B1.5.1.1-2).

Table 3-15. Screw sizes and properties

Screw Size	#6	#8	#10	#12	¼ in
Screw Diameter (in)[1]	0.138	0.164	0.190	0.216	0.250
Available Tip Point Styles[2]	2	2, 3	2, 3	2, 3, 4, 5	1, 4, 5

1. Screw shank diameter is measured out-to-out (threads are cut into the screw shank).

2. The higher the point-style number, the thicker the steel material the screw can penetrate (AISI S240 Table C-B1.5.1.1-2).

Successful installation of a screw also depends on the screw manufacturer and maximum allowed drill motor speeds. Some screws may fracture during installation if installed at too high of a drill speed. Installers typically want to use higher speed drills since they can install more screws in a given time period. Generally this is not a problem when screwing thin CFS studs together, but if the installers are screwing to structural steel members (wide flange beams, HSS sections, etc.), they can encounter a potential problem.

CFS framers may have to try several different screws from different manufacturers before finding the required screw that works well with their hand drills. Screw values can vary significantly, so it is recommended to use a screw that is listed in an evaluation report by an ANSI-accredited product certification company.

Screw-to-Screw Spacing   **AISI S100 §J4.1 and J4.2**

Center-to-center spacing (minimum):   **AISI S200 §B1.5.1.3**

    a. 3 screw diameters: 100% screw shear value

    b. 2 screw diameters: 80% screw shear value

Edge and End Distance (minimum) with the design force perpendicular to edge:

    a. 3 screw diameters: 100% screw shear value

    b. 1.5 screw diameters: Minimum edge distance   **AISI S100 §J4.2**

    c. Shear rupture   **AISI S100 §J6.1**

$$V_n = 0.6 F_u A_{nv}$$ **AISI S100 Eq J6.1-1**

    For a connection where the screw pulls through the steel toward the limiting edge:

$$A_{nv} = 2nt e_{net}$$ **AISI S100 Eq J6.1-2**

    n = Number of screws along critical cross-section

    t = Base steel thickness

    e_{net} = Clear distance from end of member and edge of screw hole

Three screw diameters is typically recommended for use in design so the tear-out distance to the perpendicular free edge is not less than the tear-out distance between the center-to-center spacing of screws.

Edge Distance (minimum) with the design force parallel to edge:

    a. 1.5 screw diameters: 100% screw shear value   **AISI S240 §B1.5.1.3**

    b. 1.5 screw diameters: Minimum edge distance   **AISI S100 §J4.2**

Screw Design Values   **AISI S100 §J4**

Screw design values for steel to steel are to be calculated per AISI S100 Section J4, and requirements for connections to other materials are found in Section J6. When screws are installed through material other than steel, such as steel to wood or steel to drywall, the screw design values will have to be evaluated based on standards for that material or published in an ANSI-accredited product-certification company evaluation report.

The Steel Stud Manufacturers Association (SSMA) "Product Technical Information" and the Steel Framing Industry Association (SFIA) "Technical Guide" provide a convenient screw design table that includes shear and pullout design values for various screw sizes, CFS stud thicknesses, and steel strength values. The screw design values in this table are for Allowable Stress Design (ASD). If the designer intends to use strength design, the screw "nominal shear strength" values can be found in Part IV of the *AISI Manual— Cold-Formed Steel Design* (D100). However, the tabulated values may have slightly different thicknesses for framing members than typically used. The nominal shear strength values have to be adjusted by either the resistance factor, ϕ, or factor of safety, Ω, to determine the screw design values.

The CFS-framed shear wall shear strength does not have to be calculated using screw connection values and scaled to those tabulated values in AISI S240 and S400, in accordance with AISI S240 Section B1.2.6, when the engineer chooses an assembly with tabulated nominal values in AISI S240 Tables B5.2.2.3-1 and B5.2.2.3-2 and S400 Tables E6.3-1, E1.3-1, and E2.3-1 for wind, seismic, and other in-plane loads.

Screws to Attach Shear Wall WSP Sheathing to CFS Framing   **AISI S240**

The design requirements for CFS-framed shear walls are covered in AISI S240. AISI S240 Section B5.2.2.3.3 limits the shear wall WSP sheathing attachment to the CFS framing to be either #8 or #10 screws. For WSP sheathing, AISI S400-15/S1-16 Table E1.3-1 (shear strength for seismic) specifies the screw size to be used with a certain framing thickness to try to preclude early shear failure of the screws. When using steel sheet sheathed shear walls, a minimum of a #8 screw is required for the steel sheet sheathing attachment to the CFS framing members, AISI S240 Table E2.3-1.

The screw sizes typically used for the attachment of WSP or steel sheet sheathing to the CFS framing are

#8 screws: For attachment of WSP sheathing to CFS studs with a designation thickness of 54 mils (16 gauge) and thinner.

#10 screws: For attachment of WSP sheathing to CFS studs with a designation thickness of 68 mils (14 gauge).

#8 screws: Minimum screw size for the attachment of steel sheet sheathing to CFS framing.

For WSP sheathing, the #8 screws and #10 screws used to install the sheathing are required to have a minimum head diameter of 0.285 inch and 0.333 inch, respectively. CFS-framed shear walls have nominal shear strengths based on sheathing type, framing thickness, and screw spacing in the following seven different design tables:

AISI S240 Table B5.2.2.3-1   Unit Nominal Shear Strength [Resistance] (V_n) for Shear Walls with Steel Sheet Sheathing on One Side of Wall

AISI S240 Table B5.2.2.3-2   Unit Nominal Shear Strength [Resistance] (V_n) for Shear Walls with Wood Structural Panel Sheathing on One Side of Wall

AISI S240 Table B5.2.2.3-3   Unit Nominal Shear Strength [Resistance] (V_n) for Shear Walls with Gypsum Board Panel Sheathing on One Side of Wall

AISI S240 Table B5.2.2.3-4   Unit Nominal Shear Strength [Resistance] (V_n) for Shear Walls with Fiberboard Panel Sheathing on One Side of Wall

AISI S400 Table E1.3-1   Unit Nominal Strength [Resistance] (V_n) per Unit Length for Seismic and Other In-Plane Loads for Shear Walls Sheathed with Wood Structural Panels on One Side of Wall

AISI S400 Table E2.3-1   Unit Nominal Strength [Resistance] (V_n) per Unit Length for Seismic and Other In-Plane Loads for Shear Walls with Steel Sheet Sheathing on One Side of Wall

AISI S400 Table E6.3-1   Nominal Shear Strength (V_n) per Unit Length for Seismic Loads for Shear Walls Sheathed with Gypsum Board Panels or Fiberboard Panels on One Side of Wall

AISI S240 Tables B5.2.2.3-1 through B5.2.2.3-4 may only be used for seismic design when the seismic response modification factor, *R*, is 3 in SDC B and C or for SDC A (AISI S400 Section A1.2.3), so it does not apply to this design example. It is important to note that AISI now requires one to design seismic force-resisting systems in SDC B through F in accordance with S400, no matter the *R*-factor, unless an *R* of 3 is used in SDC B and C.

Author's Discussion

The installation of screws for connecting CFS studs together or sheathing to CFS studs generally takes longer than nails into wood framing. Nails typically are shot-installed into wood framing members using a nail gun, whereas a screw requires a drill and the time for the installer to manually push the screws through the sheathing material and engage the CFS stud flange. Additionally, AISI S240 Commentary Section B5.2.3 states that overdriven sheathing screws will result in lower strength, stiffness, and ductility in sheathed CFS-framed assemblies, and therefore the screws should be driven flush with the sheathing.

11.2 CFS STUD DESIGN   AISI S100, S240, S400

The design requirements for CFS in studs are covered by the following documents, including supplements:

1. AISI S100 *North American Specification for the Design of Cold-Formed Steel Structural Members*, Section C and Appendix A.

2. AISI S240 *North American Standard for Cold-Formed Steel Structural Framing*, Sections A, B, and C.

3. AISI S400 *North American Standard for Seismic Design of Cold-Formed Steel Structural Systems*, Section E.

CFS studs are available in various depths. Each stud depth has several different flange widths as well as material thicknesses (gauge, mils) available. Structural CFS studs used in building design are typically manufactured using steel material with yield strengths of either 33 ksi or 50 ksi, with 54 mil and thicker framing typically using a yield strength of 50 ksi.

The material thickness used for CFS framing was previously given as a gauge thickness (example: 16 gauge). The CFS industry has moved to measuring the material thickness now as "mils," where 1 mil = 1/1000 of an inch. Table 3-16 shows the conversion for structural studs. Nonstructural studs are available in thinner material.

Table 3-16. CFS thickness properties

Designation Thickness (mils)	Minimum Thickness[1] (in)	Design Thickness (in)	Design Inside Bend Radius[2] (in)	Reference Only (gauge no.)
33	0.0329	0.0346	0.0764	20 - structural
43	0.0428	0.0451	0.0712	18
54	0.0538	0.0566	0.0849	16
68	0.0677	0.0713	0.1069	14
97	0.0966	0.1017	0.1525	12
118	0.1180	0.1242	0.1863	10

Notes for Table 3-16:

1. Minimum thickness represents 95 percent of design thickness and the minimal acceptable thickness for delivery to the job site.

2. Design inside bend radius in accordance with AISI S201 Product Data standard Table C3-1. This is used by SSMA and SFIA to calculate the CFS stud properties shown in their publications.

The CFS stud industry has also adopted a different naming nomenclature standard to specifically identify the individual CFS studs. An example of the naming nomenclature is as follows:

Table 3-17. CFS product designations

Stud Name	Depth (×/100) (in)	Style of Section[1] (S, T, U, F)	Flange Width (×/100) (in.)	Material Thickness (mils)	Material Yield Strength (ksi)
600S162-54 (50)	600	S	162	54	50
600T150-54	600	T	150	54	33

Note for Table 3-17:

1. S = Stud, T = Track, U = Channel, F = Furring Channel.

   The CFS studs are automatically assumed to have minimum yield strength of 33 ksi if the material strength is not identified. It is recommended that the engineer review AISI S201 and the SSMA and SFIA publications to further understand the naming nomenclature used to identify CFS framing.

AISI S400 Section E1.4.1.1—Limitations for Tabulated Systems (Shear Wall Studs)

The following are the minimum CFS stud dimensional requirements for shear walls utilizing CFS studs:

Table 3-18. Sheathed shear wall minimum CFS stud dimensional requirements

Style of Section	Minimum Thickness	Minimum Flange Width (×/100) (in)	MinimumWeb Depth	Minimum Flange Edge Stiffener Width (in)
C-shape	33 mils	162	350	⅜
T-shape	33 mils	125	350	N.A.

The CFS stud maximum-allowed spacing is limited to 24 inches on center for shear walls.

AISI S400 Tables E1.3-1 and E2.3-1

Table E1.3-1 requires the following additional material requirements for shear wall CFS studs and tracks:

Table 3-19. Sheathed shear wall minimum CFS stud material requirements

Stud Thickness[1] (mils)	ASTM	Structural Grade	Steel[2]
33, 43	A1003	33	Type H
54 and thicker	A1003	50	Type H

Notes for Table 3-19:

1. For WSP sheathed shear wall S400 table values, the thickest CFS stud that is permitted is 68 mils.

2. Type H steel is a high-ductility steel.

11.3 SHEAR WALL SHEATHING   AISI S240, S400

The design requirements for shear walls utilizing CFS studs are covered by AISI S240 *North American Standard for Cold-Formed Steel Structural Framing*, Section B and Commentary Section B.

The shear wall nominal shear strength depends on sheathing type, screw size and spacing, and the thickness of the CFS framing. The following are sheathed shear wall minimum requirements per AISI S400 Section E1.4.1.1 "Limitations for Tabulated Systems":

1. Fastener location from edge of sheathing (minimum edge distance):   ⅜ inch

2. Minimum width dimension of sheathing in any direction: 12 inches

    a. Panels less than 12 inches wide shall not be used for shear walls.

3. All sheathing edges shall be attached to framing or blocking.

    a. Strap blocking shall be a minimum of 1½ inches wide and not less than 33 mils in thickness.

    b. Strap blocking can be installed either under or over the sheathing.

    c. For sheathing other than steel sheet sheathing, the screw shall be installed through the sheathing to the blocking.

Section AISI S400 Section E1.4.1.1—Wood Structural Panel Sheathing

Nominal shear strength shall be as given in AISI S400 Table E1.3-1. Increases of nominal strengths shown in this table, as allowed by other standards, shall not be permitted.

Additional requirements for wood structural panel sheathing are stated in AISI notes. Those required for seismic design are noted here:

    (n) Wood structural panels shall be manufactured using exterior glue and shall comply with DOC PS1 or PS2.

    (o) Wood structural panels are permitted to be applied either parallel to or perpendicular to framing.

    (p) Wood structural panels shall be attached with minimum No. 8 countersunk tapping screws that have a minimum head diameter of 0.285 inch or No. 10 countersunk tapping screws that have a minimum head diameter of 0.333 inch in accordance with AISI S400 Table E1.3-1.

    (q) Screws used to attach wood structural panels shall be in accordance with ASTM C1513.

As noted previously, there are seven shear wall shear strength tables provided in AISI (AISI S240 Tables B5.2.2.3-1 through B5.2.2.3-4 and AISI S400 Tables E1.3-1, E2.3-1, and E6.3-1) tabulating the nominal shear strength for various sheathed CFS-framed shear wall assemblies. AISI S400 Tables E1.3-1 and E2.3-1 reproduced here as Table 3-20, is for seismic design. A review of the table indicates:

1. The maximum shear wall aspect ratio (h/w) is typically limited to 2:1.

    a. There is an exception for identified shear wall assemblies with an aspect ratio between 2:1 and 4:1 if their shear strength is reduced by $2w/h$ (2 × shear wall length/shear wall height).

2. The shear wall sheathing can be ¹⁵⁄₃₂-inch WSP Structural 1 sheathing (4-ply), ⁷⁄₁₆-inch OSB, or steel sheet sheathing.

The nominal shear strength values for in-plane lateral loads other than seismic (example: wind) for shear walls are provided in AISI S240 Section B5.2.3. The nominal shear strength values for seismic loads for shear walls are provided in AISI S400 Tables E1.3-1 and E2.3-1. The nominal shear strength values shown in Tables 3-20A and 3-20B are reduced by either the resistance factor ($\phi = 0.60$) for LRFD or the factor of safety ($\Omega = 2.5$) for ASD per AISI S400 Sections E1.3.2 and E2.3.2. Per AISI S240 Section B5.2.3 and AISI S400 Sections E1.3.1.1.2 and E2.3.1.1.3, when the same sheathing and fastener size and spacing are used on both sides of the wall, then the shear wall design values can be doubled.

Table 3-20A. AISI S400 Table E1.3-1: unit nominal strength [resistance] (V_n) per unit length for seismic and other in-plane loads for shear walls sheathed with wood structural panels on one side of wall

Assembly Description	Max. Aspect Ratio (h/w)	Fastener Spacing at Panel Edges[2] (in)				Designation Thickness[5, 6] of Stud, Track and Blocking (mils)	Required Sheathing Screw Size
		6	4	3	2		
¹⁵⁄₃₂″ Structural 1 sheathing (4-ply)	2:1[3]	780	990	—	—	33 or 43	8
	2:1	890	1330	1775	2190	43 or 54	8
						68	10
⁷⁄₁₆″ OSB	2:1[3]	700	915	—	—	33	8
	2:1[3]	825	1235	1545	2060	43 or 54	8
	2:1	940	1410	1760	2350	54	8
	2:1	1230	1850	2310	3080	68	10

Table 3-20B. AISI S400 Table E2.3-1: unit nominal strength [resistance] (V_n) per unit length for seismic and other in-plane loads for shear walls with steel sheet sheathing on one side of wall[9]

Assembly Description	Max. Aspect Ratio (h/w)	Fastener Spacing at Panel Edges[2] (in)				Designation Thickness[5, 6] of Stud, Track and Blocking (mils)	Required Sheathing Screw Size
		6	4	3	2		
0.018″ steel sheet	2:1	390	—	—	—	33 (min.)	8
0.027″ steel sheet	2:1[3]	—	1000	1085	1170	43 (min.)	8
	2:1[3]	647	710	778	845	33 (min.)	8

Notes for Tables 3-20A and 3-20B:

1. *Nominal strength* shall be multiplied by the *resistance factor* (ϕ) to determine *design strength* or divided by the safety factor (Ω) to determine *allowable strength*, as set forth in AISI S400 Sections E1.3.2 and E2.3.2.

2. Screws in the field of the panel shall be installed 12 inches (305 mm) o.c. unless otherwise shown.

3. *Shear wall* height to width aspect ratio (h/w) greater than 2:1, but not exceeding 4:1, shall be permitted provided that the *nominal strength* values are multiplied by 2w/h. See AISI S400 Sections E1.3.1.1 and E2.3.1.1.

4. See AISI S400 Sections E1.3.1.1.2, E1.3.1.1.3, E2.3.1.1.2, and E2.3.1.1.3 for requirements for sheathing applied to both sides of wall and more than a single sheathing material or fastener configuration along the same wall line, respectively.

5. Unless noted as (min.), substitution of a stud or track of a different *designation thickness* is not permitted.

6. Wall *studs* and track shall be of ASTM A1003 Structural Grade 33 (Grade 230) Type H steel for members with a *designation thickness* of 33 and 43 mils, and A1003 Structural Grade 50 (Grade 340) Type H steel with a *designation thickness* equal to or greater than 54 mils.

7. For wood structural panel sheathed shear walls, tabulated R_n values are applicable for short-term load duration (seismic loads). For other in-plane lateral loads of normal or permanent load duration as defined by the AWC NDS, the values in Tables 3-20A and 3-20B for wood structural panel sheathed shear walls shall be multiplied by 0.63 (normal) or 0.56 (permanent).

8. For SI: $1'' = 25.4$ mm, 1 foot = 0.305 m, 1 lb = 4.45 N.

9. Additional steel sheet thicknesses can be found in AISI S400 Table E2.3.1.

The original table was updated and split into two separate tables (E1.3-1 and E2.3-1) in AISI S400 based on sheathing type.

11.4 SPECIAL SEISMIC REQUIREMENTS AISI S240, S400

The design requirements for shear walls utilizing CFS studs are covered by AISI S400 Sections E1.4 and E2.4: System Requirements.

These AISI seismic design standard sections apply to shear walls sheathed with WSP or steel sheet sheathing when the building system response modification coefficient R is other than 3.0. WSP and steel-sheet-sheathed CFS-framed shear walls are typically designed using an R greater than 3.0. However, it is important to note that the seismic design standard does apply to any lateral system-resisting seismic forces, even with an R lower than 3.

1. AISI S400 Sections E1.4.1.2 and E2.4.1.2 "Chord Studs, Anchorages, Collectors (and connections)"

   a. E1.4.1.1 and E2.4.1.1: Chord studs or other vertical boundary members at the ends of wall segments that resist seismic loads, braced with sheathing, shall be anchored such that the bottom track is not required to resist uplift by bending of the track web.

   b. E1.4.1.2 and E2.4.1.2: The available strength (design strength or factored resistance) of connections and members not part of the designated energy-dissipating mechanism (DEDM) shall exceed the expected strength of the shear wall, but need not exceed the load determined from the seismic load combinations with overstrength. This includes collectors, collector connections, chord studs, hold-downs, hold-down anchorage, and bottom track shear anchorage.

2. AISI S400 Sections E1.4.1.1 and E2.4.1.1 "Limitations for Tabulated Systems"

   a. 33 mil and 43 mil wall studs and track shall be of ASTM A1003 Structural Grade 33, Type H.

   b. 54 mil or thicker wall studs and track shall be ASTM A1003 Structural Grade 50, Type H.

AISI S240 Section B5.2: Shear Wall Design

There are two types of shear walls: Type I, which is covered in AISI S240 Section B5.2.1.1 and AISI S400 Section 1.4.1, and Type II, which is covered in AISI S240 Section B5.2.1.2 and AISI S400 Section 1.4.2. The Type I shear wall is the conventional sheathed shear wall with a hold-down at each end; it is typically referred to as a segmented shear wall in wood construction. The Type II shear wall is typically referred to as a perforated shear wall in wood construction. Type II shear walls must meet the requirements of Type I shear walls except where noted in AISI S240 Section B5.2.1.2 and AISI S400 Section E1.4.2. This design example is based on using Type I shear walls. The engineer should review AISI S240 Section B5.2.1.2 and AISI S400 Section E1.4.2 for the design requirements for Type II shear walls.

12. Shear Wall Design Example: Building B

One interior three-story, stacking shear wall in Building B, Zone B1 has been selected for this design example. The CFS-framed shear wall design will follow the requirements of AISI S240 and S400.

Shear wall parameters:

1. Classification: Type I.

2. Wall sheathing: Wood structural panels (DOC PS-1 and PS-2): plywood or OSB.

3. Wall studs: CFS studs (54 mil [16 gauge]): 600S162-54 (F_y = 50 ksi) and (68 mil [14 gauge]): 600S200-68 (F_y = 50 ksi).

4. Continuous rod tie-down (hold-down) system: Resists tension (uplift) from overturning and comprises continuous rods, coupler nuts, nuts, bearing plates, take-up devices, cripple studs, and bridge blocks.

5. Chord studs: Resist compression from gravity and overturning; CFS studs.

6. Wall base connection: Elevated floors: screws.
   Podium level: anchor bolts in a 12-inch-thick structural concrete slab.

Continuous Rod Tie-Down (Hold-Down) System

The shear wall design will utilize a continuous rod tie-down system that is centered between the chord studs at each end of the shear wall and extends from the podium deck to approximately halfway between the third floor and the roof, where it terminates at a bridge block. Each individual story's shear wall uplift forces are resisted by a bearing plate on top of the floor framing above the shear wall or by a bearing plate on top of a bridge block. This story shear wall uplift force is sometimes referred to as incremental uplift. The bearing plates transfer the overturning force for each story of the building to the continuous rod. The continuous rod resists the cumulative overturning tension (uplift) force from each story's shear wall and transfers it to the concrete podium level of the building. The shear wall CFS chord studs resist the uplift force at each story in compression and bear against the wood floor or roof system or bridge block, but are typically governed by the overturning and gravity compression load.

In multistory buildings, take-up (shrinkage compensating) devices are often used to ensure the overturning restraint system is tight even after wood shrinkage or settlement occurs. Use of engineered wood framing helps reduce the wood shrinkage effect. AISI S240 Section C3.5.3 requires that structural wall studs are seated tight against the tracks and states that *tight* means a maximum gap tolerance of ⅛ inch is acceptable between the stud and the top and bottom track. This could possibly lead to up to ¼-inch vertical settlement per story. Since the steel rods are a fixed length in a continuous rod tie-down system, shrinkage and settlement accumulates over the height of the building, possibly resulting in ¾-inch vertical settlement at the top of a three-story structure.

Design Documents

AISI S100-16 *North American Specification for the Design of Cold Formed Steel Structural Members*
AISI S201-17 *North American Standard for Cold-Formed Steel Framing—Product Data*
AISI S240-15 *North American Standard for Cold-Formed Steel Structural Framing*
AISI S400-15/S1-16 *North American Standard for Seismic Design of Cold-Formed Steel Structural Systems*

LRFD and ASD

The AISI specifications and standards allow the use of either LRFD or ASD for the design of the light-frame CFS structures. Both LRFD and ASD loads are shown in the beginning sections of this design example as an aid in transitioning for those more familiar with ASD than LRFD. When deflections are to be calculated for either wood or CFS light-frame WSP-sheathed shear walls, they are to be based on using strength-level load combinations (LRFD). AISI S240 and S400 require the CFS light-frame shear wall uplift anchorage and vertical boundary members (chord studs) have the nominal strength to resist what the system can deliver, but need not exceed the amplified seismic load. The amplified loads are based on using the LRFD seismic load combinations with the overstrength factor. Since ASD amplified seismic forces are not addressed by AISI, the remainder of the design example is done using LRFD.

12.1 SHEAR WALL SHEAR AND OVERTURNING REQUIRED STRENGTH (BUILDING B, ZONE B1)

The tributary area and design shear force to the shear wall at each floor level, using the Zone B1 design forces, is as follows. The overall shear wall length is determined from the wall out-to-out dimension of 39 feet and subtracting the two exterior 6-inch CFS stud cross-walls' thickness. The cross-wall overall thickness equals 8 inches (6-inch CFS C-stud + 1-inch-thick stucco finish + ½-inch plywood one face + ½-inch gypsum wall board). The shear wall length is approximately 39 feet minus two 8-inch cross walls, which equals 37 feet 8 inches. To simplify the math, the shear wall design length is shortened to 37 feet 0 inches. The tributary area to the shear wall though is still based on the 40-foot length used in determining the seismic mass of Building B. The shear wall seismic tributary area width is 23 feet 8 inches. The story wall heights are provided in Table 3-21.

Table 3-21. Shear wall design information (LRFD)

Level	Tributary Area to Shear Wall Line (ft²)	Story Level Design Force v (psf)	Shear Wall Story Forces (lb)	Σ Shear Wall Force (lb)	ASD Forces (0.7F)
3rd Floor	(23 ft 8 in) × 40 ft = 947	10.4	947 × 10.4 = 9849	9849	6895
2nd Floor	(23 ft 8 in) × 45 ft = 1065	11.4	1065 × 11.4 = 12,141	21,990	15,393
1st Floor	(23 ft 8 in) × 45 ft = 1065	5.7	1065 × 5.7 = 6071	28,061	19,643

The location of the example shear wall can be seen on the following framing plans as well as the other shear walls for Building B.

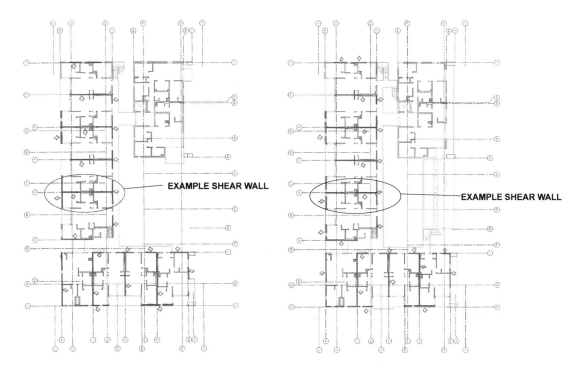

Figure 3-11. Building B—Third-floor shear walls   *Figure 3-12. Building B—Second-floor shear walls*

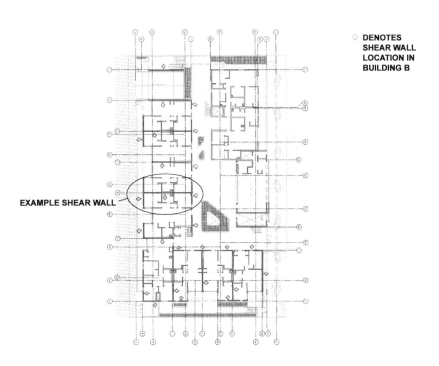

Figure 3-13. Building B—First-floor shear walls

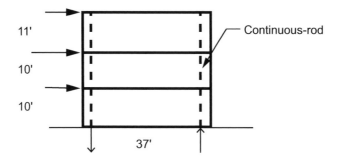

Figure 3-14. Option 1: Full-length, stacked shear wall

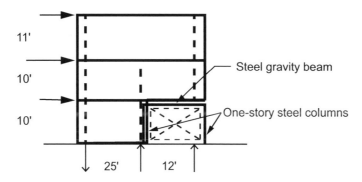

Figure 3-15. Option 2: Short first-floor shear wall

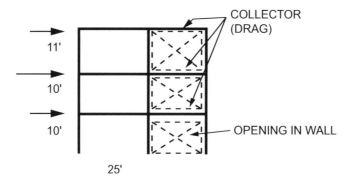

Figure 3-16. Option 3: Short, stacked shear wall

12.2 SHEAR WALL CONFIGURATION AND TYPE   AISI S400 SECTIONS E1 AND E2

Often in multifamily, multistory residential buildings there are many architectural restrictions as to where shear walls can be located, how much of the wall length can be utilized for shear walls, and how shear walls align from floor to floor. Three options are shown for the shear wall configuration at this location.

Option 1: Full-length, stacked shear walls

a. Optimum condition; smaller wall element design forces

Option 2: Full-length upper floor walls, short wall length at first floor

a. Discontinuous shear wall system at second floor

b. Second-floor beam and first-floor column design to check

c. High shear design forces on first-floor shear wall

Option 3: Short-length shear wall

a. Wall elements have higher design forces than Option 1

b. High overturning forces on wall

c. Do not have to design for discontinuity

Other multistory shear wall configurations are also possible, and the selected shear wall configuration will ultimately depend on the layout of the residential units at each floor level. Design forces for the three shear wall options are provided for comparison.

Shear walls are classified as one of two types:

1. Type I (segmented)

a. Hold-downs required at each end of each Type I shear wall

b. Design for force transfer around openings

2. Type II (perforated)

a. Hold-downs required at each end of each Type II shear wall

b. Openings permitted between the ends of a Type II shear wall without designing for force transfer around openings

c. Design for uniform uplift as well as increased unit shear between wall ends

A Type I shear wall will be used for this design example.

AISI S400 Section E1.3.1.1—Type I Shear Walls

The shear walls in this design example are resisting seismic forces and the building is located in SDC D; therefore, the design has to be in accordance with AISI S400.

The requirements of a Type I shear wall are as follows:

1. Fully sheathed and having hold-downs at each end of the wall segment.

2. When sheathed with either wood or steel sheet, then an opening is permitted in the wall between the hold-downs as long as details are provided for lateral-force transfer around the openings.

   a. Height-to-width aspect ratio (h/w) of shear wall pier on each side of a window shall be limited to 2:1, where h = window height and w = width of pier adjacent to the window.

   b. Minimum pier width = 24 inches.

3. Shear wall height-to-width aspect ratio (h/w) is limited to AISI S400 Tables E1.3-1, E2.3-1, and E6.3-1, with a maximum aspect ratio of 4:1 and walls not less than 24 inches wide. Minimum screw size restrictions for seismic design are noted in the shear wall strength tables in AISI S400.

4. AISI S240 can be used for seismic design only when the building is located in SDC B or C and the seismic response modification coefficient R is equal to 3. AISI S400 does not apply to SDC A, so AISI S240 requirements would apply.

12.3 SHEAR WALL SHEATHING AND SCREW SELECTION
AISI S400 SECTIONS E1 AND E2

The design requirements for shear wall sheathing and screws are covered by AISI S400:

1. Section E1.3.2 "Available Strength (Factored Resistance)."

2. Section E1.3.1.1 "Nominal Strength (Resistance)"—for wood structural panels.

The WSP-sheathed shear wall nominal shear strength values are taken from AISI S400 Table E1.3-1. The shear wall can be evaluated using either strength design (LRFD) or allowable stress design (ASD). The available strength is determined in accordance with AISI S400 Section E1.3.2 where the seismic resistance factor, ϕ, equals 0.6 for LRFD and the factor of safety, Ω_v, equals 2.5 for ASD (see AISI S240 Section B5.2.3 for nonseismic resistance factors and factor of safety values). Table 3-22 shows the available sheathing strength design values for one sheathing and stud combination.

Table 3-22. Shear wall strengths

Wall Sheathing	Fastener Spacing at Panel Edges (inches)				Stud Thickness (mils)	Sheathing Screw Size
	6	4	3	2		
Table E1.3-1: Nominal Shear Strength (pounds per foot)—Sheathing One Side Only						
$^{15}/_{32}$ Structural 1 (4 ply)	890	1330	1775	2190	54/68	8/10
Table E1.3-1: Available Strength Design Values (pounds) $\phi = 0.6$						
$^{15}/_{32}$ Structural 1 (4 ply)	534	798	1065	1314	54/68	8/10
Table E1.3-1: Available ASD values (pounds) $\Omega = 2.5$						
$^{15}/_{32}$ Structural 1 (4 ply)	356	532	710	876	54/68	8/10

Shear Wall Length

Earlier in the design example: the width of Building B1 was shown as 39 feet, but a width of 40 feet was used for determining the seismic mass of the building. The 39 feet is the out-to-out dimension of the building, and the shear wall sheathing is not considered to be extended to the outside face of the exterior walls; thus, the shear wall length will be shorter than 39 feet. The exterior walls are 6-inch CFS studs, so after accounting for 1-inch-thick stucco exterior finish, ½-inch plywood, and ½-inch gypsum board interior siding, the length of the shear wall is reduced as follows:

Shear wall full length = 39 ft − (2)(6 in + 1 in + ½ in + ½ in) = 39 ft − 16 in = 37 ft 8 in

To keep the design calculations easy, the full-length shear wall length is reduced to 37 feet 0 inches for design purposes. Actual shear wall construction length will be 37 feet 8 inches, so there will be a little more shear wall capacity than is being accounted for in the design.

Shear Wall Sheathing Design

The WSP sheathing selection process may utilize LRFD and ASD, and both are shown in Tables 3-23, 3-24, and 3-25 for the three shear wall options previously listed. Shear wall design is based on using $^{15}/_{32}$-inch Structural 1 (4 ply) WSP sheathing.

Table 3-23. Option 1: Shear wall lengths: Full-length shear walls each floor level (L = 37 feet)

Level	LRFD				ASD			
	Σ Shear Wall Force[1] (F) (lb)	Shear (F/L) (plf)	Design Capacity[2] (plf)	#8 or #10 Screw Spacing (in)	Σ Shear Wall Forces ASD = (0.7F) (lb)	Shear (F/L) (plf)	Design Capacity[2] (plf)	#8 or #10 Screw Spacing (in)
3rd Floor	9849	267	534	6	6895	187	356	6
2nd Floor	21,990	595	798	4	15,393	416	532	4
1st Floor	28,061	759	798	4	19,643	531	532	4

1. Shear wall forces are from Table 3-21.

2. Design capacities are from Table 3-22.

Table 3-24. Option 2: Shear wall lengths (L = third floor, second floor = 37 feet; L = first floor = 25 feet)

Level	LRFD				ASD			
	Σ Shear Wall Force[1] (F) (lb)	Shear (F/L) (plf)	Design Capacity[2] (plf)	#8 or #10 Screw Spacing (in)	Σ Shear Wall Forces ASD = (0.7F) (lb)	Shear (F/L) (plf)	Design Capacity[2] (plf)	#8 or #10 Screw Spacing (in)
3rd Floor	9849	267	534	6	6895	187	356	6
2nd Floor	21,990	595	798	4	15,393	416	532	4
1st Floor	28,061	1123	1314	2	19,643	786	876	2

1. Shear wall forces are from Table 3-21.

2. Design capacities are from Table 3-22.

Table 3-25. Option 3: Short-length shear walls each floor level (L = 25 feet)

Level	LRFD				ASD			
	Σ Shear Wall Force[1] (F) (lb)	Shear (F/L) (plf)	Design Capacity[2] (plf)	#8 or #10 Screw Spacing (in)	Σ Shear Wall Forces ASD = (0.7F) (lb)	Shear (F/L) (plf)	Design Capacity[2] (plf)	#8 or #10 Screw Spacing (in)
3rd Floor	9849	394	534	6	6895	276	356	6
2nd Floor	21,990	880	1065	3	15,393	616	710	3
1st Floor	28,061	1123	1314	2	19,643	786	876	2

1. Shear wall forces are from Table 3-21.

2. Design capacities are from Table 3-22.

The shear wall sheathing is required only on one side of the shear wall and is assumed to be installed vertically since the floor-to-floor heights are either 10 or 11 feet, and the clear CFS stud height between floor framings is either 9 or 10 feet, respectively. As an alternative design for an Option 2 and Option 3 shear wall, the first-floor sheathing could be installed on both sides of the wall using a sheathing edge-screw spacing of 4 inches on center. When sheathing is used on both sides of the stud wall, it is recommended that the sheathing panel joints should be offset to fall on different framing members, the same as for light-frame wood-frame shear walls.

Since the wall sheathing is being installed vertically, no horizontal CFS flat-strap blocking is required because all sheathing edge screwing will be to the CFS studs (vertical panel edges), bottom track, and top track (horizontal panel edges). If the wall sheathing is to be installed horizontally, then a minimum 1½-inch-wide CFS flat-strap blocking, the same thickness as the CFS wall framing, would be required at the sheathings' horizontal panel edges. Vertical panel edges are assumed to align with the wall studs.

While horizontal CFS flat-strap bracing is not required in this case for blocking when the wall sheathing is installed vertically, the horizontal CFS flat-strap bracing is still required under the wall sheathing for developing the axial capacity of the CFS bearing studs, as will be discussed later.

Full-scale shear wall testing comparing winged-tip to non-winged-tip screws attaching WSP sheathing to CFS framing has shown the peak loads for the shear wall assembly within 5 to 10 percent, but also a 20 percent design strength reduction for the winged-tip screws, probably due to the wings creating a larger hole in the WSP sheathing. Also, testing has shown significantly reduced strength, stiffness, and ductility when self-tapping screws were overdriven in the WSP sheathing of a CFS-framed shear wall assembly, as noted in AISI S240 Commentary Section B5.2.2.

12.4 OVERTURNING RESTRAINT (TIE-DOWN) SYSTEM REQUIRED STRENGTH

AISI S400 requires a hold-down (alternative terminologies used: hold-down anchor or tie-down or uplift anchorage) at each end of a shear wall to prevent the shear wall from overturning as a result of applied horizontal loads distributed vertically over the building structure's height. The hold-downs are considered uplift anchorage for the shear wall chord studs (vertical boundary members) and must comply with AISI S400 Sections E1.4.1.2, E2.4.1.2, and E6.4.1.2. AISI S240 Section F1 requires tests for hold-downs to be in accordance with AISI S100 Section F1 (K1 for S100-16) where required to determine their strength and stiffness and permits the use of test standard AISI S913 to be used for hold-downs. Figure 3-18 shows a three-story stacked CFS-framed shear wall, including the overturning restraint system, which is representative of the Option 1 and Option 3 shear walls, as the Option 2 shear wall is discontinuous.

AISI S400 Section E1.4.1.2 "Required Strength [Effect of Factored Loads] for Chord Studs, Anchorage, and Collectors"

While collectors in buildings braced entirely by wood light-frame shear walls do not have to be designed for the seismic load combinations including the overstrength factor Ω_0 per ASCE 7 Section 12.10.2.1, the collectors and collector connections for buildings using CFS frame shear walls are required to have the available (design) strength to resist the lesser of the expected strength of the shear wall and the amplified seismic load per AISI S400 Sections E1.4.1.2 and E2.4.1.2.

AISI S400 Sections E1.4.1.2 and E2.4.1.2 "Chord Studs" (vertical boundary members)

S400 Sections E1.4.1.2 and E2.4.1.2 require that the shear wall CFS chord studs (vertical boundary members) and the uplift anchorage have the available strength to resist the amplified seismic load. For ease of reference in this design example, the term *amplified seismic load* will mean the lesser of

1. The load determined from the ASCE 7 seismic load combinations with the overstrength factor Ω_0.

2. The expected strength of the shear wall ($V_n \times \Omega_E$), where $\Omega_E = 1.8$ (for WSP-sheathed shear walls per AISI S400 Section E1.3.3).

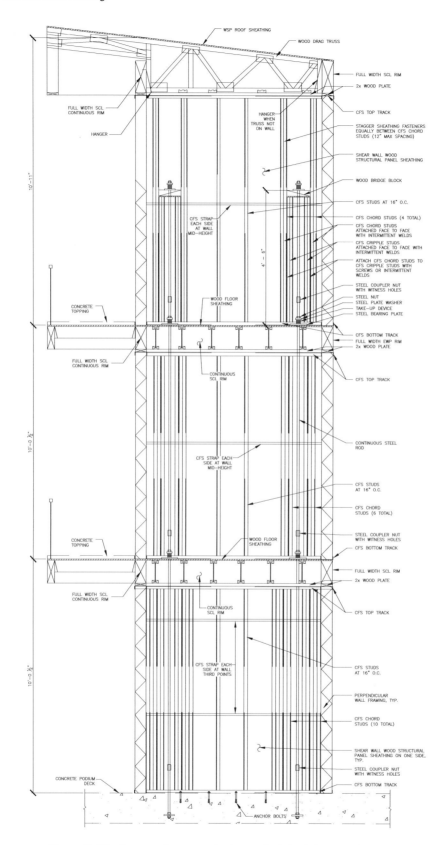

Figure 3-17. Overturning restraint in stacked CFS-framed shear wall

Since the floors and roof diaphragms are considered to be flexible in this example, the overstrength factor, Ω_0, is equal to 2.5 per ASCE 7 Table 12.2-1 Footnote b.

The available/required strength of the collectors, chord studs, other vertical boundary elements, hold-downs and anchorage connected to the shear wall, and all other components and connections of the shear wall shall be greater than or equal to the amplified seismic load.

Typically, designing for the expected strength of the shear wall will not govern over the seismic load combinations, including Ω_0. This will be shown later in the design example.

Shear Wall Overturning Forces

Tables 3-26 and 3-27 show the amplified seismic overturning forces for the three shear wall options. The overstrength factor, Ω_0, is 2.5 since Building B1 has flexible floor diaphragms and roof diaphragm. The overstrength factor, Ω_0, is used to determine the required strength that the CFS chord studs and continuous rod tie-down system's nominal strength must equal or exceed.

Table 3-26. Shear wall overturning moment (OTM) Option 1 and Option 3

	LRFD				ASD			
Level	Wall Height (h) (ft)	Σ Shear Wall Force (F) (lb)	Story-Level OTM (k-ft)	Ω_0 OTM (k-ft)	Wall Height (h) (ft)	Σ Shear Wall Force ASD = (0.7F) (lb)	Story-Level OTM (k-ft)	Ω_0 OTM (k-ft)
3rd Floor	11	9849	108,339	270,848	11	6895	75,837	189,593
2nd Floor	10	21,990	328,239	820,598	10	15,393	229,767	574,418
1st Floor	10	28,061	608,849	1,522,123	10	19,643	426,197	1065,493

1. OTM third floor = $h \times F$ = 11 × 9849 = 108,339 ft-lb = 108,339 kip-ft
    OTM second floor = OTM third floor + ($h \times F$) = 108,339 + (10 × 21,990) = 328,239 ft-lb
    $\qquad\qquad\qquad\qquad\qquad\qquad$ = 328,239 kip-ft
    OTM first floor = OTM second floor + ($h \times F$) = 328,239 + (10 × 28,061) = 608,849 ft-lb
    $\qquad\qquad\qquad\qquad\qquad\qquad$ = 608,849 kip-ft

2. The story LRFD seismic force is 9849 pounds, 12,141 pounds, and 6071 pounds at the 3rd-, 2nd-, and 1st-floor levels, respectively, per Table 3-21.

Table 3-27. Shear wall OTM Option 2: (Wall length L: 3rd, 2nd floor = 37 feet, 1st floor = 25 feet)

Level	LRFD				ASD			
	Wall Height (h) (ft)	Σ Shear Wall Force (F) (lb)	Story-Level OTM (k-ft)	Ω_0 OTM (k-ft)	Wall Height (h) (ft)	Σ Shear Wall Force ASD = (0.7F) (lb)	Story-Level OTM (k-ft)	Ω_0 OTM (k-ft)
3rd Floor	11	9849	108,339	270,848	11	6895	75,837	189,593
2nd Floor	10	21,990	328,239	820,598	10	15,393	229,767	574,418
1st Floor	10	28,061	L-R: 608,849 R-L: 280,610	L-R: 1,522,123 R-L: 701,525	10	19,643	L-R: 426,197 R-L: 196,643	L-R: 1,065,493 R-L: 491,608

Level	Col. Ht. (ft)	Σ Shear	Axial Force (P) (lb)	$\Omega_0 P$ (lb)	Col. Ht. (ft)	Σ Shear	Axial Force (P) (lb)	$\Omega_0 P$ (lb)
1st Floor	10	0	8872	22,180	10	0	6011	15,028

1. L-R = seismic lateral force applied left to right

2. R-L = seismic lateral force applied right to left

3. OTM third floor = $h \times F$ = 11 × 9849 = 108,339 ft-lb

   OTM second floor = OTM third floor + ($h \times F$) = 108,339 + (10 × 21,990)
   $$= 328,239 \text{ ft-lb}$$

   OTM first floor = L-R: OTM second floor + ($h \times F$) = 328,239 + (10 × 28,061)
   $$= 608,849 \text{ ft-lb}$$

   OTM first floor = R-L: ($h \times F$) = (10 × 28,061) = 280,610 ft-lb

   First-floor column axial = (OTM second floor/L) = (328,239/37) = 8872 lb

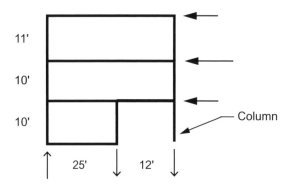

Figure 3-18. Option 2 shear wall R-L OTM and reactions

Shear Wall Overturning Resisting Force

The building dead load counters a portion or sometimes all of the shear wall uplift. The shear wall resisting force will use the floor dead load if the framing is perpendicular to the wall, and it will also use the wall self-weight. The metal-plate-connected wood roof trusses are framed parallel to the shear wall, so the roof dead load does not contribute significantly to reducing the shear wall uplift.

ASCE 7 Section 12.4.3 Seismic Load Effects, including Overstrength; Sections 2.3.6 and 2.4.5 Basic Combinations with Seismic Load Effects

Only a portion of the dead load can be used for resisting shear wall overturning forces, and for light-frame wood-frame construction, the overturning resisting forces would be based on Section 2.3.6 equations.

ASCE 7 Sections 2.3.6 and 2.4.5

LFRD: $0.9D - E_v + E_{mh}$

$[(0.9 - 0.2S_{DS})D + \rho Q_E + 1.6H] \rightarrow (0.9 - 0.2S_{DS})D = [0.9 - 0.2(1.117)]D = 0.676D$

ASD: $0.6D - 0.7E_v + 0.7E_{mh}$

$[(0.6 - 0.14S_{DS})D + 0.7\rho Q_E + H] \rightarrow (0.6 - 0.14S_{DS})D = [0.6 - 0.14(1.117)]D = 0.444D$

Per AISI S400 Section E1.4.1.2, the chord studs and uplift anchorage must have the available strength to resist the lesser of (1) the expected strength of the shear wall or (2) the load determined using the ASCE 7 seismic load combinations, including the overstrength factor, Ω_0.

ASCE 7 Section 12.4.3

LRFD: $[(0.9 - 0.2S_{DS})D + \Omega_0 Q_E + 1.6H] \rightarrow (0.9 - 0.2S_{DS})D = [0.9 - 0.2(1.117)]D = 0.676D$

ASD: $[(0.6 - 0.14S_{DS})D + 0.7(\Omega_0 Q_E) + H] \rightarrow (0.6 - 0.14S_{DS})D = [0.6 - 0.14(1.117)]D = 0.444D$

In either case, the dead load used to resist the overturning is the same, but the uplift loads will be more significant when the overstrength factor, Ω_0, is included or uplift forces are derived using the expected shear strength of the shear walls.

Author's Discussion—Loads the System Can Deliver

In previous editions, "Loads the System Can Deliver" was considered as one load combination. That practice has been discontinued. The shear wall, its components, and its collectors shall be able to resist the lesser of the shear wall expected strength or loads determined using the seismic load combinations with the overstrength factor. It is no longer allowed to be designed to a lesser capacity, as in the case where the building system framing element (say diaphragm) cannot deliver that large of a design force to the shear wall, its components, or its collectors.

Author's Discussion—Dead Loads

There are three methods designers use to determine the amount of dead load along the shear wall that can be used to counter the shear wall uplift force.

1. Neglect the dead load for conditions when it is minimal (example: floor framing parallel to shear wall), which is the most conservative approach for the uplift side, but not the compression side of the shear wall.

2. Consider the shear wall as a rigid body where the dead load is used to resist the uplift and is used as part of the gravity load demand in addition to the overturning compression load. Some justify this using a deep-beam analogy.

3. Consider the rim and top track as a beam on an elastic foundation. Such an analysis shows that typically only the dead load within a few stud bays can be mobilized to resist uplift. Further discussion can be found in FEMA 451 *NEHRP Recommended Provisions: Design Examples* Chapter 10 as well as in the book *Structural Design of Low-Rise Buildings*, Section 6.7.

This design example uses the rigid body method although good arguments could be made in support of the beam on elastic foundation approach. Therefore, the dead load of and tributary to the wall is used to resist the uplift, and it is also used as part of the gravity-load demand to the chord-stud assembly on the compression side of the shear wall.

Table 3-28 summarizes the wall and floor weights to be used for calculating the shear wall resisting moments.

Table 3-28. Shear wall OTM design information

Level	Wall Height (h) (ft)	Trib. Width to Shear Wall (ft)	Dead Load (psf)	Dead Load to Wall (W_{floor}) (plf)	Shear Wall Self-weight ($W_{wall} = h \times wt$) (plf)	Total Weight (W_{Dead}) (plf)	Σ Total Weight (W_{TD}) (plf)
3rd Floor	11	2.0	16	32	$11 \times 11 = 121$	153	153
2nd Floor	10	11.8	30	354	$10 \times 11 = 110$	464	617
1st Floor	10	11.8	30	354	$10 \times 11 = 110$	464	1081

1. Shear wall weight = 11 psf of wall surface area.
2. Metal-plate-connected wood roof trusses at 24 inches on center.

Tables 3-29, 3-30, and 3-31 show the resisting dead-load moments (RM) for the three shear wall options.

Table 3-29. Option 1 shear wall (wall length = 37 ft)

			Σ Shear Wall		
Level	Wall Height (h) (ft)	Σ Dead Load (W_{TD}) (plf)	Resisting Moment (RM) (ft-lb)	LRFD 0.676RM (ft-lb)	ASD 0.444RM (ft-lb)
3rd Floor	11	153	104,728	70,796	46,499
2nd Floor	10	617	422,336	285,499	187,517
1st Floor	10	1081	739,944	500,202	328,535

1. Resisting moment = $(W_{TD})(L \times L)/2 = (153)(37)(37)/2 = 104,728$ lb.

Table 3-30. Option 2 shear wall (wall length = 37 ft and 25 ft)

Level	Wall Height (h) (ft)	Σ Dead Load (W_{TD}) (plf)	Σ Shear Wall Resisting Moment (RM) (ft-lb)	LRFD 0.676RM (ft-lb)	ASD 0.444RM (ft-lb)
Resisting Dead Load Moments					
3rd Floor	11	153	104,728	70,796	46,499
2nd Floor	10	617	422,336	285,499	187,517
1st Floor	10	1081	L-R: 337,812 R-L: 567,336	228,360 383,519	149,988 251,897

Table 3-31. Option 2 shear wall (wall length = 37 ft and 25 ft)

Level	Col. Ht. (ft)	Σ Dead Load (plf)	Column Axial Force (lb)	0.676 Dead Load (lb)	0.444 Dead Load (lb)
Resisting Dead Load Column Axial Load					
1st Floor	10	617	3702	2502	1644

1. Resisting moment $= (W_{TD})(L \times L)/2 = (153)(37)(37)/2 = 104,728$ lb
                                          $= (617)(37)(37)/2 = 422,336$ lb

2. Resisting moment $(L - R)$ $= (W_{TD})(L)(L/2)$
                                          $= [(1081)(25)(25/2) = 337,812$ lb

3. Resisting moment $(R - L)$ $= [(W_{TD})(L \times L)/2] + [((12/2) + 25)(617)(12)]$
                                          $= [(1081)(25)(25)/2)] + (229,524) = 567,336$ lb

4. Column dead load $= (W_{TD})(12)/2 = (617)(12)/2 = 3702$ lb

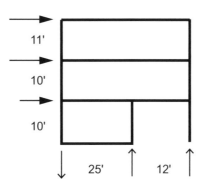

Figure 3-19. Option 2 shear wall

Table 3-32. Option 3 shear wall (wall length = 25 ft)

			Resisting Dead Load Moments (RM)		
Level	Wall height (h) (ft)	Σ Dead Load (W_{TD}) (plf)	Σ Shear Wall Resisting Moment (RM) (ft-lb)	LRFD 0.676RM (ft-lb)	ASD 0.444RM (ft-lb)
3rd Floor	11	153	47,813	32,321	21,229
2nd Floor	10	617	192,813	130,341	85,609
1st Floor	10	1081	337,813	228,361	149,989

1. Resisting moment = $(W_{TD})(L \times L)/2 = (153)(25)(25)/2 = 47,813$ lb.

Shear Wall Overturning Forces—Using Expected Shear Wall Capacity Design

The overturning forces design check is limited to LRFD only as the expected capacity of shear wall sheathing considers factored loads. To demonstrate that load combinations, including Ω_0, generate design forces less then the sheathing capacity, including Ω_E, see Table 3-32A. The provided wall sheathing shear capacity selected by the designer will always equal or exceed the seismic applied forces for ASD or LRFD to satisfy building code requirements. Basing the collector and boundary element design forces on the shear wall sheathing shear capacity, expected strength will always be greater (more conservative) than the design seismic forces resulting from load combinations, including Ω_0.

Table 3-32A. Option 1 shear wall—comparison of design forces (LRFD)

			With Overstrength	With Expected Strength
Level	Shear (F/L) (plf)	Nail Spacing (in)	$V_u \times \Omega_0$ = Shear force (plf)	$V_n \times \Omega_E$ = Shear force (plf)
3rd Floor	267	6	$267 \times 2.5 = 667.5$	$890 \times 1.8 = 1602$
2nd Floor	595	4	$595 \times 2.5 = 1487.5$	$1330 \times 1.8 = 2394$
1st Floor	759	3	$759 \times 2.5 = 1897.5$	$1775 \times 1.8 = 3195$

Ω_0 = overstrength factor = 2.5

Ω_E = expected shear wall factor = 1.8

Thus, the amplified design loads, using the lesser of the two loading types, will be controlled by the load combinations with Ω_0, as this will always be the smaller of the two. It would be conservative to design the amplified design loads using the expected strength of the shear wall sheathing.

Shear Wall Continuous Rod Tie-Down (Hold-Down) Forces

AISI S240 and S400 require shear walls to have hold-downs (also referred to as tie-downs or uplift anchorages) at the ends. Hold-downs prevent the shear wall from uplifting when the overturning forces exceed the effective resisting forces. The summation of the shear wall's effective overturning resisting force and hold-down uplift capacity has to exceed the overturning forces acting on the shear wall.

The amplified seismic overturning moments shown in the following tables are provided in terms of strength level design or LRFD from this point forward, as this example defines the amplified seismic forces as the LRFD seismic load combinations with the overstrength factor Ω_0.

The uplift forces are calculated using the distance between the continuous rods (hold-downs, uplift anchorages) that are centered in chord studs (vertical boundary members) at each end of the shear wall. The measured center of the compression CFS chord-stud pack from the end of the shear wall will vary depending on the number of chord studs, which typically is governed by the magnitude of the overturning compressive axial load. The chord studs are split symmetrically on either side of the continuous rod tie-down, typically with the gap width starting at 6 inches so the components of the tie-down system may be installed, to form a concentric overturning restraint system for the shear wall. The CFS chord studs are placed first near and on each side of the continuous rod and then, as the overturning compression force increases in each lower story, CFS chord studs are added symmetrically to the outside of the CFS chord studs on either side of the continuous rod. The center of the continuous rod is also the center of the compression chord-stud assembly.

The width of the chord-stud assembly at the lowest level of the stacked shear wall assembly will typically govern the location of the continuous rod and compression chord studs at the upper-floor levels. However, the upper-floor bridge-block detail may govern the gap width by influencing the chord-stud gap width used between the chord studs in lower stories if the engineer is aligning CFS chord studs from story-to-story.

When the force that the continuous rod tie-down resists is relatively small, it may be reasonable to assume the center of the continuous rod and CFS chord-stud pack is located 6 inches in from the end of the wall. When the force that the continuous rod tie-down resists is large, assuming the center of the CFS chord studs is 12 inches in from the end of the wall is probably more reasonable. The width of the CFS chord-stud pack varies, depending on the location and method of uplift load transfer from the continuous rod to the CFS chord studs and the required strength considering overturning and gravity loads. The uplift transfer method utilizes either a steel bearing plate nested in the stud-wall bottom track, or a steel bearing plate on a bridge-block element placed between the CFS studs several feet above the stud-wall CFS bottom track. The CFS chord-stud assembly width often ranges between 12½ to 30 inches from outside edge to outside edge. A wider chord-stud-pack width typically occurs where a bridge block is used for the uplift load transfer.

Some engineers may want to install the steel bearing plate below the CFS bottom track so as not to have to cut the CFS chord studs at a different height than other CFS wall studs, but then the floor sheathing would need to have adequate depth for the steel bearing plate, and shear transfer from the diaphragm to the shear wall below around the steel bearing plate would need to be detailed.

Tables 3-33, 3-34, 3-35A, and 3-35B show the amplified seismic uplift forces for the three shear wall options using different end distances to the center of the CFS chord studs. The non-amplified seismic uplift forces are included for the Option 3 shear wall since they are required for calculating the CFS-framed shear wall deflections, which are based on non-amplified LRFD loads.

Table 3-33. Option 1 shear wall

	Amplified Uplift Forces (LRFD)				
Level	Wall Length (L) (ft)	Wall Length (L_E) (ft)	Σ Shear Wall Ω_0 OTM (ft-lb)	0.676RM (ft-lb)	Story-Level Uplift (lb)
3rd Floor	37	36	270,848	70,796	5557
2nd Floor	37	36	820,598	285,499	14,864
1st Floor	37	36	1,522,123	500,202	28,387

1. $L_E = L$ Effective = Distance between centerline of hold-downs = (37 ft − 6 in − 6 in = 36 ft)

2. Uplift = (OTM − 0.676RM)/(L_E) = (270,848 − 70,796)/36 = 5557 lb

3. Uplift = (OTM − 0.676RM)/(L_E) = (820,598 − 285,499)/36 = 14,864 lb

4. Uplift = (OTM − 0.676RM)/(L_E) = (1,522,123 − 500,202)/36 = 28,387 lb

Table 3-34. Option 2 shear wall

	Amplified Uplift Forces (LRFD)				
Level	Wall Length (L) (ft)	Wall Length (L_E) (ft)	Σ Shear Wall Ω_0 OTM (ft-lb)	0.676RM (ft-lb)	Story-Level Uplift (lb)
3rd Floor	37	35.5	270,848	70,796	5635
2nd Floor	37	35.5	820,598	285,499	15,073
1st Floor	25 25	23 23	L-R: 1,522,123 R-L: 701,525	228,360 383,519	56,251 13,827

1. *L-R* = Seismic force in the left to right direction, *R-L* = Seismic force in the right to left direction

2. $L_E = L$ Effective = 37 ft − 1.0 ft − 0.5 ft = 35.5 ft at third and second floors; L_E = 25 ft − 1 ft − 1 ft = 23 ft at first floor

Table 3-35A. Option 3 shear wall

	Amplified Uplift Forces (LRFD)				
Level	Wall Length (L) (ft)	Wall Length (L_E) (ft)	Σ Shear Wall Ω_0 OTM (ft-lb)	0.676RM (ft-lb)	Story-Level Uplift (lb)
3rd Floor	25	23	270,848	32,321	10,371
2nd Floor	25	23	820,598	130,341	30,011
1st Floor	25	23	1,522,123	228,361	56,251

1. Uplift = (OTM − 0.676RM)/(L_E) = (270,848 − 32,321)/23 = 10,371

2. $L_E = L$ Effective = 25 ft − 1 ft − 1 ft = 23 ft

Table 3-35B. Option 3 shear wall

			Non-Amplified Uplift Forces (LRFD) for Shear Wall Deflection		
Level	Wall Length (L) (ft)	Wall Length (L_E) (ft)	Σ Shear Wall Ω_0 OTM (ft-lb)	0.676RM (ft-lb)	Story-Level Uplift (lb)
3rd Floor	25	23	108,339	32,321	3305
2nd Floor	25	23	328,239	130,341	8604
1st Floor	25	23	608,849	228,361	16,542

1. Uplift = $(OTM - 0.676RM)/(L_E) = (108,339 - 32,321)/23 = 3305$

2. $L_E = L$ Effective = 25 ft − 1 ft − 1 ft = 23 ft

Author's Discussion

The uplift forces are rather large due to the use of the load combinations with the system overstrength factor, Ω_0. The uplift forces on the building's interior transverse walls are generally smaller than forces on the perimeter shear walls due to the interior transverse walls typically being longer than the perimeter walls. The building's perimeter shear walls are typically shorter due to the presence of doors and windows. The aspect ratio (height/length) of the perimeter shear walls typically ranges between 4:1 and 1:2.

Where the shear wall aspect ratio is approximately 1:1 or greater (example: 2:1, 4:1), the uplift forces at the wall ends can be significant in a multistory light-frame structure. If the Option 3 stacked shear walls had been only 12 feet long (aspect ratio = 10 feet:12 feet, sheathing screw spacing now at 2 inches on center, both sides at first floor), the uplift design force at the podium level would have been [(1,552,123 − (77,832 × 0.676)]/10 = 149,950 pounds. This would likely be a difficult anchorage force to design and develop into the structural concrete podium, thereby most likely precluding the Option 3 shear wall being just 12 feet long.

It is very common to have shear wall uplift forces in the range of 30,000 to 50,000 pounds for ASD in multistory light-frame wall systems, especially where the building height increases from three stories to five or six stories. The uplift loads are even greater where the seismic-load combinations with the system overstrength factor, Ω_0, are used. Where the shear wall uplift loads become large, the use of continuous rods will likely be required, as opposed to using cold-formed steel hold-downs screwed or bolted to the shear wall CFS chord studs.

12.5 OVERTURNING RESTRAINT (TIE-DOWN) SYSTEM AVAILABLE STRENGTH AND DISPLACEMENT

The uplift anchorage (also referred to as overturning restraint, hold-down, or tie-down) system at each end of the shear wall in this design example is a continuous rod tie-down system that extends from the podium level to the top floor level. The continuous rod tie-down system consists of a continuous rod and multiple CFS chord studs placed on either side of the continuous rod at each floor level. The continuous rod acts as the tension component of the system and holds the uplifting shear wall down at each floor level and holds it to the podium-level base. The multiple CFS chord studs resist the compressive axial uplift load and typically bear against the wall top track and floor framing on the uplift end of the shear wall unless a bridge block at near mid-height of the shear wall is used. In that case, the CFS chord studs are fastened to CFS cripple studs that bear against the bridge block, as shown in Figure 3-20. The chord studs also resist the combined gravity and seismic overturning compressive axial down load on the compression side of the shear wall.

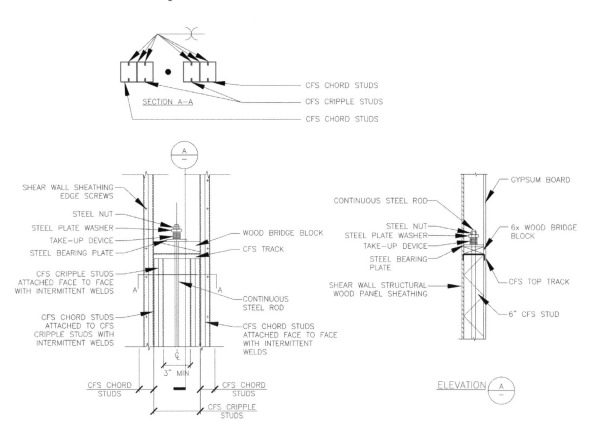

Figure 3-20. Detail of the third-floor bridge-block termination of the continuous rod tie-down system

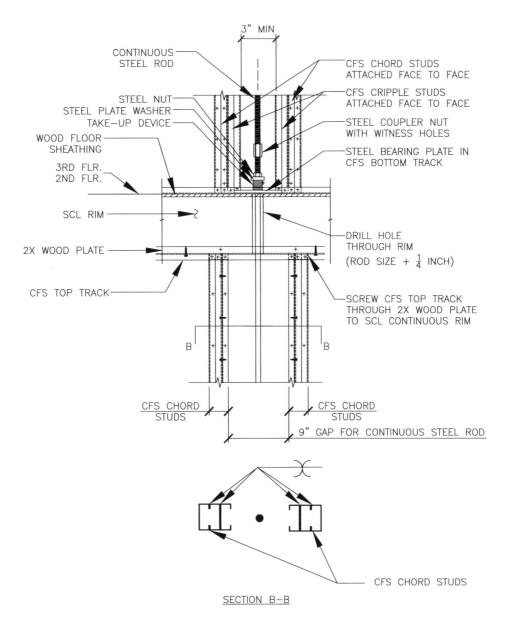

Figure 3-21. Typical chord-stud assembly of the floor line. Continuous rod tie-down (hold-down) system chord studs at the second and third floors.

The continuous tie-down system design is based on the Option 3 short-stacked shear wall forces, since it has the largest uplift forces. The continuous rod extends above the third floor, but terminates at a bridge block several feet below the third-floor wall top track.

In a continuous rod tie-down system, uplift caused when a lateral load acts on a shear wall is typically resisted by a steel bearing plate attached to the continuous rod at the floor above the shear wall or a bearing plate on top of a bridge block within the height of the shear wall, as shown in Figure 3-21. The bearing plate or load transfer point at each floor level resists the overturning (uplift) force of the shear wall below (sometimes referred to as *incremental bearing*), while the continuous rod resists the cumulative overturning force from the top of the continuous rod tie-down system run down to the floor level under consideration. The lowest level in the design example is the concrete podium deck to which the continuous rod is anchored and that resists the cumulative overturning force.

AISI S400 requires in SDC B through F that components of the seismic-force-resisting systems (SFRS) not part of the designated energy-dissipating system (e.g., chord studs, tie-downs, shear anchorage, and collectors), regardless of R-factor used unless exempted otherwise, have the available strength to resist the lesser of (1) the expected strength of the shear wall ($\Omega_E V_n$) or (2) the load determined using the seismic load combinations with the overstrength factor Ω_0. This is different from light-frame wood structures where the shear wall chord (end) studs, hold-down or tie-down system, shear anchorage, and collectors are designed only for the ASD or LRFD seismic load. However, buildings are exempt from having to comply with S400 where located in SDC A, or located in SDC B or C and using an SFRS with an R equal to 3, or an SFRS with a higher R-factor but assigned an R of 3 in SDC B or C. But these exempted buildings must still comply with S100 or S240.

The *available strength* is defined by the AISI standard as the material nominal strength (V_n) modified by a resistance factor (ϕ) when using LRFD or dividing by a factor of safety (Ω) when using ASD. The values for ϕ and (Ω) are defined in the AISI specifications.

Available strength (LRFD) = $V_n(\phi)$

Available strength (ASD) = $V_n/(\Omega)$

Table 3-36 shows the continuous rod area required and the provided strength and rod sizes. The continuous rod is required to have the available strength to resist the amplified seismic force per AISI S400 Sections E1.4.1.2 and E2.4.1.2. Displacement of the overturning restraint system (including tension rod elongation, take-up device deflection or the gap distance from settlement and/or shrinkage if take-up devices are not used, wood crushing, and bearing plate bending) also needs to be determined in order for the engineer to determine if the horizontal deflection at the top of the shear wall is in accordance with the ASCE 7 drift limit as well as the ICC-ES and/or local jurisdiction story vertical displacement limit.

Table 3-36. Continuous rod tie-down system required, provided strength, and rod sizes (Option 3: Shear wall)—LRFD

Level	Floor-to-Floor Height (L) (ft)	Story-Level Amplified Seismic Uplift Force[1] (P_{amp}) (lb)	Rod Gross Area Required[4]/Area Provided (A_b) for Strength (in^2)	Story-Level Seismic Uplift Force[2] (P) (lb)	Rod Net Tensile Area Required[3]/Area Provided (A_e) for Vertical Story Displacement[6] (in^2)	Rod Diameter Provided (in) (rod tensile strength [ksi])
3rd Floor	11	10,371	0.318/0.442	3305	0.063/0.334	¾ ($F_u = 58$ ksi)
2nd Floor	10	30,011	0.920/0.994	8604	0.150/0.763	1⅛ ($F_u = 58$ ksi)
2nd Floor	10	30,011	0.427/0.442	8604	0.150/0.334	¾ ($F_u = 125$ ksi)
1st Floor	10	56,251	0.800/0.994	16,542	0.288/0.763	1⅛ ($F_u = 125$ ksi)

1. Story-level amplified seismic uplift force is from Table 3-35A.

2. Story-level seismic uplift force is from Table 3-35B.

3. Rod material: ASTM A36 $F_y = 36$ ksi $F_u = 58$ ksi, $E = 29,000,000$
               ASTM A193 B7 $F_y = 105$ ksi $F_u = 125$ ksi, $E = 29,000,000$

4. Rod available strength (LRFD) = $0.75(0.75F_u)A_b$, so $A_{req} = P_{amp}/(0.56F_u)$ from AISC 360 Equation J3-1, Table J.3.2, and corresponding commentary.

5. System vertical story displacement limit = 0.170 = 0.20 inch − 0.030 inch take-up device initial seating, Δ_R, and design deflection, Δ_A, per manufacturer's evaluation report (ASD) × 1.4 = 0.170 × 1.4 = 0.238 inch (LRFD). System vertical story displacement limit = δ = 0.238 inch.

$$\delta = PL/A_{req}E$$

$$A_{req} = PL/0.238(E)$$

6. Rod net tensile area tabulated in the 15th Edition of AISC *Steel Construction Manual* Table 7-17 or per the following equation: $A_e = 0.7854 \times [d - (0.9743/n)]^2$ where n = threads per inch and d = rod diameter.

Author's Discussion

Continuous rod tie-down systems are not only designed to have the strength to resist the seismic overturning force but must also be designed to ensure compliance with the code seismic-drift limit and the local building jurisdiction's story-elongation limit. The allowable story drift limit is shown in ASCE 7 Table 12.12-1 and is taken as $0.025h_{sx}$ for this design example. Devices that expand to take up the gap between the bearing plate and the continuous rod nut are called *take-up* (shrinkage compensating) *devices*, and these are often used in multistory buildings to ensure the overturning restraint system is tight.

The ICC-Evaluation Service's publically developed acceptance criteria for shrinkage compensating devices, AC316, has a 0.20-inch total vertical displacement limit, including the steel rod elongation and the take-up device deflection, using the more restrictive rod length at each story or between restraints at ASD. The 0.20-inch limit needs to be confirmed with the local jurisdiction where the building project occurs as it may have a more stringent limit such as 0.125 inch. Continuous rods should be considered standard strength unless clearly identified with markings as high-strength, and special inspection should be required to ensure high-strength rod is used where specified. Also, high-strength rods and coupler nuts are usually not weldable, but may be if certain supplementary requirements are followed (e.g., ASTM F1554 Grade 55 with Supplementary Requirement S1).

The use of smaller diameter high-strength rods, such as ASTM A193 B7 with $F_u = 125$ ksi, will elongate more than larger-diameter standard-strength rods, such as ASTM A36 with $F_u = 58$ ksi, when sized for the same load and so will increase the top of shear wall drift with their use.

Continuous Rod Tie-Down Steel Bearing Plate Design

As the shear wall attempts to uplift, the uplift force is transferred through compression of the CFS studs located under the wood framing (floor blocking, floor rim joist, wall bridge block) and steel bearing plate. A nut or take-up-device nut is used to transfer the uplift force from the bearing plate to the continuous rod. The steel bearing plate is designed for both bending and shear.

The wood framing often becomes the weakest element of the continuous rod tie-down system since it is typically governed by compression perpendicular to grain. The wood rim joist and blocking wall framing is used as a load transfer element to help spread the compression loads under the steel bearing plate to the ends of the CFS chord-stud pack under the floor/roof wood framing. The steel bearing plate width and length are designed and fabricated to fit within the CFS wall track, accounting for the CFS bottom-track radius and some construction erection tolerance. When a bridge block is used within the shear wall, the steel plate is similarly designed and fabricated for some construction erection tolerance and to not extend over the edges of the bridge block.

The steel bearing plate is designed to have the available strength to resist the amplified overturning uplift load (differential or story-uplift load) in the shear wall below at each floor level or load transfer point. So for this design example, the following occurs:

1. The steel bearing plate at the third-floor wood bridge block resists the overturning uplift from the third-floor shear wall.

2. The steel bearing plate in the third-floor CFS-framed-wall bottom track resists the overturning uplift force from the second-floor shear wall.

3. The steel bearing plate in the second-floor CFS-framed-wall bottom track resists the overturning uplift force from the first-floor shear wall.

Table 3-37. Option 3 amplified design forces (Ω_0) and tie-rod bearing plate sizing—LRFD

Shear Wall Level	Floor-to-Floor Height (L) (ft)	Story-Level Uplift ($P\Omega_0$) (lb)	Differential Uplift Loads (lb)	Bearing Plate Level[1]	Rod Diameter Provided (in) (nominal diameter, rod area)
3rd Floor	11	10,371	10,371	3rd flr. bridge blk.	¾ (0.442) ($F_u = 58$ ksi)
2nd Floor	10	30,011	19,640	3rd flr. b. track	1⅛ (0.994) ($F_u = 58$ ksi)
2nd Floor	10	30,011	19,640	3rd flr. b. track	¾ (0.442) ($F_u = 125$ ksi)
1st Floor	10	56,251	26,240	2nd flr. b. track	1⅛ (0.994) ($F_u = 125$ ksi)

1. b. track = CFS stud-wall bottom track

The steel bearing plate at the second-floor CFS bottom track is shown below. The design is similar for the other steel bearing plates at the third-floor CFS bottom track and third-floor bridge block.

1. Bearing plate work space:

   a. CFS stud size and spacing: 6-inch CFS studs at 16 inches on center

   b. Clear area between CFS chord studs and track flanges = (16 in − 1.625 in)(6 in − 0.25 in) = 82.66 in^2

   c. Wood block or rim joist: Douglas Fir-Larch, $F_{c\perp} = 625$ psi

   d. Continuous rod size = 1.125-inch diameter

2. Bearing plate forces—second-floor level:

   As wood bearing perpendicular to grain and the steel bearing plate are part of the CFS-framed shear wall overturning-restraint (hold-down) system, AISI S400 Sections E1.4.1.2 and E2.4.1.2 require that they must have the available strength to resist the minimum of (1) the expected strength of the shear wall and (2) the load determined using the ASCE 7 seismic load combinations with the overstrength factor. AWC NDS Section 4.2.6 notes that wood reference compression design values perpendicular to grain ($F_{c\perp}$) are based on an average compression resistance at a deformation of 0.04 inch. NDS Equation 4.2-1 is used to calculate the compression design value perpendicular to grain for a reduced deformation level of 0.02 inch:

   $$F_{c\perp 0.02} = 0.73 F_{c\perp}$$

   The ASD value is then multiplied by K_F equal to 1.67 and ϕ equal to 0.9 to obtain the design value for LRFD, as can be seen in AWC NDS Table 4.3.1 and shown here:

   Douglas Fir-Larch Perpendicular-to-Grain Deformation and $F_{c\perp}$ Design Values

Approximately 0.02 inch of crush/deformation	Approximately 0.04 inch of crush/deformation
ASD: 456 psi	625 psi
Nominal: 456 × 1.67 = 762 psi	625 × 1.67 = 1044 psi
LRFD: 456 × 1.67 × 0.9 = 685 psi	625 psi × 1.67 × 0.9 = 939 psi

   The question arises regarding the appropriate application of the AISI S400 required strength provisions to the wood bearing design values based on a serviceability limit state.

   While AISI requires that the shear wall chord studs and uplift anchorage have the available strength to resist the amplified seismic loads (primarily to prevent CFS open-shape, singly symmetric studs from buckling under compression loading, but also helpful to preclude premature failure of the tension anchorage), this is not a requirement for wood design. If the floor joist framing or wall bearing bridge had been a CFS member instead of wood framing or structural steel, these members would have to develop the amplified seismic loads.

   Using either the ASD or LRFD seismic loads, the bearing plate in this design example should be sized such that the resulting bearing pressure is equal to or less than the selected wood-compression-perpendicular-to-grain value ($F_{c\perp}$) that has a starting ASD base value of 625 psi. Using LRFD, the wood ASD $F_{c\perp}$ value is multiplied by 1.67 and 0.9 per AWC NDS Table 2.3.5 and Table 2.36 (or Table 4.3.1). Per AWC NDS Appendix Table N3, time-effect factors (λ) equal 1.0 when used in load combinations including earthquake, so there is no additional increase allowed for wood bearing capacity when design forces include earthquake.

Neither load-duration (C_D) increases for ASD nor time-effect factors (λ) for LRFD are permitted when evaluating wood framing members for perpendicular-to-grain loading per NDS Table 4.3.1. However, a bearing area factor, C_b, is applicable for bearing lengths up to 4 inches measured parallel to grain per NDS Section 3.10.4.

Example Forces

1. LRFD differential non-amplified seismic uplift force = 16,542 − 8604 = 7938 lb

   a. Non-amplified seismic uplift forces are from Table 3-35B of this design example

2. ASD differential non-amplified seismic uplift force = 7938(0.7) = 5557 lb

   a. The use of 0.7 as a factor to convert from LRFD to ASD is not exact, but it is considered close enough for design purposes because the difference in differential amplified seismic loading between ASD and LRFD is expected to be less than three percent.

3. Bearing-plate hole size for continuous rod: $\pi d^2/4 = \pi(1\frac{1}{8} + \frac{1}{16})^2/4 = 1.11 \text{ in}^2$

   a. A standard hole is used in the bearing plate whose diameter is defined as the continuous rod diameter plus $\frac{1}{16}$ inch (0.0625 inch)—see NDS Section 12.1.3.2.

   b. The use of Equation NDS 3.10-2 is permissible, but is ignored in this calculation as plates often have dimensions equal to or larger than 6 inches, even though this example shows a plate size of 3 in × 5 in. The increase in capacity per Equation 3.10-2 is not that much.

Bearing-Plate Sizing for Wood (ASD)

1. Plate area (minimum): $5557/625 = 8.89 \text{ in}^2 <$ trial plate size = 3.0 in × 5.0 in = 15.0 in^2

2. Wood bearing stress: $P/A_{net} = 5557/(15.0 - 1.11) = 400 \text{ psi} < 625 \text{ psi}$

3. Plate shear: $V = P(A_{net})/2 = 400 \times (15.0 - 1.11)/2 = 2778 \text{ lb}$

4. Plate bending: $M = 400 \text{ psi} \times (3.0 \text{ in})(5.0/2) \times (5.0/4) = 3750 \text{ in-lb}$

Bearing-Plate Sizing for Wood (LRFD)

$K_F = 1.67, \phi = 0.9, \lambda = 1.0$

1. Plate area (minimum): $P_u/(F_{c\perp}K_F\phi) = 7938/(625 \times 1.67 \times 0.9) = 8.45 \text{ in}^2$
   Trial plate size = 3.0 in × 4.0 in = 12.0 $\text{in}^2 > 8.45 \text{ in}^2$

2. Wood bearing stress: $P_u/A_{net} = 7938/(12.0 - 1.11) = 729 \text{ psi} < 625 \times 1.67 \times 0.9 = 939 \text{ psi}$

3. Plate shear: $V_u = P_u(A_{net})/2 = 729 \times (12.0 - 1.11)/2 = 3969 \text{ lb}$

4. Plate bending: $M_u = 729 \text{ psi} \times 3.0 \text{ in} \times (4.0/2) \times (4.0/4) = 4374 \text{ in-lb}$

For the ASD and LRFD plate bending-moment calculations, the area of the hole is conservatively not subtracted out to simply the calculation.

Steel Bearing-Plate Design (AISC 360)

The steel-plate yield strength is $F_y = 36$ ksi. The plate design for bending will consider the continuous rod hole in plate. A standard hole is assumed, where the hole's diameter is equal to the rod diameter plus $\frac{1}{16}$ inch (0.0625 inch) per AISC 360 Table J3.3.

1. Plate thickness—Flexure   AISC 360 §F11 "Rectangular Bars and Rounds"

$$M_n = M_p = F_y Z \leq 1.6 M_y \hspace{3cm} \text{AISC 360 Eq F11-1}$$

ASD ($\Omega = 1.67$)	LRFD ($\phi = 0.9$ AISC)
$M_n/\Omega > M_{acting}$	$\phi M_n > M_{acting}$
Z required $= M\Omega/F_y$ $= 3750(1.67)/36{,}000$ $= 0.174$ in^3	Z required $= (M/\phi)/F_y$ $= (4374/0.9)/36{,}000$ $= 0.135$ in^3
$Z = bd^2/4$ $b = 3.0 - (1.125 + \frac{1}{16})$ $b = 1.813$ in	$Z = bd^2/4$ $b = 3.0 - (1.125 + \frac{1}{16})$ $b = 1.813$ in
$t = \sqrt{4Z/b}$ $= \sqrt{(4)(0.174)/(1.813)}$ $= 0.620$ in	$t = \sqrt{4Z/b}$ $= \sqrt{(4)(0.135)/(1.813)}$ $= 0.546$ in
Use 0.625-inch-thick plate minimum.	Use 0.625-inch-thick plate minimum.

$1.6M_y = 1.6F_y S_x$ $S_x = bh^2/6 = 3(0.625)^2/6 = 0.1953$ in^3

       $= 1.6(36)(0.1953)$

       $= 11.25$ in-kip

    $M_p = F_y Z = (36)(3)(0.625)^2/4 = 10.55$ in-kip < 11.25 in-kip $\ldots$ OK

2. Plate thickness—Shear   AISC 360 §G1 and G2

Shear is typically not a problem for the bearing plate, but it is checked for completeness of the bearing-plate design.

ASD ($\Omega = 1.67$)

LRFD ($\phi = 0.9$)

      $V_n = 0.6F_y A_w C_v$ AISC 360 Eq G2-1

      $C_v = 1.0$ for flat plates

      $A_w = 3.0$ in $\times$ 0.625 in $= 1.88$ in^2

$V_n = 0.6(36)(1.5)(1.0) = 32.4$ kips

$\phi V_n = 0.9(32.4) = 29.2$ kips $> 3969/0.7 = 5674$ lb

$V_n/\Omega = 29.2/1.67 = 17.5$ kips > 3969 lb

It is acceptable to use: ASD: a 3.0-inch $\times$ 5.0-inch $\times$ 0.625-inch-thick bearing plate

                      LRFD: a 3.0-inch $\times$ 4.0-inch $\times$ 0.625-inch-thick bearing plate

A smaller 3-inch × 3-inch plate could be used if the C_b increase in allowable bearing was considered. The plate would have been the same thickness and the deformation of the wood would be a little more than 0.04 inch due to the smaller bearing area.

While LRFD allows for smaller bearing plates, the resulting sill plate crushing deformation is greater than the 0.02 and 0.04 crush limits established for ASD service values. LRFD uses KF to adjust the E-value for strength design, resulting in larger perpendicular-to-grain bearing values. The increase in crush associated with 939 psi and 1044 psi can be determined from the load-displacement curve shown in Figure 1-18 and associated equations of Design Example 1 of this manual. The authors recommend that bearing plates be sized to limit the compression perpendicular to grain to 625 psi (crush = 0.04 inch) or less when using LRFD to reduce deflections of the tie-down assembly.

Podium Connection (anchorage to concrete)

The shear wall continuous rod tie-down tension (uplift) base connection occurs at the first-floor podium level. The amplified seismic uplift force is 56,215 pounds (Table 3-35A) and the LRFD seismic uplift force is 16,542 pounds (Table 3-35B). The amplified compression force (OTM compression plus gravity) for this design example is 91,318 pounds (Table 3-39).

The elevated podium structural slab is currently considered to be a discontinuity for the shear wall system.

1. Anchorage: Similar to requirements for light-frame wood structures, ASCE 7 Section 12.3.3.3 requires that the connections of the discontinuous element to the supporting structure be designed for the forces used to design the discontinuous element. AISI S400 Sections E1.4.1.2 and E2.4.1.2 require the uplift anchorage, which includes the anchor rod, have the available strength to resist the amplified seismic force. Using AISC 360, the steel anchor rod material and size are selected to comply with AISI S400. Then one designs the anchorage in accordance with ACI 318 Chapter 17 using the rod material and size selected to satisfy AISI S240, S400, and the LRFD seismic-load combinations, except where ACI 318 Chapter 17 requires the use of the seismic-load combinations with the overstrength factor. This ensures the concrete will not be the governing limit for the rod material and size selected unless it is designed using the seismic-load combinations with the overstrength factor.

2. Podium slab design: The concrete podium deck, since it represents the element the discontinuous shear wall is sitting on, is to be designed to resist the load determined using the ASCE 7 seismic-load combinations with the overstrength factor Ω_0. This applies to both wood and CFS light-frame structures.

The lateral-resisting system for the concrete podium structure is likely a load-bearing wall system with special reinforced concrete shear walls, special reinforced masonry bearing shear walls, or a combination of the two, where R is equal to 5.0. Per ASCE 7 Section 12.3.3.3, when the lower podium base structure is ten times stiffer than the light-frame construction upper portion, the upper and lower portions of the structure are to be analyzed as two different structures, which is likely the case for this building. The design force V for the lower podium structure lateral-resisting elements will be amplified by the ratio of R-values of the light-frame building above, divided by the R-value of the podium structure below (6.5/5.0 = 1.30).

The design of the concrete podium deck will be controlled by the light-frame construction forces and its overstrength factor, Ω_0 (the podium slab is considered to be a discontinuous element), since $\Omega_0 = 3.0$ is greater than evaluating the podium deck using the 1.3 force amplification associated with the ratio of the upper and lower lateral-resisting system R-values.

The design of the continuous rod-to-podium connection is not part of this design example, and it is assumed the engineer is familiar with ACI 318 Chapter 17. The design of the podium slab is also not part of this design example.

Author's Discussion

Multistory residential buildings typically have many shear walls, and typically a symbol mark is shown on the framing plans representing the locations of the continuous rod tie-downs (hold-downs) for each of the shear walls. These marks then refer back to a continuous rod (hold-down) schedule that identifies all of the components of the continuous rod tie-down system, usually with a generic detail showing how the continuous rod tie-down system is assembled. Projects may use a combination of different hold-down types such as CFS strap hold-downs, embedded CFS strap hold-downs, conventional CFS hold-downs, and continuous rod tie-down systems. As the buildings become taller, continuous rod tie-down systems are used, as they typically have more strength than conventional hold-downs.

When designing multistory buildings, the framing contractor should be required to provide the engineer of record installation drawings showing all the different types of continuous rod tie-down runs, along with framing plans that show where these continuous rod tie-downs occur in plan. Some building departments, or the jurisdictions having responsibility, will require these continuous rod tie-down installation drawings be submitted for permitting as a deferred submittal.

There are continuous rod tie-down component manufacturers that will produce these shear wall continuous rod tie-down installation drawings as part of their service to the framing contractor who purchases the components from them. The continuous tie-down component manufacturer may also consider and suggest alternative materials (steel-rod material, CFS stud material, bearing-plate sizes, etc.) for substitution based on what is currently available in the construction marketplace. Any substitutions by the continuous rod tie-down component manufacturer are to be submitted to the engineer of record as well as to the jurisdiction for review and approval if the substitution is proposed during or after plan check.

12.6 SHEAR WALL CHORD STUDS

Chord studs (vertical boundary members, end studs) are at each end of a shear wall and primarily resist the shear wall overturning and gravity-compression loads. The chord studs are placed symmetrically on either side of the shear wall continuous rod tie-down use to resist the uplift forces. In this design example, there are two overturning-restraint (tie-down) system configurations used.

1. The third-floor shear wall continuous rod terminates at the bridge block several feet below the top of the wall. As the wall lifts up from overturning, the fastener connection of the CFS chord studs to CFS cripple studs, located under the wood bridge block, transfers the uplift force to the CFS cripple studs, which then transfers the force to the underside of the bridge block through bearing. Then the steel bearing plate on top of the wood bridge block resists the uplift force through bearing and is supported by the continuous rod.

2. The second- and first-floor shear wall continuous rods extend through the floor above, and as the wall lifts up from overturning, the CFS chord studs resist the uplift force through bearing in the CFS top track, which in turn bears on the underside of the wood floor rim joist. The continuous rod steel bearing plate is placed in the CFS bottom track of the wall at the floor level above, and it holds down the wood rim floor joist.

The chord studs are checked for two different compressive axial loading conditions:

1. Chord studs used for transferring the overturning uplift load are located on each side of the continuous rod and under the steel bearing plate in the bottom track of the wall above and any wood filler block or rim joist under the steel bearing plate.

2. Chord studs resisting downward overturning and gravity compression forces are located on each side of the steel bearing plate in the wall bottom track or possibly bear on top of the bearing plate.

When R is other than 3.0, the CFS chord studs are required to have the available strength to resist the compressive axial force equal to the lesser of (1) the seismic load combinations with the overstrength factor or (2) the expected strength of the shear wall. The expected strength of the shear wall is the nominal shear strength, V_n, multiplied by the expected strength factor, Ω_E. The expected strength factor is 1.8 for shear walls with wood structural panels per AISI S400 Section E1.3.3. This typically governs the design of the CFS chord studs rather than the differential load, as the overturning and gravity loads are cumulative downward.

Only the overturning uplift load at each floor level (differential load) should be considered for the compression design of the uplift studs at that floor level. The differential uplift loads were derived earlier using the amplified loads subtracting out the resisting dead loads.

In this design example, the CFS chord studs resisting uplift bear on the top track, which bears on a wood top plate, which bears on a wood rim joist, which is held down by the steel bearing plate in the wall above. AISI D110-16 *Cold-Formed Steel Framing Design Guide* Appendix F has a design example for designing an axially load steel stud-to track-to concrete bearing condition, which may provide guidance for a steel stud-to steel track-to wood bearing condition. In addition, there will be crushing or bearing deformation at the steel chord stud to wood top plate, the wood top plate to the wood rim joist, and the wood rim joist to the steel bearing plate. AWC NDS Commentary Section C4.2.6 states the amount of deformation is approximately two and one-half times a metal plate to wood bearing joint when a joint contains two wood members loaded perpendicular to grain. This bearing deformation should be added to the vertical overturning-restraint-system displacement portion of the shear wall deflection equation.

AISI D110-16 *Cold-Formed Steel Framing Design Guide* Appendix F provides an example of one methodology for calculating the approximate bearing area when designing CFS compression studs in a bottom track bearing on concrete.

Chord-Stud Assembly Compression Loads

The design forces shown are for the Option 3 shear wall (LRFD).

Roof-Level Design Loads (Third-Floor Shear Walls)

Wall gravity-compression loads:
        Dead load = 153 plf
        Live load = 0 plf (roof live load not used in load combinations)
        Load combination = $(1.2 + 0.2(S_{DS}))D + 0.5L$ ASCE 7 Eq 6 §2.3.6
                = $[1.2 + 0.2(1.117)](153) + 0.5(0) = 218$ plf

        Chord stud boundary gravity load = (25-ft-long wall/2)(218 plf) = 2725 lb
        Assumed chord stud boundary width = 2 ft

Wall seismic forces (amplified seismic loads – compression loads):

OTM (including the seismic overstrength factor Ω_0) = 270,848 ft-lb

Lever arm = centerline of hold-down to centerline of hold-down = 25 ft – 2(1 ft) = 23 ft

$C = T = 270,848/23 = 11,776$ lb

Expected shear wall strength – compression loads:

Wall length = 25 ft, #8 screws at 6 in o.c., $V_{nominal} = V_n = 890$ plf, $\Omega_E = 1.8$

OTM = (25 ft)(890)(1.8)(11 ft)/1000 = 440.55 kip-ft

Lever arm = centerline of hold-down to centerline of hold-down = 25 – 2(1 ft) = 23 ft

$C = 440,550/23 = 19,154$ lb > 11,776 lb; therefore, use 11,776 lb

Continuous rod tensile capacity (for uplift comparison):

Continuous rod = ¾-inch diameter (0.442 in^2)

$R_t = 1.2$ (ASTM A36 material)   AISC 341 TA3.1

Continuous rod nominal tension strength = (0.442)(0.75 × 58 ksi)(1.2) = 23.07 kips

AISC 360 §J3.6

Summary of chord-stud assembly axial loads:

23.07 kips (rod uplift capacity)   > 19.154 (expected – compression)

> 11.776 kips (amplified – compression)

> 10.371 kips (rod amplified differential uplift)

Third-Floor Design Loads (Second-Floor Shear Walls)

Wall gravity-compression loads:

Dead load = 153 + 464 = 617 plf

Live load = (11.8 ft × 40 psf) = 472 plf

Load combination = $(1.2 + 0.2(S_{DS})D + 0.5L$ ASCE 7 Eq 6 §2.3.6

= [1.2 + 0.2(1.117)](617) + 0.5(472) = 1115 plf

Chord stud boundary gravity load = (25-ft-long wall/2)(1115 plf) = 13,938 lb

Assumed chord-stud assembly boundary width = 2 ft

Wall seismic forces (amplified seismic loads – compression loads):

OTM = 820,598 ft-lb

Lever arm = 23 ft

$T = C = 35,679$ lb

Expected shear wall strength – compression loads:

Wall length = 25 ft, #8 screws at 3 in o.c., $V_{nominal} = V_n = 1775$ plf, $\Omega_E = 1.8$

OTM = (25 ft)(1775)(1.8)(10 ft)/1000 = 799 kip-ft

OTM total (roof + third floor) = 440.55 + 799 = 1239.55. Use 1240 kip-ft

Lever arm = centerline of hold-down to centerline of hold-down = 25 – 2(1 ft) = 23 ft

$C = 1,240,000/23 = 53,913$ lb > 35,679 lb; therefore, use 35,679 lb

Continuous rod tensile capacity (for uplift comparison):

Continuous rod = ¾-inch diameter (area = 0.44 in^2)($F_u = 125$ ksi)

$R_t = 1.1$ (assumed for ASTM A193 B7 material)

Continuous rod nominal tension strength   = (0.44)(0.75 × 125 ksi)(1.1)   AISC 360 §J3.6

= 45.375 kips

Summary of chord-stud assembly axial loads:

45.375 kips (rod uplift capacity)   < 53.913 kips (expected compression)
              > 35.679 kips (amplified compression)
              > 19.640 kips (rod amplified-differential uplift)

Second-Floor Design Loads (First-Floor Shear Walls):

Wall gravity-compression loads:
  Dead load = 153 + 464 + 464 = 1081 plf
  Live load = (11.8 ft × 40 psf) + 472 plf = 944 plf
  Load combination   = $(1.2 + 0.2(S_{DS}))D + 0.5L$ ASCE 7 Eq 6 §2.3.6
          = [1.2 + 0.2(1.117)](1081) + 0.5(944) = 1539 plf + 472 plf = 2011 plf
  Chord stud boundary gravity load = (25-ft-long wall/2)(2011 plf) = 25,138 lb
  Assumed chord-stud assembly boundary width = 2 ft

Wall seismic forces (amplified seismic loads – compression loads):
  OTM = 1522.123 kip-ft
  Lever arm = 23 ft
  $T = C = 66,180$ lb

Expected shear wall strength – compression loads:
  Wall length = 25 ft, #8 screws at 2 in o.c., $V_{nominal} = V_n = 2190$ plf, $\Omega_E = 1.8$
  OTM = (25 ft)(2190)(1.8)(10)/1000 = 986 kip-ft
  OTM total (roof + third floor + second floor) = 441 + 799 + 986 = 2226 kip-ft
  Lever arm = centerline of hold-down to centerline of hold-down = 25 – 2(1 ft) = 23 ft
  $C = 2226/23 = 96,783$ lb > 66,180 lb; therefore, use 66,180 lb

Continuous rod tensile capacity (for uplift comparison):
Continuous rod = 1⅛-inch diameter (area = 0.994 in^2) ($F_u = 125$ ksi)
$R_t = 1.1$ (assumed for ASTM A193 B7 material)
Continuous rod nominal capacity = (0.994)(0.75 × 125 ksi)(1.1)   AISC 360 §J3.6
            = 102.51 kips

Summary of chord-stud assembly axial loads:

102.51 kips (rod uplift capacity)   > 96.783 kips (expected compression)
              > 66.18 kips (amplified compression)
              > 26.240 kips (rod amplified differential uplift)

Governing Loads for Compression CFS Chord Studs

Table 3-38 shows the governing CFS chord stud design loads for both the story-level differential uplift and accumulative downward compression loads due to the shear wall overturning for each story level of the building. In a typical continuous rod tie-down system for CFS construction, the chord studs are required to

1. Have the available strength to resist the compressive axial load due to the cumulative overturning downward compression design loads, including the design gravity loads.

2. Have the available strength to resist the compressive axial load when bearing against the floor framing or wall above on the tension (uplift) side of the shear wall.

The chord stud design on the compression side of the shear wall governs the chord stud design, as the compressive axial load is cumulative with each successive story and includes the gravity loads.

Table 3-38. Option 3 shear wall: summary of CFS chord stud differential uplift and accumulative downward compression design loads

Level	OTM Differential Uplift Loads (kips)	Load Type[1]	OTM Compression Downward Loads (kips)	Load Type[2]	Gravity Loads (kips)
3rd Floor	10.371	amplified differential	11.776	amplified	2.725
2nd Floor	19.640	amplified differential	35.679	amplified	13.938
1st Floor	26.240	amplified differential	66.180	amplified	25.138

1. The uplift loads are the amplified differential story loads from Table 3-37.

2. The downward compression design loads are the smaller of the calculated overstrength and expected loads.

Chord Stud Resisting Compression Due to Overturning and Gravity Loads

The CFS-chord studs are designed for the governing compression forces utilizing commercially available CFS design software.

The selected CFS stud sizes for the three floor levels that have an available compressive axial strength to resist the lesser of (1) the expected strength of the shear wall or (2) the load from the seismic load combinations with the overstrength factor (amplified seismic load).

The engineer may want to increase the CFS stud thickness over that used in the story above to keep the CFS chord studs aligned from top to bottom. However, the increased stud thickness and corresponding required screw size are required to be in accordance with AISI S400 Tables E1.3-1 and E2.3-1.

Table 3-39. Option 3 shear wall: CFS chord stud size, number, and strength

Level	Stud Height[1] (ft)	Individual Chord Stud Size	Available Stud Strength[5] (kips)	Number of Chord Studs	Available Chord Assembly Axial Strength (kips)	Amplified LRFD[2] Axial Design Load (kips)	Chord Stud Assembly Width[4]
3rd Floor	10	600S162-54(50)	4.48	4	17.92	14.489	$(8 \times 1.625 \text{ in}) + 3 \text{ in}$ = 16 in
2nd Floor	9	600S200-68(50)	9.34	6	56.0	49.617	$(6 \times 2.0 \text{ in}) + 9 \text{ in}$ = 21 in
1st Floor	9	600S200-68(50)	11.1	10	110.8	91.318	$(10 \times 2.0 \text{ in}) + 9 \text{ in}$ = 29 in

1. Stud height uses floor height minus 12 inches for rim joist height on stud wall.

2. Amplified LRFD axial design load = OTM compressive load + gravity = (e.g., first floor = 66.18 + 25.138 = 91.318 kips); these loads can be found in Table 3-38.

3. In accordance with IBC Section 1607.14, a horizontal live load of 5 psf is applied uniformly across the vertical face of the interior shear wall and is assumed to be acting concurrently with the seismic OTM compression and gravity axial loads on the shear wall chord studs.

4. This design example uses a 3-inch space between the CFS cripple studs below the bridge block on either side of the continuous rod at the third floor and a 9-inch width between the CFS chord stud packs at the second and third floors. The gap needs to be adequate to install the uplift restraint system, which includes the continuous rod to the coupler nut, the take-up device, etc.

5. The shear wall CFS studs are mechanically braced by steel straps on each side and periodic intermittent blocking at midpoint at the third and second floors and at third points at the first floor.

The compressive axial strength of the individual CFS studs is dependent on the presence of bracing. If mechanical steel bracing is used, the axial capacity also depends on the spacing of the bracing. As is discussed later in Section 14.1 on wall-stud bracing, the bracing must be adequately secured to prevent lateral twisting and buckling of the CFS studs and must have anchorage to resist the cumulative bracing force for axially loaded studs.

While the third-floor shear wall CFS studs are braced by steel straps on each side and periodic intermittent blocking at the midpoint, the engineer might use wood structural panel sheathing on one side and gypsum board sheathing on the other side. But the bracing strength of the gypsum board sheathing is weaker and therefore governs in accordance with AISI S240 Section B1.2.2.1(b). If wall sheathing is used as stud bracing, Section B1.2.2.2 also requires that the engineering construction documents identify the wall sheathing as a structural element on the plans. AISI S240 Table B3.2-1 limits the nominal axial load for a CFS stud to 6.7 kips when braced by ½-inch-thick gypsum board sheathing using #8 screws and so would have worked only for the third floor.

When the engineer selects the CFS strap-bracing heights on the wall, they should consider the location of electrical boxes, light switches, recessed wall pockets for fire extinguishers, and other wall openings. The CFS continuous strap bracing should not be used as backing for objects to be supported off the face of the shear wall, so the engineer should consider the location and elevation of wall fixtures, wall-hung cabinets, and the tops of floor-supported cabinets.

Stud Strap Bracing for CFS Stud Axial Capacity (Bracing Force and Bracing System)

IBC Section 2211 states that structural walls shall be designed in accordance with AISI S240, which references S100, and that seismic-force-resisting systems shall be designed using AISI S400. This design example will conform to AISI S240, in which Section B3.4 requires that each stud brace be designed for 2 percent of the design compression force in the member. Therefore, the CFS stud bracing anchorage is designed to have the available strength (LRFD) to resist the maximum of:

1. The cumulative bracing force for the CFS chord studs on the compression side of the shear wall determined using the compression force of the lesser of (1) load from the seismic load combinations with the overstrength factor, Ω_0, or (2) the expected strength of the shear wall with just the gravity load from that same load combination on the intermediate studs for half the length of the shear wall (conservatively, as the rigid-body assumption would have only axial compression on the chord studs).

2. The cumulative bracing force on all the CFS chord and intermediate studs along the entire shear wall based on the LRFD gravity-load combinations.

The Option 3 shear wall in the design example is 25 feet long with 15 intermediate CFS studs at 16 inches on center. The first-floor chord-stud assembly has a pack of five chord studs on each side of the continuous rod tie-down (ten chord studs total) with an overall width of 29 inches on each end of the shear wall. The first-floor shear wall CFS studs are mechanically braced at the third points using continuous horizontal CFS straps on each face of the wall. The two cases noted above are checked for the horizontal CFS stud strap bracing design utilizing a vertical bracing system of CFS strongback studs turned flat on each face of the wall (see Figure 3-28) spaced uniformly along the length of the shear wall to transfer the wall-stud horizontal bracing forces to the floor level above and below the wall. Flat-strap bracing requires access to both sides of the wall and may cause "bump outs" in the wall sheathing, so bridging through the stud punchouts may be a more desirable stud bracing method.

Case 1: Determining CFS Stud Compressive Axial Load Using Seismic Load Combinations with Ω_0

For Case 1, the amplified LRFD axial load for the ten 600S200-68(50) by 9-foot-tall CFS chord stud pack is 91.3 kips per Table 3-38, and the intermediate CFS wall studs have an LRFD axial load of 2.68 kips [2011 plf × 16-inch spacing/(12 inches/foot)].

a. Strap-to-stud connection design force

$$P_{br,2\ chord} = 0.02P = 0.02(91.3\ \text{kips}/10\ \text{chords studs})$$
$$= 0.183\ \text{kips}/2\ \text{straps (one on each side of stud)} = 0.092\ \text{kips}$$
$$P_{br,2\ inter} = 0.02P = 0.02(2.68\ \text{kips}) = 0.054\ \text{kips}/2\ \text{straps (one on each side of stud)} = 0.027\ \text{kips}$$

Attach the CFS strap to the CFS stud flange with a #8 self-tapping screw connection having an LRFD shear strength of 114 pounds at the individual chord studs and 27 pounds at the intermediate studs. Strap thickness does not have to be the same thickness as the wall stud.

b. Strongback bracing system design force

$$P_{anch} = (0.092\ \text{kips} \times 10\ \text{chord studs}) + (0.027\ \text{kips} \times 8\ \text{intermediate studs in half of shear wall})$$
$$= 1.136\ \text{kips}$$

Try four pairs of 800S162-54(50) by 9-foot-tall CFS strongback studs starting with the first pair near the chord stud packs on each end of the wall and then equally spaced along the length of the wall between the chord studs and on each side of the stud wall resisting the load from the strap bracing. The strongback studs are designed unbraced for their full height and are attached with CFS clip angles at the top and bottom tracks. Because strap bracing only works in tension, the engineer must take special care in determining anchorage locations to ensure there is an adequate load path for bracing forces acting in either direction along the length of the wall.

$$P_{anch\ sb} = 1.136\ \text{kips}/4\ \text{strongback stud locations along wall length}$$
$$= 0.284\ \text{kips at a 3-foot and 6-foot height along each 9-foot-tall CFS strongback stud}$$

Attach the CFS strap to the CFS strongback web with a #8 self-tapping screw connection having an LRFD shear strength of 284 pounds. Use a minimum of two screws for the strap connection to the strongback web. Use CFS clip angles with an LRFD shear strength of 284 pounds to attach the strongback to the top and bottom tracks of the shear wall. Use a minimum of two screws or other appropriate fastener in each leg of the CFS clip angle (example: expansion anchors in a concrete podium).

The horizontal CFS straps shall be designed for a minimum LRFD load of 284 pounds. The CFS strap width and thickness is sized to resist the required tension load, but does not have to be the same thickness as the shear wall CFS framing members as long as it is not less than the minimum structural thickness of 33 mils. Typically, the strap widths used by designers are 1½ to 2 inches wide to accommodate the minimum two-screw attachment to the vertical bracing system framing member. For this design example, a 1½-inch-wide by 33-mil (20 ga) strap ($F_y = 33$ ksi) could be used with two #8 self-tapping screws for the attachment to the CFS strongback.

The four pairs of 800S162-54(50) CFS strongback studs, with point loads at third points along their height from the strap bracing, starting with the first pair near the chord-stud packs and then spaced equally along the shear wall length, are determined to be adequate in flexure using commercially available CFS design software. This example assumes that the strongback studs are not axially loaded. If a diagonal flat-strap anchorage method is used instead of strongbacks, such as strap "X" bracing (Figure 3-29), then the wall stud that the flat diagonal strap attaches to must also be checked for the additional axial load from the diagonal flat strap.

Case 2: Determining CFS Stud Compressive Axial Load Using Gravity Load Combinations

For Case 2, the LRFD axial load for each of the CFS chord studs is 0.486 kips [2011 plf × (29 inches/(12 inches/foot))/10 chord studs] and 2.681 kips for each of the intermediate CFS wall studs [(2011 plf × 16-inch spacing)/(12 inches/foot)]. The studs are braced with steel-strap bracing on each side of the studs at third points (two strap braces at 3 feet on center) with CFS stud strongbacks, as shown in Figure 3-28.

a. Strap-to-stud design force

$$P_{br,2\text{ chord}} \quad = 0.02P = 0.02(0.486 \text{ kips}) = 0.010 \text{ kips/two straps (one on each side of stud)}$$
$$= 0.005 \text{ kips}$$

$$P_{br,2\text{ intermediate}} = 0.02P = 0.02(2.681 \text{ kips}) = 0.054 \text{ kips/two straps (one on each side of stud)}$$
$$= 0.027 \text{ kips}$$

Attach the CFS strap to the CFS stud flange with a #8 self-tapping screw connection having an LRFD shear strength of 5 pounds at the individual chord studs and 27 pounds at the intermediate studs.

b. Strongback bracing system design force

$$P_{anch} = (0.005 \text{ kips} \times 20 \text{ chord studs}) + (0.027 \text{ kips} \times 15 \text{ intermediate studs}) = 0.505 \text{ kips}$$

Try two pairs of 800S162-54(50) by 9-foot-tall CFS strongback studs starting with the first pair near the chord stud packs on each end of the wall and then equally spaced along the length of the wall and on each side of the stud wall resisting the load from the strap bracing. The strongback studs are designed unbraced for their full height and are attached with CFS clip angles at the top and bottom tracks. Because strap bracing only works in tension, the engineer must take special care in determining anchorage locations to ensure there is an adequate load path for bracing forces acting in either direction along the length of the wall.

$$P_{anch\ sb} = 0.505 \text{ kips/2 strongback stud locations along wall length}$$
$$= 0.253 \text{ kips at a 3-foot and 6-foot height along each 9-foot-tall CFS strongback stud}$$

Attach the CFS strap to the CFS strongback web with a #8 self-tapping screw connection having a LRFD shear strength of 253 pounds. Use a minimum of two screws for the strap connection to the strongback web. Use CFS clip angles with an LRFD shear strength of 253 pounds to attach the strongback to the top and bottom tracks of the shear wall. Use a minimum of two screws or other appropriate fastener (example: expansion anchors into a concrete podium) in each leg of the CFS clip angle. The CFS straps shall be designed for a minimum LRFD tension load of 253 pounds.

The two pairs of 800S162-54(50) CFS strongback studs, with point loads at third points along their height from the strap bracing, starting with the first pair near the chord stud packs and then spaced equally along the shear wall length, are determined to be adequate in flexure using commercially available CFS design software.

Since Case 2 requires fewer strongbacks than Case 1, the Case 1 bracing design using the seismic load combinations governs, and four pairs of 800S162-54(50) CFS strongback studs are required. The spacing of these strongbacks typically ranges between 6 to 16 feet on center along the length of the stud wall and is highly dependent on the floor system gravity loads as well as the resulting overturning axial loads imposed on the chord-stud assemblies at the end of the shear walls. In multistory buildings, the strongback spacing will typically get closer together from the upper-most floor level to the lowest floor level. Where strongback spacing exceeds 8 feet on center, full-depth stud bridging blocks should be provided at not more than 8 feet on center spacing for the continuous CFS strap-bracing attachments. Where CFS horizontal bracing straps are to be spliced, it is preferable to splice the straps on full-depth stud bridging between the wall studs than on the vertical bracing system strongbacks.

Other anchorage solutions for the stud bracing might work as well, such as anchoring into a cross wall [where the wall studs, in-wall posts, columns, or other wall material (example: concrete or CMU wall) are designed for the strap-bracing force] or using diagonal strap bracing, taking the bracing force down to the bottom track from the lowest bracing line and up to the top track from the highest bracing line. This is discussed further in Section 14.1.

Where tall sheathed shear walls are used (example: over 10 feet tall), the engineer should consider the vertical spacing of continuous strap bracing with the layout of the sheathing so it will not be used as edge blocking for the wall sheathing. This includes considering any horizontal stagger of sheathing panel edges. Separate CFS flat-strap blocking should be used for sheathing edge screwing and not combined with the continuous horizontal CFS straps used to brace CFS stud flanges. The author recommends a note be placed on the structural drawings that states something like the following:

> The layout of the shear wall sheathing shall be such that any CFS flat-strap blocking for either the sheathing edge screwing or for any items attached to the wall surface shall be placed separate from the CFS stud wall continuous strap bracing. Where a conflict between blocking and CFS stud wall continuous strap bracing placement occurs, contact the structural engineer for direction.

The assumption for CFS stud walls less than 10 feet tall is that the sheathing shall be placed vertically so no horizontal CFS flat-strap blocking is required since sheathing edges will be attached directly to the CFS studs (vertical panel edges), bottom track, and top track (horizontal panel edges).

The designer is also reminded that a structural note needs to be placed on the engineering construction drawings stating something like the following:

> All cold-formed-steel (CFS) stud wall strap bracing and bridging shall be installed and adequately anchored per details shown on plans prior to applying any axial loads to the CFS studs resulting from the placement of the floor/roof framing level immediately above the CFS studs. Shear wall sheathing shall be installed prior to placing of any floor toppings over the floor sheathing at the floor level immediately supported by the CFS studs and also before placement of the next immediate floor/roof level framing above being supported on CFS stud walls, unless the building structure is otherwise adequately laterally braced by the contractor, until the installation of all sheathed shear walls and any other lateral-resisting systems are completed.

Chord Stud Alignment between Floors

In this design example, the third-floor chord-stud assembly width includes the CFS flange width (1⅝ inches) of the cripple studs under the bridge block, as the cripple studs are on either side of the 3-inch gap width under the bridge block. The inside face of the chord-stud assembly using a 9-inch gap at the first and second floors below aligns almost directly with the inside face of the chord studs at the third floor where the gap at the third floor, excluding the cripple studs, is 9.5 inches; see Figure 3-22. Since the floors are wood framed, the depth of the wood rim joist or blocking sitting on the wall can be used to horizontally transition axial loads resulting from any minor alignment offsets between chord studs above the floor line to the chord studs below the floor line. If CFS floor framing was used, it would be more important to have the chord studs aligning above and below the floor line, and this might change the number of required chord studs for alignment between floors. Also a larger bearing plate extending across all the CFS chord studs would probably be required.

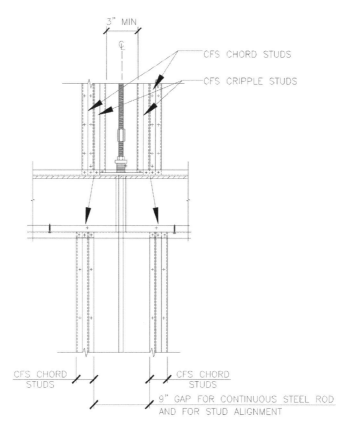

Figure 3-22. Chord stud alignment

Location Check of Continuous Rod Tie-Down from End of Shear Wall

As a last check, the engineer reviews the original assumption of the continuous rod tie-down location from the end of the shear wall. The assumption used in the Option 3 shear wall was 12 inches from the end of the wall. Table 3-40 shows the comparison.

Table 3-40. Option 3 shear wall: continuous tie-down rod location check from end of wall

Level	Chord-Stud Assembly Width, W (in)	Shear Wall End Distance, W/2 (in)	Corrected End Distance (in)	Original Assumption (in)
3rd Floor	16	8.0	14.5	12
2nd Floor	21	10.5	14.5	12
1st Floor	29	14.5	14.5	12

1. Since the continuous rod tie-down is to be installed vertically with no offsets, the first-floor location of the continuous rod tie-down from the end of the shear wall dictates the location at the higher floor levels, but the bridge block may dictate the size of the chord stud pack gap width.

2. W = individual chord stud flange width + gap (9 inches per Figure 3-22)

In this design example, at the third- and second-floor levels, the location of the continuous rod tie-down from the end of the wall is less than the original assumption. At the first-floor level, the assumption was slightly off (14.5 in > 12 in).

1. When the actual continuous rod tie-down location is less than the assumed distance from the end of the shear wall, this is conservative, since the uplift design forces are less than the calculated design force.

2. If the end distance is greater than the original assumption, then the designer must determine if the uplift forces need to be recalculated. In this design example, the change in distance between the centerline of the tie rods is minimal:

   25 ft − 2(14.5 in/12) = 22.58 ft

   23 ft/22.58 ft = 1.019   The change is less than 2 percent, so it is deemed acceptable and does not have to be recalculated.

   Since the rod is centered in the largest chord pack, and the rod stacks from floor to floor, the corrected end distance is now 14½ inches.

Author's Discussion

If the end distance to the continuous rod tie-down is 6 inches or greater from the end of the shear wall than the original assumption, and the shear wall aspect ratio is 1:1 or greater, then perhaps the uplift force should be recalculated. This depends on the overall length of the shear wall and whether the shear wall design forces are calculated using just a tributary-area diaphragm analysis, a rigid-diaphragm analysis, or an envelope procedure (comparison between tributary area and rigid diaphragm). A rigid-diaphragm analysis depends on the shear wall stiffness and is directly impacted by the distance between continuous rod tie-down/chord-stud assemblies at the ends of the shear wall. Using a shear wall length longer or shorter than the design assumptions will impact the accuracy of the rigid-diaphragm analysis, resulting in a redistribution of seismic design forces between shear walls.

If the actual continuous rod tie-down location is less than 6 inches beyond the original assumption from the end of the shear wall to the continuous rod tie-down, and the shear wall aspect ratio is less than 1:1, this probably will not result in a large increase in uplift and compression design forces. Most likely there is enough reserve capacity in the chord-stud assembly and continuous rod tie-down to be able to support the slightly increased design forces resulting from a shift of 6 inches or less from the original assumed location. Similarly, if the continuous rod tie-down location is less than the original assumption from the end of the shear wall by 6 inches or less, and the shear wall aspect ratio is less than 1:1, the uplift and compression design forces should be less and not impact the design of the chord-stud assembly and continuous rod tie-down.

12.7 BRIDGE BLOCK AND CHORD-STUD ASSEMBLIES

Bridge Block

At the third-floor wood bridge block, shown in Figure 3-23, two CFS cripple studs under the bridge block and on each side of the continuous rod (four total) are attached to the CFS chord studs and transfer the third-floor shear wall overturning uplift force from the chord studs to the bridge block. The two full-height CFS chord studs on each side of the bridge block (four total) are also used to resist the third-floor shear wall overturning compressive axial load. In lieu of a wood bridge block, a steel HSS section or a steel channel (turned flat) could be designed to be used as the bridge block.

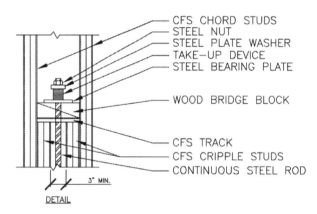

Figure 3-23. Chord-stud assembly at wood bridge block

The bridge block needs to be the same width as the CFS cripple studs under the bridge block for uplift-force transfer. If it is not, then a filler plate the same depth as the CFS cripples needs to be provided between the bridge block and the CFS track into which the CFS cripple studs frame. The bridge block also needs to be stiff enough to uniformly transfer the uplift loads to the steel bearing plate on the top of the bridge block.

In the case of a wood bridge block (spanning between CFS cripple studs), the depth of the block needs to be checked for shear just as would be done for a wood beam. As a guideline, the depth of the wood bridge block should be not less than half the gap distance of the chord-stud assembly (clear distance between the inside face of the chord studs). This helps to assure a 1:1 slope for uplift-force transfer from the underside of the wood bridge block to the steel bearing plate on the bridge block. If a steel bridge block is used, then deflection of the steel bridge block end relative to the continuous rod tie-down should be evaluated. This generally is not a problem unless a very thin steel plate is used for the bridge block.

Sheathing Attachment at Bridge Block, Cripple Studs, and Chord Studs

There are multiple ways to accomplish the uplift-force transfer from the wall sheathing to the bridge block through the cripple studs and adjacent chord studs. The one detail common to all of the uplift-force transfer methods is to have the CFS chord stud directly adjacent to each end of the bridge block attached to the first CFS cripple stud under the bridge block. This specific connection detail between the chord stud and cripple stud provides the load path for transferring wall uplift forces to the cripple studs. The required number of sheathing edge fasteners are divided equally into the chord studs, not exceeding 12 inches on center, connecting the wall sheathing to the chord studs, to resist the required design uplift force and downward compression force. The designer may use field screw spacing of 12 inches on center for the cripple studs. There are various sheathing-fastener placement configuration options that designers can use, but all still require investigation to determine the appropriate force transfer design between the chord studs and cripple studs adjacent to the end of the bridge block. Typically, the design-force transfer between the chord studs and cripple studs is accomplished using screws or welds. The wall sheathing should not be attached to bridge blocks because wood blocks could shrink and steel blocks restrain vertical movement.

Chord Stud and Cripple Stud Orientation

One CFS chord stud-to-cripple stud connection option would be to have the CFS chord stud directly adjacent to the end of the bridge block oriented so its web could be screwed to the web of the CFS cripple stud under the wood bridge block. If this option was used, the CFS chord studs and the CFS cripple-stud flanges would be attached with intermittent welds to form a box shape, but the screw connection between the webs of the CFS chords and the CFS cripple studs would need to be completed prior to welding to make the box shapes. The engineer might decide to use an all-welded connection approach with just intermittent welds on either side of the chord studs to the cripple studs rather than screw them together. Figure 3-24 shows an all-welded chord and cripple stud arrangement with individual chords and cripple studs welded toe-to-toe and the back of the chord stud box welded to the back of the cripple stud box.

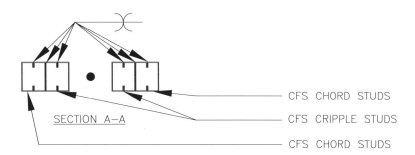

Figure 3-24. Chord and cripple studs oriented toe-to-toe (plan view)

Another CFS chord stud-to-cripple stud connection option would be to have the CFS chord studs oriented back-to-back using screws or welds to attach them together and the CFS cripple studs oriented back-to-back using screws or welds to attach them together. Then the CFS chord studs would be attached to the CFS cripple studs with intermittent welds to the flanges between the CFS chord studs and the cripple studs.

Steel Bearing Plate at Floor Line

The steel bearing plate that is in the CFS bottom track of the third-floor shear wall, which is used to resist the overturning uplift force from the second-floor shear wall below, is also designed to resist the overturning compressive force from the third-floor shear wall. The third-floor CFS chord studs' nominal compressive strength and the bearing strength of the bottom track and wood floor system are to be equal or greater than the overturning amplified seismic compressive load. The CFS-framed shear wall CFS chord studs align from floor to floor, centered on the continuous rod tie-down. The CFS chord studs may transfer some of the overturning compressive force to the cripple studs below the bridge block through the screw connection or welded connection, and this is taken through the steel bearing plate in the third-floor CFS bottom track and the wood floor system, so CFS chord studs directly below the third-floor CFS cripple studs do not need to be added to the shear wall system below. The third-floor CFS cripple studs might also be cut short so they only transfer the overturning uplift force from the CFS chord studs to the wood bridge block.

Wall Bridge Block

The wood bridge block for uplift is used in the wall at the third floor since a roof-drag, metal-plate-connected wood truss will be connected to the shear wall double top plate/top track to transfer roof lateral forces to the shear wall. If the uplift continuous rod tie-down system bearing plate was placed on the top of the shear wall double plate, it would likely interfere with the roof-drag metal-plate-connected wood-truss connection. The bridge block is generally located between one-half to about two-thirds of the wall height above the floor level.

Author's Discussion

The vertical boundary element (chord-stud assembly) at each end of the shear wall consists of several CFS studs. The CFS studs should be placed symmetrically on each side of the continuous rod. Each of the individual chord studs shall be screwed to the shear wall sheathing. The screwing of the shear wall sheathing to the chord studs does not have to be the same as for the other CFS framing members of the shear wall at the wood structural panel edges.

> Example: The second floor has six CFS chord studs. The second-floor shear wall wood structural panel sheathing has screws at 3 inches on center. Because there is more than one member in the chord-stud assembly, the edge screws may be divided equally between them; however, the edge spacing should not exceed 12 inches on center on any of the individual chord or intermediate studs.
>
> 3-inches-on-center edge-screw spacing × 6 chord studs = 18-inches-on-center edge-screw spacing at each chord stud. However, the designer should not exceed 12-inches-on-center spacing.

This is a savings in time and material since the wall framer does not have to install screws at 3 inches on center to each individual chord stud of the chord-stud assembly (boundary member).

Where a bridge block is used, each of the individual chord studs shall be screwed to the shear wall sheathing with edge screws staggered equally between them. Typically, the bridge block CFS cripple studs are not screwed to the shear wall sheathing with edge screws, but with field screws at 12 inches on center. In this case, the total uplift force is transferred from the welded or screwed attachment of the CFS chord studs to the CFS cripple studs below the bridge block, which then bear on the underside of the bridge block. See Figure 3-20 for CFS cripple and chord-stud attachments.

However, if the CFS chord studs-to-cripple studs connections are not designed to transfer the entire uplift load from the chord studs as discussed previously, then the cripple studs need to have shear wall sheathing edge screws adequate to transfer the force not being transferred by the chord studs. This might occur if the engineer considers that only the individual chord stud immediately adjacent to each end of the bridge block will transfer only a portion of the overturning uplift force to the adjacent cripple stud.

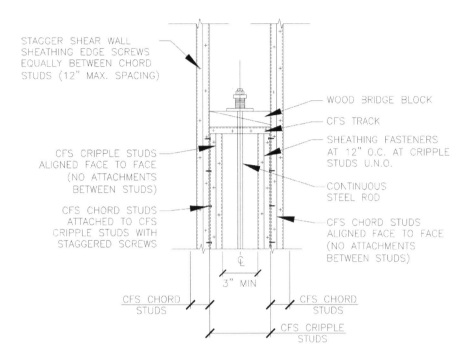

Figure 3-25. Wood bridge block at third-floor chord-stud assembly

Chord-Stud Assembly at Bridge Block; Sheathing-Screw Uplift Force Transfer Examples

Example 1: The third-floor uplift bridge block uses the chord-stud sheathing edge-screw design but without edge screws to the cripple studs, instead using field screws to the cripple studs under the bridge block.

> Uplift = 10,371 lb (LRFD amplified force)
>
> Stud height to wall rim joist = 11 ft − 1 ft = 10 ft
>
> Shear per foot of stud height = 10,371/10 = 1037 lb/ft
>
> Shear per foot of height per stud = 1037/4 chord studs = 260 lb
>
> #8 screws at 6 inches on center in plywood sheathing (nominal strength) = 890 lb
>
> 890 lb > 260 lb

However, shear wall edge fasteners are divided equally between chord studs in shear walls using continuous rod tie-down systems (but they should not exceed 12 inches on center). The third-floor shear wall uses #8 screws at 6 inches on center, and there are four chord studs.

> 6-inches-on-center edge-screw spacing × 4 chord studs = 24-inches-on-center edge-screw spacing at each chord stud. However, the designer must not exceed spacing of 12 inches on center.

Use #8 screws at 6 inches on center for general wall-sheathing edge screwing, except use 12 inches on center to each of the chord compression studs on each side of the bridge block. Stagger the screws between adjacent chord studs. Attach sheathing to cripple studs using field spacing of 12 inches on center.

Load Transfer between the Chord Stud and the Cripple Stud

Use #8 screw attachments between the 54-mil CFS chord stud web and the 54-mil CFS cripple stud web for uplift force transfer to the bridge block:

> Transfer force = 10,371/2 chord stud packs = 5186 lb/chord pack
>
> #8 screw capacity (ϕP_{ss}) = 0.5 × 1278 = 639 lb   (from Table 3-40)
>
> $(\phi P_{ss}) < (\phi P_{ns})$ for bearing and tilting
>
> See Section 12.8 for screw design information.
>
> Quantity of #8 screws = 5186/639 = 8.1 screws; therefore, use eight #8 screws minimum.
> #8 screw spacing = (3.67 ft × 12)/((8/2 rows) − 1) = 14.68 in > 12 in
> Since the required screw spacing is greater than 12 inches, it is recommended to not exceed 12-inch spacing.
>
> Use two rows of #8 screws at 12 inches on center.

Load Transfer between Individual Chord Studs and Individual Cripple Studs

> The chord studs must be designed to transfer 10,371/4 = 2593 pounds between them using welds, and the pairs of cripple studs at each end of the bridge block also need to be designed to transfer 5186/2 cripples = 2593 pounds between them using welds. Instead of screwing the one chord stud to the one cripple stud, it may be easier for the fabricator to shop weld the chord stud to the cripple stud and bring it out as one assembly, since the welding between individual chord studs (face to face) and cripple studs (face to face) will likely be done in the shop.

Example 2: At the third-floor uplift bridge block, the chord-stud sheathing edge-screw design includes the edge screws to the shorter cripple studs under the bridge block. Chord and cripple studs are not attached together except for a single chord stud web screwed to a single cripple stud web at each end of the bridge block (see Figure 3-25).

> Uplift = 10,371 lb (LRFD amplified force). The bridge block is assumed to be 10 inches deep.
>
> The stud height to the underside of the bridge block = 4.5 ft − 10 in = 3 ft 8 in = 3.67 ft
>
> The uplift above the bottom of the bridge block = 10,371 × [(10 ft − 3.67 ft)/10 ft] = 6565 lb
>
> The shear per foot of stud height above the bottom of the bridge block = 6565/(10 ft − 3.67 ft)
> $\qquad\qquad\qquad$ = 1037 lb/ft
>
> The shear per foot of chord stud above the bottom of the bridge block = 1037/(2 chord studs)
> $\qquad\qquad\qquad$ = 519 lb/ft
>
> The uplift below the bottom of the bridge block = 10,371 − 6565 = 3806 lb
>
> The shear per foot of stud height below the bridge block = 3806/3.67 = 1037 lb/ft
>
> The shear per foot of chord stud/cripple height below the bottom of the bridge block:
>
> Shear = 1037/(4 cripple studs + 2 chord studs) = 173 lb
>
> #8 screws at 6 inches on center in plywood sheathing (nominal strength) = 890 lb
>
> #8 screws at 4 inches on center in plywood sheathing (nominal strength) = 1330 lb

Summary with screws at 6 inches on center: 890 lb > 519 lb > 173 lb

with screws at 4 inches on center: 1330 lb > 1037 lb

4-inch-on-center edge-screw spacing (4 cripple studs) = 16-inch-on-center edge spacing

16 inches on center > 12-inch-on-center spacing; therefore, use 12 inches on center.

> Use #8 screws at 6 inches on center to all chord studs since individual chords studs are not interconnected by screws or welds, and use #8 screws at 12 inches on center to the individual cripple studs below the bridge block.

Load Transfer between the Chord Stud and the Cripple Stud

> #8 screw attachments between the 54-mil chord stud web and the 54-mil cripple stud web for uplift force transfer:
>
> Transfer force = $(519 \times 6.33 \text{ ft}) + (173 \times 3.67 \text{ ft}) = 3921$ lb
>
> #8 Screw capacity $(\phi P_{ss}) = 0.5 \times 1278 = 639$ lb (from Table 3-40)
>
> $(\phi P_{ss}) < (\phi P_{ns})$ for bearing and tilting
>
> See Section 12.8 for screw design information.
>
> Quantity of #8 screws = $3921/639 = 6.1$ screws; therefore, use six #8 screws minimum
>
> #8 screw spacing = $(3.67 \text{ ft} \times 12)/(6 - 1) = 8.8$ in
>
> Use #8 screws at 8 inches on center, staggered.

Wood Bridge Block Horizontal Shear and Bending Check

The wood bridge block must also be designed. The bridge block was previously checked for bearing when the engineer was designing the steel bearing plate. The bridge block also needs to be checked for horizontal shear and bending. ASD is used for evaluating the bridge block. C_D is conservatively taken as 1.0.

> Bridge length = $(4 \times 1.625) + 3$-inch gap around continuous rod = 9.5 in
>
> Bridge reaction (simple beam): $R = (10,371 \times 0.7)/2 = 3630$ lb
>
> Bridge flexure (simple beam): $M = PL/4 = (10,371 \times 0.7)(9.5)/4 = 17,242$ in-lb
>
> Wood area required = $1.5(3630)/170 = 32.03 \text{ in}^2 < 41.25 \text{ in}^2 = 6 \times 8$
>
> Wood $S_x = 17,242/1350 = 12.77 \text{ in}^3 < 51.56 \text{ in}^3 = 6 \times 8$
>
> Use a 6×8 bridge block minimum (Douglas Fir-Larch #1, $F_b = 1350$ psi, $F_v = 170$ psi).

12.8 SHEAR TRANSFER

The shear transfer between floor levels utilizes screws from the CFS wall tracks to the wood framing members (floor sheathing and floor wood framing members), as shown in Figure 3-26.

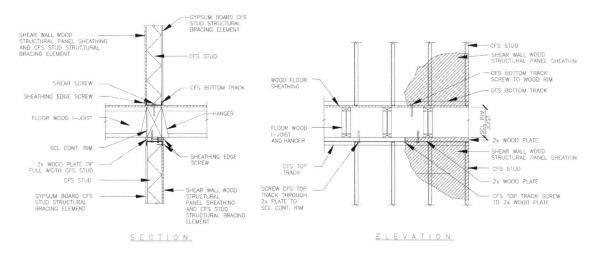

Figure 3-26. Shear transfer through wood floor framing

The shear transfer at the podium uses anchor bolts embedded into concrete with standard cut washers over the CFS track web. While standard cut washers may be used for the shear anchor bolts, some designers use plate washers in case the shear anchor bolt holes are oversized or if they want to weld the plate washer to the CFS track web. The design forces for the Option 3 shear wall are used for this design example.

Just as occurs in lumber, the design values for screws and bolts are limited by steel sheet sheathing edge, end, and spacing distances. The location of the screws and bolts will be such that they are not controlled by these minimum distances.

Screw Selection: AWC NDS Section 12.3 Reference Lateral Design Values
             (Tables 12.3.1.A, 12.3.1.B, 12M)

NDS Section 12.1.5.3 requires lead holes for wood screws loaded laterally: "For G ≤ 0.6 (see Table 12.3.3A), the part of the lead hole receiving the shank shall be about ⅞ the diameter of the shank and that receiving the threaded portion shall be about ⅞ the diameter of the screw at the root of the thread." Therefore, the designer should use a lag screw or wood screw installed through predrilled holes in the CFS track-to-wood connection if a self-drilling tapping screw has a drill tip that drills a larger than ⅞-root diameter hole in the wood. If the lead hole is too large, the lag screw or wood screw threads do not have as much "bite," so the lateral values would be some reduced value, and the withdrawal could be significantly less than the lag screw or wood screw design value.

To make the shear connection more economical between floor levels and reduce the number of required screws, larger #12 screws should be used instead of #8 screws. Typically, the screws are installed in two parallel rows in the bottom track of the CFS stud shear wall into the wood floor sheathing and framing. AWC NDS Table 12M does not provide #12 screw design values (Z) for 0.048-inch or 0.060-inch-thick material, but does have #12 screw design values (Z) for 0.075-inch (14 gauge) material of 147 pounds for Douglas Fir-Larch.

The #12 screw shear design values will therefore be calculated for use with CFS 54-mil framing thickness material (16 gauge, 0.0566 inch thick) attached to wood framing.

Screw design values

1. CFS Connections (AISI S100 Section J4 Screw Connections)

Screw notations:

d = nominal screw diameter

d_h = screw head diameter

T_1 = thickness of material under screw head or washer

T_2 = thickness of material not in contact with screw head or washer

F_{u1} = tensile strength of member in contact with screw head or washer

F_{u2} = tensile strength of member not in contact with screw head or washer

Screw spacing:

Minimum screw spacing = $3d$	AISI S100 §J4.1
Minimum screw edge and end distance = $3d$	AISI S240 §B1.5.1.3
(force perpendicular to edge)	
Minimum screw edge and end distance = $1.5d$	AISI S100 §J4.2, S240 §B1.5.1.3
(force parallel to edge)	

Shear (AISI S100 Section J4.3)

A. Connection Shear—Limited by Tilting and Bearing (P_{ns})   **AISI S100 §J4.3.1**

The designer must determine which of two sets of limit state equations, based on the thickness of the two materials (T_1, T_2) being joined by the screw, is to be used to determine the screw nominal shear capacity. Shear transfer connection design materials are as follows:

T_1 = track material thickness: 54 mils = 0.0566 in (F_y = 50 ksi, F_u = 65 ksi)
Tracks are to match shear wall stud material thickness and properties.

T_2 = plywood sheathing: ¾ in
#12 screw diameter: shank = 0.216 in, head diameter = 0.340 in

Screw limit state equations:

$T_2/T_1 = 0.75/0.0566 = 13.3 > 2.5$

$T_2/T_1 < 1.0$ (P_{ns} = smallest of the three equations)

1. Tilting:	$P_{ns} = 4.2(t_2^3 d)^{1/2} F_{u2}$	AISI S100 §J4.3.1-1
2. Bearing:	$P_{ns} = 2.7 t_1 d F_{u1}$	AISI S100 §J4.3.1-2
3. Bearing:	$P_{ns} = 2.7 t_2 d F_{u2}$	AISI S100 §J4.3.1-3

$T_2/T_1 > 2.5$ (P_{ns} = smallest of the two equations) . . . governs

1. Tilting:	Not applicable	
2. Bearing:	$P_{ns} = 2.7 t_1 d F_{u1} = 2.7(0.0566)(0.216)(65,000)$	AISI S100 §J4.3.1-4
	$= 2146$ lb	
3. Bearing:	$P_{ns} = 2.7 t_2 d F_{u2}$ = Not applicable for wood	AISI S100 §J4.3.1-5

LRFD = ϕP_{ns} = (0.5)(2146) = 1073 lb
ASD = P_{ns}/Ω = (2145/3.0) = 715 lb

B. Screw Shear (P_{ss})   **AISI S100 §J4.3.2**

The average screw shear values (P_{ss}) are taken from CFSEI Technical Note F701-12, which provides an average screw shear value based on review of several manufacturers' test reports. The nominal screws shear values are shown in Table 3-41. Higher screw shear values are possible based on the designer specifying screws that are evaluated in an evaluation report in accordance with publically developed and publically available acceptance or evaluation criteria.

Table 3-41. Nominal screw shear values (P_{ss}) from CFSEI Technical Note F701-12

Screw Size	Nominal	LRFD ($\phi = 0.5$)	ASD ($\Omega = 3.0$)
	P_{ss} (lb)	ϕP_{ss} (lb)	P_{ss}/Ω (lb)
#8	1278	639	426
#10	1644	822	548
#12	2330	1165	777
¼″	3048	1524	1016

C. Shear Rupture (V_n) if Screw Pulls toward Limiting Edge   **AISI S100 §J6.1**

$$V_n = 0.6 F_u A_{nv}$$ AISI S100 Eq J6.1-1

For a connection where the screw pulls through the steel toward the limiting edge:

$$A_{nv} = 2nte_{net}$$ AISI S100 Eq J6.1-2

   n = number of screws along critical cross-section (assume 1 screw)

   t = base steel thickness

   e_{net} = clear distance from end of member and edge of screw hole (assume 3 in)

$$A_{nv} = 2(1)(0.0566)[(3)(0.216)] = 0.07335 \text{ in}^2$$

$$V_n = 0.6(65,000)(0.07335) = 2861 \text{ lb}$$

$$\text{LRFD} = \varphi V_n = (0.5)(2861) = 1431 \text{ lb}$$

$$\text{ASD} = V_n/\Omega = (2861/3.0) = 954 \text{ lb}$$

Controlling Screw Value (in CFS) for This Design Example

   ASD: #12 screw shear value in 54-mil (16 ga) track = 715 lb (P_{ns}) < 777 lb = P_{ss}

   LRFD: #12 screw shear value in 54-mil (16 ga) track = 1073 lb (P_{ns}) < 1165 lb = P_{ss}

2. Wood (AWC NDS) and Wood Member with Steel Side Member (ASD and LRFD)

The wood to steel single shear lateral design values are determined from the AWC *National Design Specification for Wood Construction* (NDS) using a steel side member on one side.

Screw size: #12 (AWC NDS Section 12.3.7.1)

> Nominal diameter $D = 0.216$ in
>
> Root diameter $D_r = 0.171$ in
>
> Required screw length: Full design shear $(Z) = 10d$ (only when using tabulated values)
> Minimum design value $(Z) = 6d = 0.6V$ (NDS Section 12.1.5.6)
>
> Length required   = track thickness + sheathing thickness + receiving member penetration
> $= 0.0566 + 0.75 + (10)(0.171) = 2.517$ in
> Note: Use 10d for penetration as a starting design estimate. Since calculating the capacity, one could use a shallower penetration, say 2.5 or 2.0 inches. Use a #12 × 3.0-in-long screw minimum > 2.517 inches.

Side member thickness: CFS track (Grade 50): 54 mil (0.0566 in)
Wood member (Douglas Fir-Larch): thickness not less than screw length

AISI S201 Table B2-1:   CFS track design thickness = 0.0566 in
(Minimum base steel thickness = 0.0538 in)

AWC NDS Table12M:

> Since the shear wall design requires the use of 16 gauge ASTM A653, ($F_y = 50$ ksi) material, and AWC NDS Table 12M design values (Z) are based on the steel side member material being ASTM A653, ($F_y = 33$ ksi), which is different from the CFS track being used in this design example, lateral design values will have to be calculated using NDS yield equations.
>
> The dowel bearing strength is derived from AWC Technical Report 12, Table A1 and is equal to $2.2F_u/1.6$.
>
> Dowel bearing strength (F_e):
>
>> Associated with ASTM A653, $F_y = 33$ ksi, $F_u = 45$ ksi, is established as being 61,850 psi
>>
>> Associated with ASTM A653, $F_y = 50$ ksi, $F_u = 65$ ksi, is established as being 89,375 psi
>
> The screw bending yield strength, F_{yb}, is dependent on the diameter of the screw. As the screw diameter becomes smaller, the bending yield strength typically increases. NDS Table 12M footnotes provide minimum screw bending yield strengths ranging from $F_{yb} = 70,000$ psi for screws around ¼-inch diameter up to 100,000 psi for screws that are around ⅛-inch diameter. Higher screw bending yield strengths are possible by using proprietary screws that have product evaluation reports (example: ICC, IAPMO) by an ANSI-accredited product certification company that could allow for higher screw capacities. See NDS Appendix E and AWC Technical Report 12 for more information on dowel bearing strength and bending yield strength.

#12 Screw Z values in 54-mils CFS (16-gauge or 0.0566-inch design thickness)

> #12 screw in 0.0566-mils (16-gauge) CFS ($F_y = 50$ ksi)
>
> #12 screw length = 3.0-inch-long screw

AWC NDS Wood Screw Lateral Design Values

D_r = screw root diameter = 0.171 in   T12.3.1A, §12.3.7.1

l_s = bearing length: side member = 0.0566 in   T12.3.1A

l_m = bearing length = 3.0 − 0.75 − 0.0566 = 2.19   T12.3.1A

F_{em} = main member dowel bearing strength = 4650 psi (Douglas Fir-Larch: G = 0.50)   T12.3.3

F_{es} = side member dowel bearing strength = 89,375 psi (ASTM A653, Grade 50)

F_{yb} = dowel bending yield strength (0.177 < D ≤ 0.236) = 80,000 psi (used)   T12M Footnote 2
 = dowel bending yield strength (0.142 < D ≤ 0.177) = 90,000 psi

R_d = reduction term = K_D = 10D + 0.5 = 10(0.216) + 0.5 = 2.66   T12.3.1B

$R_e = F_{em}/F_{es}$ = 4650/89,375 = 0.0520   T12.3.1A

$R_t = l_m/l_s$ = 2.19/0.0566 = 38.69   T12.3.1A

AWC NDS Yield Limit Equation Constants (Calculated from Table 12.3.1.A Notes)

k_1 = 0.821, k_2 = 0.4769, k_3 = 14.977

Table 3-42. NDS Table 11.3.1A "Yield Limit Equations"

Yield Mode	Z Lateral Value (ASD) (lb) (single shear)	NDS Equation Number
I_m	654	12.3-1
I_s	325	12.3-2
II	267	12.3-3
III_m	282	12.3-4
III_s	123 (governs)	12.3-5
IV	168	12.3-6

Per NDS Table 11.3.1, the calculated lateral design value, Z, is to be adjusted by applicable factors, including the load duration factor for ASD, C_D. Therefore, the adjusted lateral design value, Z' = 123(1.6) = 197 lb for ASD. For LRFD, Z' = 123(3.32)(0.65)(1.0) = 265 lb.

Note: Per the AWC NDS Commentary Section C12.3, the design values for screws are indexed to average short-term proportional limit test values divided by 1.33. The NDS Table 12.3.1A equations represent the possible screw failure modes, but do not account for the load durations typically associated with wood design. The 1.33 factor is based on the original reduction factor of 1.6 increased 20 percent for normal loading and experience (1/1.6) × 1.2 = 0.75. The 20 percent increase was introduced as part of the World War II emergency increase in wood design values. After the war, the 20 percent increase was codified as 10 percent for change from permanent to normal loading and 10 percent for experience.

Instead of calculating the screw shear design values in wood when connecting CFS framing members, as shown above, the designer can refer to the the Cold-Formed Steel Engineers Institute (CFSEI) Technical Note F101-12 (September 2012), which provides screw design values for both withdrawal and shear.

Author's Discussion: AWC, NDS, and AISI Steel Thickness and Connections

The various steel thicknesses (inches) listed in AWC NDS Table 12M "Wood Screws" are different from the typical steel minimum and design thicknesses (mils/inches) used by CFS stud manufacturers. AWC NDS references steel up to 3 gauge (0.239 inch) in terms of gauge (inches), whereas AISI and the CFS industry have moved away from using the term *gauge* and refer to mils (inches) for thickness.

When using multiple materials, designers need to evaluate various material standards to determine which material might control the design for each element in the load path. Both ASD and LRFD methodologies are available for common construction materials. Care should be taken to ensure appropriate adjustment factors are used that might be material specific. For example, NDS Section 11.2.3 states the following:

11.2.3 Design of Metal Parts

Metal plates, hangers, fasteners, and other metal parts shall be designed in accordance with applicable metal design procedures to resist failure in tension, shear, bearing (metal on metal), bending, and buckling. When the capacity of a connection is controlled by metal strength rather than wood strength, metal strength shall not be multiplied by the adjustment factors in this Specification. In addition, metal strength shall not be increased by wind and earthquake factors if design loads have already been reduced by load combination factors.

Typically, the wood members will control screw design values as compared to the CFS framing elements or individual screw shear capacity. When connecting CFS materials together, the screw shear capacity can be the governing factor, depending on the CFS material strength and thickness used. A comparison example is shown below using 33 ksi and 50 ksi CFS material and comparing it to the CFS individual screw shear capacity per Technical Note F701-12.

$\qquad$ #8 Screw: shank diameter = 0.164 in

$\qquad$ 54-mil CFS framing materials: $\quad F_y = 33$ ksi, $F_u = 45$ ksi
$$F_y = 50 \text{ ksi}, F_u = 65 \text{ ksi}$$

$\qquad$ Bearing: $\; P_{ns} = 2.7 t_1 d F_{u1} = 2.7(0.0566)(0.164)(45,000) = 1128$ lb
$$P_{ns} = 2.7 t_1 d F_{u1} = 2.7(0.0566)(0.164)(65,000) = 1629 \text{ lb}$$

$\qquad$ LRFD $= \phi P_{ns} = (0.5)(1128) = 564$ lb $< 639 < \phi P_{ns} = (0.5)(1629) = 815$ lb
$\qquad$ ASD $= P_{ns}/\Omega = (1128/3.0) = 376$ lb $< 426 < P_{ns}/\Omega = (1629/3.0) = 543$ lb

As shown above, the #8 screw is weaker than the 54 mil material with a yield strength of $F_y = 50$ ksi, but it is stronger than $F_y = 36$ ksi.

Author's Discussion: Screws in CFS and Wood

As noted in the previous discussion, a comparison of the screw nominal shear design values in thin CFS members (P_{ns}) and wood members (Z) shows that the shear design values will typically be governed by the lower wood values. A #12 screw was selected for its larger wood shear transfer design values as opposed to using #8 screws, which was the fastener size used for the CFS stud shear wall sheathing attachment. Table 3-43 shows a comparison of ASD and LRFD shear design values for the #12 screw with AISI-calculated design values. Even when including the seismic short-term load duration (C_D) increase of 1.6 for wood, the #12 screw shear value is still less than the shear strength in the CFS framing materials.

Table 3-43. Screw shear design value comparison between wood and CFS

Screw Size	Type of Framing Material	ASD Design Values	LRFD Design Values
#12	54-mil CFS ($F_u = 65$ ksi)	$P_{ns}/\Omega = 715$ lb	1072
#12	Wood (Douglas Fir-Larch)	$Z' = (1.6)(123) = 196$ lb	$Z' = 256$ lb

Shear transfer between framed floors is based on ASD loads since lateral forces are transferring into a wood member for this example. LRFD loads could also be used if the designer prefers not to use ASD. AISI S400 requires the bottom track shear anchorage to have the available strength to resist the lesser of (1) the expected strength of the shear wall or (2) the load determined using the seismic load combinations with overstrength. When the latter governs, which is typical, ASCE 7 Section 2.4.5 permits the ASD capacity to be multiplied by 1.2 when using the ASD seismic load combinations with overstrength. So the #12 screw in wood strength of 196 pounds then becomes 235 pounds.

Table 3-44. Shear wall sheathing shear design

Level	Σ Shear Wall Forces ASD = (0.7F) (lb)	Shear (0.7F/L) (plf)	Design Capacity (plf)	#8 or #10 Screw Spacing (in)	Shear from Ω_0 Load Combinations (plf)
3rd Floor	6895	276	356	6	690
2nd Floor	15,393	616	710	3	1540
1st Floor	19,643	786	876	2	1965

Floor shear transfer:

3rd Floor: #12 screws required: $V = 1540$ plf/(2 rows $\times$ 235) = 3.28 screws/ft and 12/3.28 = 3.66 in o.c. Use two rows of #12 screws at 3 inches on center, staggered.

2nd Floor: #12 screws required: $V = 1965$ plf/(2 rows $\times$ 235) = 4.18 screws/ft and 12/4.18 = 2.87 in o.c. Use two rows of #12 screws at 2 inches on center, staggered.

The second-floor screw spacing should probably be three rows spaced at 4 inches on center staggered. The wood member would need to be wide enough to accommodate three rows of fasteners.

3. Wood (AWC NDS) and Wood Member with Wood Side Member (ASD)

Depending on how the floor/wall framing assembly is constructed, there may be several filler wood plates-to-bottom of wood rim joist connections using lags, screws, or wall sheathing nailing to complete the required shear transfer. The load path through the shear wall that is selected for the lateral design determines the connections.

Assuming the wall rim joist sits on a wood plate to distribute gravity loads to the top of the CFS stud wall, then a wood-to-wood shear transfer may be required. This would be a more traditional wall sheathing attachment using nailing of the wall sheathing to the wood plate with lags/screws for the shear transfer from the wood plate to the underside of the rim joist. The wall sheathing should have edge nailing to both the wood plate and CFS top track. The shear transfer to the rim joist would be through screws/lags installed through both the CFS top track and wood filler plate to the underside of the rim joist.

Screw Design Shear Value (Wood-to-Wood Member)

AWC NDS Table12L: 1½-in side member to main member
                    #12 screw = 0.216-in diameter
                    Z = 147 lb

The wood side member-to-wood main member shear value, Z, exceeds the calculated CFS 54-mil CFS side member-to-wood main member connection where Z equals 123 pounds. Therefore, the spacing of the #12 screws will be governed by Z equals 123 pounds.

If the wood rim joist is the same width as the stud wall, then the CFS top track would be screwed directly to the underside of the rim joist.

Anchor-Bolt Design—Shear Transfer Shear Wall Bottom Track to Concrete Base

1. Concrete   **ACI 318 Chapter 17 and IBC §1905.1.8**

The anchor bolt in concrete shear capacity is determined using ACI 318 Chapter 17. IBC Section 1905.1.8 amends ACI 318 Section 17.2.3.5.2 by adding exemptions for the calculation of the in-plane shear strength of anchor bolts used to attach wood sill plates or CFS tracks to concrete. This exception permits the in-plane shear strength to be determined in accordance with AWC NDS Table 12E and AISI S100 J3.3.1, respectively, rather than comply with ACI 318 Section 17.5.2, "Concrete breakout strength of anchor in shear," Section 17.5.3, "Concrete pryout strength of anchor in shear," and Section 17.2.3.5.3. The applicability of each of these revised provisions to light-frame CFS structures is discussed below.

2018 IBC Section 1905.1.8 Exceptions 1, 2, and 3 discuss the design of shear anchors anchoring light-frame wood mudsills or cold-formed steel tracks to a concrete element near the edge of the concrete.

Exceptions 2 and 3 for CFS tracks for both bearing and nonbearing walls may be used when the following conditions are satisfied:

    2.1. The maximum anchor nominal diameter is ⅝ inch.

    2.2. Anchors are embedded into concrete a minimum of 7 inches.

    2.3. Anchors are located a minimum of 1¾ inches from the edge of the concrete parallel to the length of the track.

    2.4. Anchors are located a minimum of 15 anchor diameters from the edge of the concrete perpendicular to the length of the track.

    2.5. The sill track is 33 to 68 mil designation thickness.

The last part of the exception indicates that concrete anchors less than or equal to 1 inch in diameter that attach a wood sill plate or CFS bottom track to a foundation need not satisfy ACI 318-14 Sections 17.2.3.5.3(a) through (c) if the design strength is determined using Section 17.5.2.1(c), nominal concrete breakout strength in shear parallel to an edge.

ACI 318 Section 17.5.2.1 "Concrete Breakout Strength of Anchor in Shear"

Since the interior shear wall meets the requirements of IBC Section 1905.1.8, replacement Section 17.2.3.5.2, Exception 2, this calculation is not required but is included for completeness of the design example. As will be seen, the shear wall bottom track shear capacity will limit the shear transfer as compared to the anchor strength in concrete.

ACI Section 17.5.2.1(c) states the method for determining the anchor-bolt shear strength when the shear force is parallel to the slab edge. Since this is an interior shear wall, the anchor-bolt slab-edge distance is not a factor, and anchor bolts will be spaced far enough apart such that spacing will not be a limitation factor either.

Podium slab:

Thickness: 12 in

Concrete: $F_c' = 4000$ psi

Hex-headed anchor bolt $= d_a = \frac{5}{8}$-in diameter $= 0.625$ in (height of hex head $= \frac{1}{2}$ in)

End distance $= 15d = (15)(0.625) = 9.375$-in minimum $=$ minimum distance from perpendicular edge of concrete slab to centerline of anchor bolt

Bolt load bearing length in concrete $= l_e = 7$ in $- \frac{1}{2}$ in $= 6.5$ in

$\lambda = 1.0$ (normal weight concrete)

$$V_{cb} = \frac{A_{vc}}{A_{vco}} \psi_{ed}, v\psi_c, v\psi_h, vV_b \qquad \text{ACI 318 Eq 17.5.2.1a}$$

$\psi_{ed} = 1.0$ $\qquad$ ACI 318 §17.5.2.6

$v\psi_c = 1.0$ (conservative) $\qquad$ ACI 318 §17.5.2.7

$v\psi h = \sqrt{(1.5c_{a1})/h_a}$ $\qquad$ ACI 318 §17.5.2.8

$\qquad = \sqrt{14.06/12.0}$

$\qquad = 1.082$

$V_b = (7(l_e/d_a)^{0.2} \sqrt{d_a})\lambda \sqrt{f_c'}(c_{a1})^{1.5}$ $\qquad$ ACI 318 §17.5.2.2

$\qquad = (7(6.5/0.625)^{0.2} \sqrt{0.625})(1.0)\sqrt{4000}(9.375)^{1.5}$

$\qquad = 16{,}048$

$c_{a1} = 15d = 9.375$ in

$1.5c_{a1} = 14.06 > 12$-in thickness of podium slab; therefore, $h_a = 12.0$ in

$A_{vc} = 2(1.5c_{a1})h_a = 2(14.06)(12) = 337.44$ in^2

$A_{vco} = 4(c_{a1})^2 = 4(14.06)^2 = 790.7$ in^2

$V_{cb} = (337.4/790.7)(1.0)(1.0)(1.082)(16{,}048) = 7409$ lb

$\phi = 0.70$ $\qquad$ ACI 318 §17.3.3(c) Condition B

$\phi V_{cb} = 0.70(7409) = 5186$ lb

2. CFS Connections (AISI S100—Section J3 "Bolted Connections") Shear Transfer Shear Wall Bottom Track to Concrete Base

Bolt notations:

$d =$ nominal bolt diameter

$t =$ uncoated thickness of thinnest connected material

$e =$ distance measured in line of force from center of standard hole to nearest edge of adjacent hole or to end of connected part

$F_u =$ tensile strength of connected CFS member as defined in AISI S100 Sections A3.1 and A3.2

$C =$ bearing factor (AISI S100 Table J3.3.1-1)

$m_f =$ modification factor for type of bearing connection (AISI S100 Table J.3.3.1-2)

Bolt spacing and bolt-hole size:

Minimum bolt spacing (center line to center line) $= 3d$ \hfill AISI S100 §J3.1

Minimum bolt edge and end distance from centerline of bolt $= 1.5d$ \hfill AISI S100 §J3.2

Bolt-hole size (bolts larger than ½-in diameter) \hfill AISI S100 Appendix A TE3a

Using standard bolt hole $= d + \frac{1}{16}$ in

Bolt bearing (AISI S100 Section J3.3):

Track material thickness: $t = 68$ mils $= 0.0713$ in

Track material $F_y = 50$ ksi, $F_u = 65$ ksi

Anchor bolt diameter $(D) = \frac{5}{8}$ in $= 0.625$ in

$A_b =$ gross cross-sectional area of bolt $= 0.31$ in^2

Bolt type: A307 bolt, Grade A

Bearing strength (resistance) without consideration of bolt hole deformation (AISI S100, Section J3.3.1):

$P_n = Cm_f dtF_u$ \hfill AISI S100 §J3.3.1-1

$\Omega = 2.50$ (ASD) \qquad $\phi = 0.60$ (LRFD)

$D/t = (0.625/0.0713) = 8.77 < 10$; therefore, $C = 3.0$ \hfill AISI S100 §J3.3.1-1

$m_f = 1.0$ (with washer under anchor bolt nut) \hfill AISI S100 §J3.3.1-2

$P_n = (3.0)(1.0)(0.625)(0.0713)(65,000) = 8690$ lb

ASD: \qquad $P_n/\Omega = 8690/2.50 = 3476$ lb

LRFD: \qquad $\phi P_n = 0.6(8690) = 5214$ lb

Author's Discussion: Since this is a shear wall, the designer should also consider the AISI bolt shear equation, which considers bolt hole deformation in the sheet metal (AISI S100 Section J3.3.2). Shear walls resisting seismic forces are deformation limited by the ASCE 7 story drift limitation. Due to possible combinations of bolt diameter and sheet metal thickness, AISI S100 Section J3.3.2 requires that the calculated bearing strength "with consideration of bolt hole deformation" not exceed the calculated bearing strength "without consideration of bolt hole deformation." The bolt hole considering deformation calculation is shown below.

$P_n = (4.64\alpha t + 1.53)dtF_u$ \hfill AISI S100 §J3.3.1-2

$\Omega = 2.22$ (ASD) \qquad $\phi = 0.6$ (LRFD) \qquad $\alpha = 1.0$

$P_n = [4.64(1.0)(0.0713) + 1.53](0.625)(0.0713)(65,000) = 5390$ lb

ASD: \qquad $P_n/\Omega = 5390/2.22 = 2428$ lb < 3476 lb \hfill AISI S100 §J3.3.1

LRFD: \qquad $\phi P_n = 0.65(5390) = 3504$ lb < 5214 lb \hfill AISI S100 §J3.3.1

As can be seen, the difference in shear capacity is significant when the designer considers bolt hole deformation in this design example (1857 pounds vs. 2000 pounds). The value for Ω is larger and the value for ϕ is smaller to address the bolt hole elongation deformation limit of 0.25 inch, which occurs before reaching the limited bearing strength of the sheet metal. Therefore, sheet metal bearing strength with consideration of bolt hole deformation governs in this design.

Controlling Shear Transfer Design (Concrete Embedment and Cold-Formed Steel Tracks)

The bottom-track anchor-bolt attachment to the concrete podium deck is restricted to strength design since 2018 IBC Section 1901.3 requires the anchor to concrete to be in accordance with ACI 318. The anchor-bolt governing strength design shear value is controlled by the bottom track's 68-mil thickness and is limited to 3504 pounds (LRFD).

Shear Transfer Summary

Table 3-45. Option 3 shear wall: shear wall fastener spacing at floor line

Level	$\Omega_0 (F)$ Load Combo (lb)	Anchor Type	Connector Design Capacity (Z')	Number of Fasteners	Max. Spacing Allowed (in)	Spacing Used
ASD—Superstructure—above Podium Deck						
3rd floor	17,238	#12 screw	235 lb	73	8.5	8 in on center, 2 rows
2nd floor	38,483	#12 screw	235 lb	164	5.6	5 in on center, 3 rows
LRFD—Concrete Podium Deck						
1st floor	70,153	⅝-in Diameter Anchor Bolt	3504 lb	20	15.8	15 in on center

1. Wall length = 25 ft, Ω_0 = 2.5, shear forces (F) taken from Table 3-25

2. Max spacing = (25 ft × 12)/(73/2 − 1) = 8.5 in
   = (25 ft × 12)/(164/3 − 1) = 5.6 in

3. Max spacing (single row of anchor bolts) = (25 ft × 12)/(20 − 1) = 15.8 in

Author's Discussion: Spacing of anchor bolts is calculated based on applying omega forces. Practical spacing of the anchor bolts is 16 inches on center, which is a module of the wall stud spacing. While the suggested maximum spacing is 15 inches on center, it may be more practical to space the bolts at 12 inches on center.

The shear wall connection to the concrete slab will typically be controlled by the thickness of the cold-formed steel track. If the diameter of the anchor bolt is reduced, and the thickness of the cold-formed steel track is increased, it is possible that the anchor-bolt strength would control the connection design to the concrete.

In this design example, the controlling shear design value is per AISI S100 Section J3.3.1 or the bearing of the steel bottom track against the anchor bolt (3504 pounds < 5186 pounds). A lower bottom track bearing capacity against the anchor bolt could be obtained by using a track with an F_y = 33 ksi (F_u = 45 ksi), but then it would not match the wall stud material strength used (F_y = 50 ksi, F_u = 65 ksi).

12.9 DISCONTINUOUS SHEAR WALL

The Option 2 shear wall is a discontinuous shear wall that sits on a steel beam at the second floor, which in turn is supported by a first-floor steel column.

A discontinuous shear wall situation occurs when the shear wall directly below is eliminated and the remaining shear walls at the floor below are offset either horizontally to a parallel grid line (Type 4 horizontal irregularity) or horizontally along the same grid line (Type 4 vertical irregularity). In this design example, the Option 2 shear wall at the first floor is shorter than the shear wall immediately above at the second- and third-floor levels, so this would be considered a vertical irregularity. The design of the supporting members of the discontinuous shear wall has to comply with ASCE 7 Section 12.3.3 "Elements Supporting Discontinuous Walls or Frames."

The steel beam and column supporting the discontinuous shear wall are required to be designed using the seismic load combinations with the overstrength factor. The following elements supporting the discontinuous shear wall are required to be designed to resist this amplified seismic load:

1. The second-floor steel beam.

2. The first-floor steel columns.

3. The beam-to-column connections.

4. The connection of the column to the podium level.

The amplified seismic load is not used for the hold-down or chord studs or their attachment to the supporting member for light-frame wood stud shear walls. AISI S400 requires that the CFS-framed shear wall hold-downs (uplift anchorage) and CFS chord studs (vertical boundary compression elements) have the available strength to resist the amplified seismic force.

13. Shear Wall Deflection AISI S400 §E1.4.1.4 "Design Deflection"

The designer of the rigidity of a CFS-framed shear wall must consider several factors: bending deformation, shear deformation, fastener slip, and hold-down movement. When there are multiple shear walls along the wall line, the forces are to be distributed based on the rigidity of the shear walls along that wall line.

The rigidity of the individual shear wall is determined from the deflection of the sheathed CFS stud shear wall. AISI S400 provides design equations to estimate the deflection of either sheet steel or blocked wood structural panels (WSPs) on CFS stud shear walls. The design equations can be found in AISI Section E1.4.1.4 "Design Deflection."

The distribution of horizontal shear forces between shear walls in a line is not covered in this design example.

AISI S400

Deflection is an important consideration in design; excessive deflection of lateral-force-resisting systems may lead to undesirable building performance or even collapse. AISI S400 Sections E1.4.1.4 and E2.4.1.4 state the deflection of a blocked wood structural panel or steel-sheet-sheathed CFS-stud-framed shear wall may be determined by using the four part equation shown here.

$$\delta = \frac{2vh^3}{3E_s A_c b} + \omega_1 \omega_2 \frac{vh}{\rho G t_{sheathing}} + \omega_1^{5/4} \omega_2 \omega_3 \omega_4 \left(\frac{v}{\beta}\right)^2 + \frac{h}{b}\delta_v$$

The four parts of the equation take into account linear elastic cantilever bending, linear elastic sheathing shear, overall nonlinear effects, and the top-of-wall horizontal deflection contribution from the vertical displacement of the hold-down or tie-down system (uplift anchorage).

Linear elastic cantilever bending: $\delta_1 = \dfrac{2vh^3}{3E_s A_c b}$

Linear elastic sheathing shear: $\delta_2 = \omega_1 \omega_2 \dfrac{vh}{\rho G t_{sheathing}}$

Overall nonlinear effects: $\delta_3 = \omega_1^{5/4} \omega_2 \omega_3 \omega_4 \left(\dfrac{v}{\beta}\right)^2$

Lateral contribution from anchorage/hold-down deformation: $\delta_4 = \dfrac{h}{b} \delta_v$

ASCE 7 Table 12.12-1 limits the story drift for Risk Category II three-story buildings to $0.025h_{sx}$, where h_{sx} is the story height. This three-story light-frame building is considered to comply with the Table 12.12-1 requirement that interior walls, partitions, ceilings, and exterior walls have been designed to accommodate the story drifts. If it did not, or the number of stories was five stories or more, the story drift would be limited to $0.020h_{sx}$.

The shear wall deflection (δ) is calculated per ASCE 7 Equation 12.8-15:

$\delta_x = C_d \delta_{xe}/I_e$

Shear wall deflection calculation:

First story: chord studs A_{Gross}, $Ac = (10) - 600S200\text{-}68 = 10 \times 0.7643 \text{ in}^2 = 7.643 \text{ in}^2$ AISI D100 TI-2

Second B story: chord studs A_{Gross}, $Ac = (6) - 600S200\text{-}68 = 6 \times 0.7643 \text{ in}^2 = 4.586 \text{ in}^2$ AISI D100 TI-2

Second A story: chord studs A_{Gross}, $Ac = (6) - 600S200\text{-}68 = 6 \times 0.7643 \text{ in}^2 = 4.586 \text{ in}^2$ AISI D100 TI-2

Third story: chord studs A_{Gross}, $Ac = (4) - 600S162\text{-}54 = 4 \times 0.5560 \text{ in}^2 = 2.224 \text{ in}^2$ AISI D100 TI-2

Structural 1 (4 ply, 32/16) plywood sheathing shear modulus per AISI S400 Commentary Section E1.4.1.4 and AWC SDPWS Commentary Table C4.2.2A:

$G = G_v t_v / t = (45{,}500 \text{ lb/in})/0.469 \text{ in} = 97{,}015 \text{ psi}$

Table 3-46. Option 3 shear wall: deflection variables

Floor Level	Wall Height, h (in)	Wall Width, b (in)	LRFD Required Strength, v (lb/in)	LRFD Story Level Uplift Force, P (lb)	End Studs Gross Area, A_c (in^2)	Sheathing Thickness, t (in)	Sheathing Shear Modulus, G (psi)	Rod Net Tensile Area (A_e)(in^2)/ LRFD Rod Elongation[2,3] d_{v1} (in)	Take-Up Device Deflection[4] d_{v2} (in)
3rd	132 (54)[1]	300	32.8	3305	2.224	0.469	97,015	0.334/0.018	0.030
2nd A	120	300	73.3	8604	4.586	0.469	97,015	0.763/0.046	0.030
2nd B	120	300	73.3	8604	4.586	0.469	97,015	0.334/0.107	0.030
1st	120	300	93.5	16,542	7.643	0.469	97,015	0.763/0.088	0.030

See notes for Table 3-47.

Table 3-47. Option 3 shear wall: deflection variables

Floor Level	CFS Modulus of Elasticity, E_s (psi)	Fastener Spacing, s (in)	Framing Designation Thickness t_{stud} (in)	Sheathing Factor, ρ	Fastener Spacing Factor, $\omega_1 = s/6$	Framing Designation Thickness Factor, $\omega_2 = 0.033/t_{stud}$	Aspect Ratio Factor, $\omega_3 = ((h/b)/2)^{0.5}$	Sheathing Material Factor, ω_4
3rd	29.5E6	6	0.054	1.85	1.00	0.611	0.469	1
2nd A	29.5E6	3	0.068	1.85	0.50	0.485	0.447	1
2nd B	29.5E6	3	0.068	1.85	0.50	0.485	0.447	1
1st	29.5E6	2	0.068	1.85	0.33	0.485	0.447	1

Notes for Table 3-47:

1. Rod length at third-floor bridge block = 4 ft 6 in = 54 in.

2. Vertical rod elongation = $\delta_{v1} = PL/A_e E$.

3. Modulus of elasticity (E) for tie rod = 29,000,000 psi.

4. Reference manufacturer's evaluation report evaluated to ICC-ES AC316 for take-up device initial (seating increment) deflection, Δ_R, and allowable load deflection, Δ_A, to determine the total device deflection, Δ_T, which for this design example is δ_{v2}. $\Delta_T = \delta_{v2} = \Delta_R + \Delta_A (P_D/P_A)$. Shrinkage and estimated building settlement are to be taken as part of the deflection computation if a take-up device is not used.

5. Total vertical deformation of uplift anchorage system = δ_v = rod elongation (δ_{v1}) + total take-up device deflection (δ_{v2}) + stud bearing crushing at wood floor + bearing plate crushing at wood floor. The wood crushing terms are not shown in this design example, but should be added.

For 3rd-floor shear wall:

$$\delta_1 = \frac{2vh^3}{3E_s A_c b} = 0.0026 \text{ in}$$

$$\delta_2 = \omega_1 \omega_2 \frac{vh}{\rho G t_{sheathing}} = 0.0314 \text{ in}$$

$$\delta_3 = \omega_1^{5/4} \omega_2 \omega_3 \omega_4 \left(\frac{v}{\beta}\right)^2 = 0.0677 \text{ in}, \ \beta = 67.5 \text{ for plywood sheathing} \qquad \text{AISI S400 §E1.4.1.4}$$

$$\delta_4 = \frac{h}{b}\delta_v = \frac{132}{300}(0.018 + 0.030) = 0.0211 \text{ in}$$

There are additional contributors to the deflection of multistory shear walls that need to be taken into account, including rotation at the top of the shear wall below; axial shortening and lengthening of the compression and tension chords, respectively, of the shear wall below; and hold-down deflection of the shear walls below.

2nd-floor shear wall additional top-of-wall deflection contributors:

1. Rotation at top of 1st-floor shear wall due to cantilever bending caused by seismic overturning forces. Angle of rotation for a fixed-base, cantilever beam with a concentrated load at its end:

   $\alpha = PL^2/(2EI)$

   I for the shear wall $= A_c b^2/2$

   $\alpha = PL^2/(EA_c b^2)$

   $\alpha_{1st\,Floor} = 28,061 \text{ lb} \times (120 \text{ in})^2/(29,500,000 \text{ psi} \times 7.643 \text{ in}^2 \times (300 \text{ in})^2) = 1.99\text{E-5 radians}$

   Top of 2nd-floor shear wall deflection due to rotation at top of 1st-floor shear wall is then

   $\delta_{rot\text{-}2} = h_2 \times \alpha_1 = 120 \text{ in} \times 1.99\text{E-5 radians} = 0.0024 \text{ in}$

2. Additional rotation at top of 1st-floor shear wall caused by tension and compression from 2nd-floor shear wall chords:

   $T_2 = 8604 \text{ lb} \quad C_2 = (328,239 \text{ lb} + 130,341 \text{ lb})/23 \text{ ft} = 19,938 \text{ lb}$ \qquad Table 3-35B

   $\delta_{chds\text{-}1} = PL/AE$

   $\delta_{chds\text{-}1T} = 8604 \text{ lb} \times 120 \text{ in}/(7.643 \text{ in}^2 \times 29,500,000 \text{ psi}) = 0.0046 \text{ in for } T \text{ 1st-floor shear wall chord}$

   $\delta_{chds\text{-}1C} = 19,938 \text{ lb} \times 120 \text{ in}/(7.643 \text{ in}^2 \times 29,500,000 \text{ psi}) = 0.0106 \text{ in for } C \text{ 1st-floor shear wall chord}$

   Additional deflection at top of 2nd-floor shear wall due to 1st-floor shear wall chord axial deformations:

   $\delta_{2\text{-}chds\text{-}1} = (\delta_{chds\text{-}1T} + \delta_{chds\text{-}1C})(h_2/b_2) = (0.0046 \text{ in} + 0.0106 \text{ in})(120 \text{ in}/300 \text{ in}) = 0.0061 \text{ in}$

3. Additional 2nd-floor shear wall deflection due to 1st-floor tie-down system deformation. Note that this accounts for only the rod elongation and take-up device deflection. It should also include stud bearing crushing and bearing plate crushing at wood floor when they occur.

   Deflection per Table 3-46 $= \delta_v = 0.088 \text{ in} + 0.030 \text{ in} = 0.118 \text{ in}$

   Top of 2nd-floor deflection due to tie-down system deformation is then

   $\delta_{2\text{-}TDS\text{-}1} = \delta_v \times (h_2/b_2) = 0.118 \text{ in} \times (120 \text{ in}/300 \text{ in}) = 0.0472 \text{ in } (0.0304 \text{ in for 2nd-Floor Wall Option 1})$

3rd-floor shear wall additional top-of-wall deflection contributors:

1. Rotation at top of 2nd-floor shear wall due to cantilever bending caused by seismic overturning forces. Angle of rotation for a fixed-base, cantilever beam with a concentrated load at its end:

$\alpha = PL^2/(2EI)$

I for the shear wall $= A_c b^2/2$

$\alpha = PL^2/(EA_c b^2)$

$\alpha_{1st\,Floor} = 21{,}990 \text{ lb} \times (120 \text{ in})^2/(29{,}500{,}000 \text{ psi} \times 4.586 \text{ in}^2 \times (300 \text{ in})^2) = 2.60\text{E-}5 \text{ radians}$

Top of 3rd-floor shear wall deflection due to rotation at top of 2nd-floor shear wall is then

$\delta_{rot-2} = h_2 \times \alpha_1 + \delta_{rot-1} = 120 \text{ in} \times 2.60\text{E-}5 \text{ radians} + 0.0024 \text{ in} = 0.0055 \text{ in}$

2. Additional rotation at top of 2nd-floor shear wall caused by tension and compression from 3rd-floor shear wall chords:

$T_2 = 3305 \text{ lb} \quad C_2 = (108{,}339 \text{ lb} + 32{,}321 \text{ lb})/23 \text{ ft} = 6116 \text{ lb}$ Table 3-35B

$\delta_{chds-1} = PL/AE$

$\delta_{chds-2T} = 3305 \text{ lb} \times 120 \text{ in}/(4.586 \text{ in}^2 \times 29{,}500{,}000 \text{ psi}) = 0.0029 \text{ in}$ for T 2nd-floor shear wall chord

$\delta_{chds-2C} = 6116 \text{ lb} \times 120 \text{ in}/(4.586 \text{ in}^2 \times 29{,}500{,}000 \text{ psi}) = 0.0054 \text{ in}$ for C 2nd-floor shear wall chord

Additional deflection at top of 3rd-floor shear wall due to 2nd-floor shear wall chord axial deformations:

$\delta_{3-chds-2} = (\delta_{chds-2T} + \delta_{chds-2C})(h_2/b_2) + \delta_{2-chds-1} = (0.0029 \text{ in} + 0.0054 \text{ in})(120 \text{ in}/300 \text{ in}) + 0.0061 \text{ in}$
$= 0.0094 \text{ in}$

3. Additional 3rd-floor shear wall deflection due to 2nd-floor tie-down system deformation. Note that this accounts for only the rod elongation and take-up device deflection. It should also include stud bearing crushing and bearing plate crushing at wood floor when they occur.

Deflection per Table 3-46 $= \delta_v = 0.107 \text{ in} + 0.030 \text{ in} = 0.137 \text{ in}$

Top of 3rd-floor deflection due to tie-down system deformation is then

$\delta_{3-TDS-2} = \delta_v \times (h_2/b_2) + \delta_{2-TDS-1} = 0.137 \text{ in} \times (120 \text{ in}/300 \text{ in}) + 0.0472 \text{ in} = 0.102 \text{ in}$

Amplify story drift using ASCE 7 Equation 12.8-15 to ensure it is less than the allowable story drift, Δ_a.

$\Delta_a = 0.025 h_{sx} = 0.025(120 \text{ in}) = 3.0 \text{ in (first and second floors)}$ ASCE 7 §12.12-1
$= 0.025(132 \text{ in}) = 3.3 \text{ in (third floor)}$

$\delta_x = C_d \, \partial_{xe}/I_e$ ASCE 7 Eq 12.8-15
$I_e = 1.0$

Table 3-48. Summary of top-of-wall deflections

Floor Level	δ_1 (in)	δ_2 (in)	δ_3 (in)	δ_4 (in)	δ_{rot} (in)	δ_{chrds} (in)	δ_{TDS} (in)	δ_{Total} (in)	δ_x (in)	Δ_a (in)	$\delta_{Total} < \delta_x$
3rd 1	0.0026	0.0314	0.0677	0.0211	0.0055	0.0094	0.1020	0.2397	0.9587	3.3	Yes, OK
2nd A	0.0021	0.0254	0.1076	0.0304	0.0024	0.0061	0.0304	0.2043	0.8172	3.0	Yes, OK
2nd B	0.0021	0.0254	0.1076	0.0548	0.0024	0.0061	0.0472	0.2455	0.9820	3.0	Yes, OK
1st	0.0016	0.0213	0.1041	0.0472	—	—	—	0.1742	0.6970	3.0	Yes, OK

1. 3rd-floor shear wall top-of-wall deflection calculation based on 2nd B rod size.

Each line of vertical elements of the seismic-force-resisting system complies with allowable story drifts per ASCE 7 Table 12.12-1.

This design example uses Type I shear walls, and the AISI S400 deflection equation is for that type of wood structural panel or steel-sheet-sheathed CFS-framed shear wall. However, while there are currently no provisions given in AISI S400 to calculate the deflection of a Type II shear wall, the designer might consider using a similar methodology as shown in AWC SDPWS Section 4.3.2.1 where v and b in AISI S400 Equation E1.4.1.4-1 are equal to v in AISI S400 Equation E1.4.2.2-1 and the sum of widths of Type II shear wall segments, ΣL_i, respectively.

Seismic Separation

The story drifts are also used to determine the size of any required structural seismic separation between adjacent building structures as well as seismic joints between individual buildings. ASCE 7 Section 12.12.3 requires the minimum structural separation between buildings of $\delta_m = C_d \delta_{max}/I_e$ for each story level of the building where δ_{max} includes both the translational and amplified torsional displacements of each floor level and roof of the building. δ_m is the minimum setback requirement from the property line, unless other building code requirements stipulate a larger setback.

The required separation distance (δ_{mt}) between adjacent edges of structures on the same property is calculated using the equation:

$$\delta_{mt} = [(C_{d1}\delta_{m1}/I_{e1})^2 + (C_{d2}\delta_{m2}/I_{e2})^2]^{1/2} \qquad \text{ASCE 7 Eq 12.12-2}$$

δ_{m1} = Maximum displacement of adjacent structure 1, as determined by an elastic analysis

δ_{m2} = Maximum displacement of adjacent structure 2, as determined by an elastic analysis

The summation of the Building B Option 3 shear wall elastic story drifts equals 0.240 + 0.246 + 0.174 = 0.660 inches. Assuming this shear wall deflection is representative of all the shear walls in Building B and accounts for amplified torsion of the floor/roof diaphragms, the roof-level deflections are as follows:

1. Roof-level maximum elastic horizontal displacement (deflection) = 0.660 inches.

2. Roof-level maximum inelastic response horizontal displacement = (4.0)(0.660)/1.0 = 2.64 inches.

The calculated Building B rooftop drift of 2.64 inches is significantly less than the code default value limit of 0.025H, or what would be (10.0 + 10.0 + 11.0)(12)(.025) = 9.3 inches.

The width of the seismic joint at the bridge between Buildings A and B will have to be determined from the calculated seismic horizontal deflections of both Building A and Building B in accordance with the building code requirements for building separation. But as can be seen for the Building B shear wall calculation, sizing the seismic joint width based on the actual shear wall deflections of both Building A and Building B will likely be significantly less than sizing the seismic joint width based on using the maximum allowable shear wall deflections permitted by the building code.

14. Discussion: Framing with Cold-Formed Steel

14.1 WALL STUD BRACING

Because CFS framing members are typically made up of singly symmetric (C-studs, tracks) or point-symmetric shapes (Z-purlins, angles) with thin elements, they often require supplemental bracing. In the case of exterior wall studs in bearing-wall construction, intermittent bracing is required to resist weak-axis buckling due to axial loads and torsion resulting from lateral loads (wind or seismic) not applied through the shear center of the member in either the strong or weak axis. The following discussion provides an overview of stud-wall bracing design. For further discussion, illustrations, and design examples, the reader is referred to *Cold-Formed Steel Framing Design Guide* (AISI D110). A more in-depth discussion of bracing can also be found in *Bracing Cold-Formed Steel Structures—A Design Guide*, by Thomas Sputo and Jennifer L. Turner.

Two basic methods are recognized for bracing CFS studs: sheathing braced design and all-steel design (also referred to as mechanical bracing). Sheathing braced design relies on the diaphragm action of the sheathing attached to the studs and top and bottom tracks. Mechanical bracing consists of the addition of discrete bracing elements, typically comprised of a combination of bridging channel, flat strapping, connectors, and blocking, that are designed to provide the required resistance.

Sheathing Braced Design of CFS Wall Studs

Sheathing braced design is prescriptive in nature and is addressed in the *North American Standard for Cold-Formed Steel Structural Framing* (S240) and *North American Standard for Seismic Design of Cold-Formed Steel Structural Systems* (S400). Since sheathing is typically required for architectural reasons, use of a sheathing braced design is attractive for cost reasons. However, studies show that gypsum board that is commonly used may not provide adequate bracing for members with a design thickness greater than 0.0346 inch (20 gauge or 33 mils). In addition, many feel the bracing performance of gypsum board deteriorates quickly under cyclic loading and if exposed to moisture. Even when sheathing braced design is used, it is standard practice for the engineer to provide some amount of mechanical bracing to align members and provide stability during construction.

AISI S240 Section B3.2.1.1 addresses axial load design of the CFS stud. The connection of the stud ends to the bottom track and top track prevents twist of the stud at the ends. The type of sheathing and fastener size may limit the maximum axial capacity the stud can support unless supplemental steel bracing is provided between the CFS studs. The maximum spacing of the sheathing fastener is 12 inches on center, as typically occurs in the field area of the sheathing attachment to the stud. Closer spacing of the sheathing fasteners is not credited to increase the stud axial capacity.

In shear walls, it is common to have wood sheathing on just one side, while gypsum wall board is provided on the opposite side as the wall finish material, which may be used to brace the CFS stud flanges. The wood sheathing fastener attachment, gypsum board fastener attachment, and CFS stud need to be checked to determine the limiting axial capacity of the CFS stud. The lesser value of the three checks shall be used to determine the stud axial capacity. The designer may only use twice the bracing strength of the weaker attached sheathing when determining the CFS stud axial capacity, assuming sheathing occurs on both faces of the shear wall.

Since the design equations for determining axial capacity are based on a single fastener attached to one side of the stud, when that sheathing is attached to both flanges of the wall stud, the nominal axial capacity of the wall stud is twice the calculated capacity based on the single fastener attachment to just one flange of the CFS stud. The AISI S240 Commentary discusses how to determine the sheathing bracing strength of the stud. Section B1.2.2 of the new S240 CFS light-frame standard now permits load bearing and non-load bearing walls to have sheathing bracing on one wall stud flange and discrete bracing on the other flange rather than requiring either an all-steel braced design of stud flanges or an all-sheathing braced design of stud flanges for wall stud bracing. However, the authors recommend using either an all-sheathing braced design or an all-steel braced design of the stud bracing for (1) load bearing and (2) non-load bearing walls designed for lateral forces in excess of 6 psf unless research is identified substantiating wall stud brace load sharing between the sheathing on one face of the wall and discrete bracing on the other face of the wall.

This CFS-framed shear wall design example utilizes horizontal steel strap bracing to brace the CFS bearing stud wall flanges with a full-depth block placed every 8 feet, with a minimum of two blocks per shear wall, along the length of the wall. The vertical spacing of the continuous horizontal straps at each floor level was selected based on the engineer assuring the chord-stud assembly would have sufficient capacity to support the imposed compressive axial and flexural design loads.

As discussed earlier, sheathing braced design could be used at the third-floor shear wall level of the building since the axial loads are small. It is preferable to stay with a steel-braced design for two reasons:

1. For shear walls, it is preferable to have the sheathing used to resist just the seismic lateral forces as opposed to including the sheathing to also stabilize the steel studs for axial loads.

2. If the wall sheathing has to be removed for any reason (example: access a leaking pipe or the gypsum wall board becomes wet), the CFS studs are still braced by the continuous strapping.

Steel (Mechanical)-Braced Design of CFS Wall Studs

Requirements for the design of all steel bracing, or mechanical bracing, are included in AISI S100 Section C2. The design approach is somewhat different for the bracing of axially and laterally loaded studs. For axial loading, bracing is designed for a percentage of the axial load in order to prevent buckling of the stud, similar to AISC 360 for compression member nodal bracing. AISI S100 provides design requirements for both the strength and stiffness of the bracing. For bracing of laterally loaded studs, bracing is designed to resist the torsion created due to the fact that the lateral load is not applied through the shear center. In this case, AISI S100 provides design requirements for the strength of the steel bracing, but does not currently include requirements for stiffness.

Design of bracing can prove challenging for several reasons. Prior to the 2007 edition, the AISI Specification required that members be braced, but no design equations were provided. As a result, many engineers designed bracing based on the "2 percent rule," or other rules of thumb, or prescriptive guidelines. With the addition of explicit strength and stiffness requirements, designers must now be more rigorous with their bracing design. AISI D110 contains design examples that include bracing design. Recent testing of typical bracing details has been performed, and AISI is working on improved bracing provisions based on this research. Also, the calculation of bracing system stiffness can prove to be quite complicated and inaccurate. Several manufacturers have recently started to publish design values for proprietary bridging connectors in accordance with AISI S915, *Test Standards for Through-the-Web Punchout Cold-Formed Steel Wall Stud Bridging Connectors.*

The two most common steel bracing systems consist of:

1. 1½-inch U-channel bridging installed through the web punch-out of the studs and attached to the stud web with a connector. The connector generally extends across the stud web out to both stud flanges.

2. Flat-strap bracing installed on each face of the stud in combination with intermittent blocking between the CFS studs.

Both of these bracing methods have their advantages and disadvantages, and the decision of which to use is often based on designer and/or installer preference.

U-Channel Bridging

The use of U-channel bridging is probably more common, but requires coordination with other building elements in the stud bays, including plumbing pipes, electrical conduit, and continuous rods used for overturning restraint.

1. For the design of axially loaded studs, the bracing force accumulates over a number of studs, requiring that the bracing be anchored to the structure periodically. One bridging anchorage option is to use strongbacks (CFS studs turned 90 degrees within the stud wall for strong axis bending to resist strap-braced loads) periodically along the wall, and this is shown in Figure 3-27. This aspect of bracing design is sometimes overlooked, but is critical to the performance of the bracing system.

2. For the design of laterally loaded studs using U-channel bridging, torsion in the stud is resisted by bending of the U-channel, so no additional anchorage is required because the system is in equilibrium without the anchorage. The only horizontal shear reaction that needs to be resolved is at the ends of the U-channel run, or how the U-channel connects to a cross wall or the last stud in the wall.

3. While not a code limit, this U-channel bridging system is typically limited to CFS stud depths of 8 inches or less.

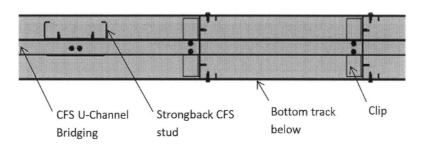

CFS U-Channel Bridging   Strongback CFS stud   Bottom track below   Clip

Figure 3-27. CFS stud-wall U-channel bridging—strongback anchorage (plan view)

Flat-Strap Bracing

Flat-strap bracing on each side of the CFS stud wall with periodic stud blocking is generally stiffer than U-channel bridging and eliminates conflicts within the stud bays, but installation requires access to both sides of the wall.

1. Periodic anchorage to the structure is required when the engineer is bracing axially loaded CFS studs, similar to U-channel bridging. Anchorage of bracing can occur several ways:

   a. Strongbacks (CFS studs turned 90 degrees within the stud wall for strong axis bending to resist strap-braced loads) spaced periodically along the wall. This is shown in Figure 3-28.

   b. Periodic flat-strap diagonal bracing attached to the flat-strap stud bracing extending and anchoring to the top and bottom tracks of the stud wall, as shown in Figure 3-29.

   c. Stud bracing might also be achieved using sheathing diaphragm action to deliver loads to the top and bottom tracks of the stud wall.

   d. Stud bracing can also be achieved by attaching bracing to some other structural member (steel column/post, shear wall, etc.) that is substantially anchored itself between floor levels.

2. But unlike U-channel bridging, flat-strap bracing only acts in tension, so this system also requires intermittent blocking (bridging) between the CFS studs when bracing laterally loaded studs, which may have an impact on installation costs.

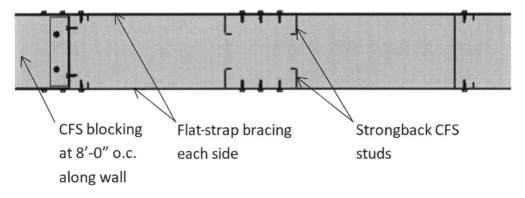

CFS blocking at 8'-0" o.c. along wall   Flat-strap bracing each side   Strongback CFS studs

Figure 3-28. CFS stud-wall flat-strap bracing and blocking—strongback anchorage (plan view)

3. While flat-strap and blocking bracing were used for this design example, some may prefer to use a bridging and clip bracing solution, as discussed previously, to avoid the wall sheathing being "pushed out" by the thickness of the CFS strap and screw attaching it to the CFS stud or CFS track framing.

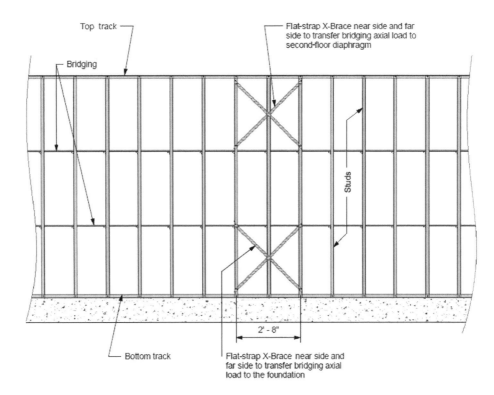

Figure 3-29. CFS stud-wall flat-strap bracing—diagonal strap bracing anchorage (elevation view)

Determination of CFS stud capacities (axial and flexure) based on steel-brace spacing is accomplished most easily using computer programs. Most commercially available computer programs for CFS stud design allow the designer to evaluate combinations of axial loads and lateral loads based on various vertical spacings of the CFS stud flange braces to determine the nominal capacities of the selected CFS stud.

14.2 WALL STUD HEIGHT: BEARING AND NONBEARING STUDS

Out-of-plane wind loads and axial gravity loads are typically going to govern the design of the CFS wall studs, other than possibly the design of the boundary studs at the end of shear walls for in-plane seismic loads. Design aids, such as the Steel Stud Manufacturers Association (SSMA) and Steel Framing Industry Association (SFIA) publication "Product Technical Information," provide CFS stud-design information for use in interior nonbearing stud design, exterior nonbearing curtain-wall design, and bearing stud wall design.

The size of bearing stud walls will depend on the axial load on the stud as well as the out-of-plane loading. SSMA and SFIA's "Product Technical Information" publication typically provides design values for bearing stud walls up to 16 feet in height. This is probably a good cut-off height. If taller stud walls are required due to floor-to-floor heights, then an alternative gravity framing system should be considered, such as beams and columns, to support the floor/roof gravity loads. The CFS studs would then be strictly considered as nonbearing stud walls and only need to be designed for out-of-plane loads.

Taller bearing studs may be possible, but the stud depth will likely have to be deeper, or the thickness will need to be increased to resist out-of-plane forces. As a reminder, CFS studs used in sheathed shear walls have limits on the CFS stud thickness, so at taller heights a deeper stud will be required to keep the thickness of stud within thickness limitations. The alternative solution is to make the shear wall CFS studs nonbearing in order to achieve taller stud heights. The shear wall CFS studs would be infill studs installed below a floor/roof beam supported by columns or posts to transfer gravity loads to the foundation or podium level in this design example. Where infill studs are used below a beam, they should be installed only after the floor/roof beam above, and after all tributary framing dead loads to the beam have been placed, to minimize gravity axial load transfer to the studs. Both non-shear and shear wall infill studs may still need to be checked for imposed live loads from the floor/roof framing.

14.3 FLOOR SYSTEMS

This design example intentionally used engineered wood I-joists rather than CFS joists for the floor framing system to demonstrate that wood joists can also be considered for use. Generally the assumption when using CFS bearing stud walls is that the floor joist will also be of CFS, which is not always the case. Figures 3-30 and 3-31 show platform and ledger CFS light-frame construction methods, respectively, of which the ledger method currently seems popular for three-story and taller structures. CFS bearing studs have also been used with other floor systems such as concrete topping over steel deck as well as precast plank floors. Each of these floor systems has special considerations for the enginner to keep in mind when designing the CFS bearing studs to support the floor framing.

1. CFS Floor Joist   **AISI S240 Section B1.2.3 "In-Line Framing"**

Since the CFS top track does not have much flexural capacity about its weak axis to support the reaction of horizontal framing members, the centerline (mid-width) of the CFS floor joist, CFS rafter, CFS truss, and CFS structural wall stud (above or beneath) must be aligned vertically within the tolerances of AISI S240 Figure B1.2.3-1.

As can be seen in Figure 3-32, a fair amount of coordination is required in placing the framing members to limit the amount of offset between them. Even with a ¾-inch offset, there can be a fair amount of reduction in the axial capacity of the stud.

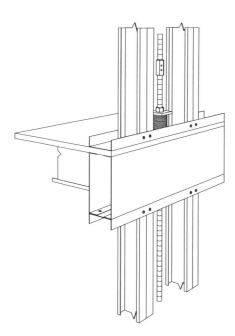

Figure 3-30. Floor-joist platform-framed CFS light-frame construction

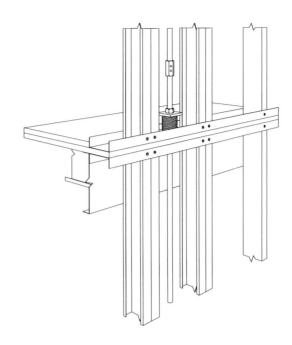

Figure 3-31. Ledger-framed CFS light-frame construction

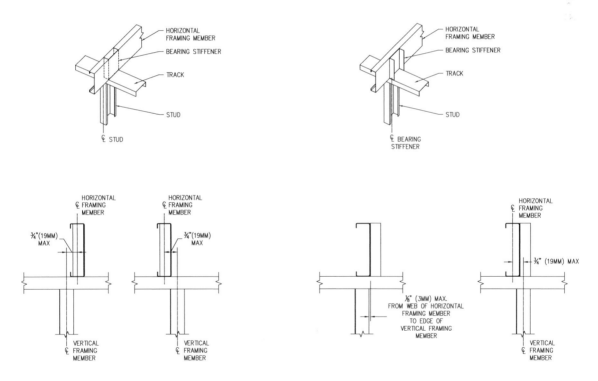

Figure 3-32. AISI S240 Figure B1.2.3-1: "In-Line Framing" (figure courtesy of AISI)

2. Wood Floor Joist

Since the wall top track does not have much flexural capacity about its weak axis, typically a wood single plate or double plate is added to the top of the stud wall. On longer-span floor joists, where heavy floor live loads occur or the design includes partition loads, the single or double wood top plate may not be adequate in flexure about the weak axis either. In such cases, studs and joists must be aligned similar to in-line framing described previously, or a full-depth wood rim joist can be framed on top of the wood top plate with the joists hung from the rim joist using hangers. The shear strength, flexural strength, and stiffness of the wood rim joist allow the floor joist to occur anywhere along the length of the rim joist without the designer needing to worry about alignment with the wall studs. This is consistent with AISI S240 Figure B1.2.3-1 "In-Line Framing," where the framing member alignment tolerance is not required when a structural load distribution member is specified in accordance with an approved design or approved design standard.

Since the nominal widths of available wood framing members used as rim joists are typically narrower than the depth of the CFS studs (4× rim on 4-inch-deep CFS studs, 4× or 6× rim on 6-inch-deep CFS studs, etc.), the wood single or double top plate needs to be cut to be the same width as the CFS top track. This provides a load path from the narrower rim joist to the full width of the CFS stud. Where beams frame into the wall rim joist, then multiple studs should occur under the rim joist where the beam connection occurs, as required to support the beam reaction force.

3. Steel Deck with Concrete Topping and Precast Plank Floors, with or without Concrete Topping

CFS stud walls are used in both residential and commercial structures to support floor systems constructed from steel deck and precast planks that may or may not have concrete topping. Figure 3-33 shows concrete over a steel-deck floor system framing over a CFS-framed wall. The use of these types of floor systems is beyond the scope of this design example.

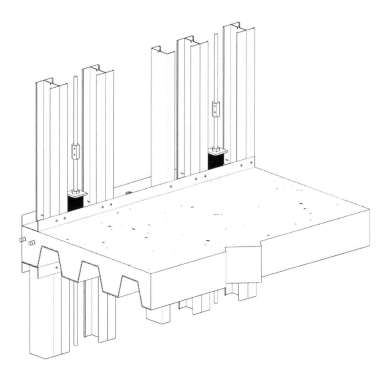

Figure 3-33. Concrete over steel-deck floor

Author's Discussion

Bare precast planks and both steel-deck and precast planks with concrete topping are floor systems that are significantly heavier than the floor joist systems used in traditional light-frame construction. Light-frame construction is defined in Chapter 2 of the IBC as "A type of construction whose vertical and horizontal structural elements are primarily formed by a system of repetitive wood or cold-formed steel framing members." The use of bare precast concrete planks and both steel-deck and precast planks with a concrete topping as a horizontal framing system clearly does not fit within this definition of light-frame construction. Where CFS stud walls, or wood stud walls for that matter, are to be used with these heavier floor/roof framing systems, these building structures should not be considered as light-frame construction and should not be designed to use a response modification coefficient *R* associated with light-frame construction.

ASCE 7 Table 12.2.1 provides response modification coefficients *R* based on the seismic-force-resisting system that the building uses, but does not differentiate as to the mass of the floor system when utilizing light-frame construction. As a comparison, the response modification coefficient *R* for the different steel moment-frame types used in high seismic zones varies, and there are height and weight limitations. The use of light-frame wood stud walls or CFS stud walls sheathed with shear panels or CFS diagonal straps may not be appropriate as the lateral-resisting system for this type of building system in high-seismic regions. Lateral-resisting systems using structural steel frames (brace frames, moment frames, and steel-plate shear walls), concrete, or masonry shear walls are more appropriate to resist the seismic lateral horizontal forces induced from the larger mass of these building structures.

In SDC D, both ordinary and intermediate steel moment frames would not be permitted in these structures using precast plank or concrete topping over a steel deck, since the floor mass likely exceeds the 35 psf weight limitation and implied expected ductility performance of these steel frames associated with their response modification coefficients *R*. Similarly, the implied ductility performance of sheathed wood stud shear walls, CFS stud shear walls, or CFS diagonal strap-braced walls, based on their light-frame response modification coefficient *R*-values for construction, may be reduced related to the greater associated building mass in buildings that have floor/roof systems constructed of precast planks or metal decking and precast planks with a structural concrete topping slab.

AISI S400 Section B1.5 "Seismic Load Effects from Other Concrete or Masonry Components" does permit CFS systems to be designed to resist seismic forces from other concrete and masonry components (other than walls), including masonry veneers as well as floor systems utilizing concrete topping over a steel deck or structural reinforced concrete floors. The design then has to also be in accordance with AISI S100 and required deflection limits as specified in the concrete and masonry standards or model building codes.

AISI S400 Section B1.4 "Seismic Load Effects Contributed by Masonry and Concrete Walls" is similar to what is permitted by AWC for light-frame wood construction (single-story limit, two-story exceptions, etc.), which are reasonable limits since a combination of lateral-resisting systems are being utilized (concrete or masonry shear walls with light-frame construction wood or CFS-framed shear walls). The author's concern is for taller buildings that have the heavier weight floor systems previously discussed that depend on *only* using light-frame sheathed CFS or wood-frame shear walls or diagonally strapped CFS studs with the associated response modification coefficients *R* for the lateral-resisting system (no combination of lateral-resisting systems), and achieving the same expected ductility performance of the light-frame sheathed shear wall system.

The designer needs to use caution when using a combination of lateral-resisting systems (examples: concrete shear walls, steel-braced frames) with the light-frame sheathed shear walls or CFS diagonal strap-braced walls, particularly with these heavy floor systems in any seismic region. The lateral loads go where the stiffness occurs, and the light-frame sheathed or diagonally strap-braced walls are not going to have near the same stiffness and strength as properly detailed masonry shear walls, concrete shear walls, or steel-braced frames.

15. Discussion: Seismic Joints

As occurs with many large multistory residential light-frame building projects, there can be several buildings on a single podium slab. Where the buildings are distinctly separate, they must satisfy the minimum separation distance between buildings as required in the building code. In many cases, these light-frame buildings are typically continuous buildings arranged in a doughnut shape or very long buildings with distinct areas where the floor plan is greatly reduced in width, often reducing down to 10 or 15 feet or possibly narrower. In some cases the buildings are interconnected with pedestrian bridges.

Historically most multistory light-frame buildings have ignored the use of seismic joints in those areas where the footprint of the building significantly narrows relative to the building footprint on each side of this narrowed area. Depending on the actual width and length of this narrow building strip, the buildings on each side of the narrow strip area may be behaving more as separate individual buildings as opposed to a single building, possibly moving in opposite directions during an earthquake. The opposite-direction movement of the buildings could tear apart the narrow strip area diaphragm or cause it to pull away from one of the buildings. This could be particularly true where pedestrian bridges are used to connect the various floor levels of individual buildings.

If an engineer was designing a multistory all-steel-frame building with concrete topping over a steel deck, or all-concrete cast-in-place or precast buildings for a given footprint, and the engineer determined that a seismic joint was required, then a multistory light-frame building with the same footprint should probably also have a seismic joint in the same location.

15.1 BUILDING SEISMIC JOINTS

Designers need to give serious consideration to providing seismic joints at those locations where the light-frame building footprint significantly narrows in width. When the narrowed portion of the building is only 10 to 15 feet wide or less and the remaining footprint on each side of this narrowed region is 40 to 60 feet wide, the diaphragm cannot be realistically expected to transfer the design loads across this narrow building width. In such locations a seismic joint should be introduced to allow the building to move as two individual structures. Often these narrow areas are paths of egress, so it may be prudent for the engineer to design the narrow areas so that they remain functional after an earthquake. Consideration will also have to be given to utilities passing across the seismic joint that have to remain in service after the seismic event.

15.2 PEDESTRIAN BRIDGES

In this design example there were two separate buildings, A and B, and a pedestrian bridge was provided between them at the second- and third-floor levels. A seismic joint was provided between the pedestrian bridge and Building A at both the second and third floors. A two-story steel moment frame was provided at the end of the bridge at Building A to provide lateral stability, orthogonal to the direction of the bridge span. The bridge longitudinal framing members were checked as drag members to transfer the bridge seismic design forces back into both the second- and third-floor framing levels of Building B when the bridge seismic movement is in the direction of the bridge span. As a path of egress, it was determined that the two-story bridge should have a seismic joint to increase the likelihood the pedestrian bridge will remain functional after an earthquake.

16. Discussion: Elevators

16.1 SEISMIC AND FRAMING CONSIDERATIONS

Multistory light-frame construction introduces issues with elevators and elevator guide-rail supports, particularly in high seismic regions. In light-frame construction, the floor construction is typically nominal wood-frame construction, engineered I-joists, or CFS joists. When the floor construction is conventional dimension-lumber framing, there are issues with vertical shrinkage of the floor joist and to a much lesser extent with engineered wood-framing products. CFS joists do not have the shrinkage issues but do experience settlement as studs settle into the tracks if they are not built completely seated. Since lumber shrinkage occurs over time as the wood framing dries out, the elevator cab stops at each floor level will likely have to be reset a couple of times to account for the vertical shrinkage of the wood floor framing, so that when the elevator cab doors open, the elevator cab floor is flush with the finish floor level at each floor level of the building. The amount of vertical movement will be greatest at the upper floor levels of the building as the amount of vertical shrinkage is cumulative over multiple floor levels.

Elevator manufacturers also have concerns regarding attaching the elevator cab guide-rail supports in the elevator shaft walls to the floor framing, typically not wanting the cab guide-rail supports to be attached to wood framing due to concerns with wood shrinkage and because the attachments of the wood framing can become loose over time. The elevator cab guide-rail is attached by horizontal brackets, provided by the elevator manufacturer, to the elevator cab guide-rail support placed within the elevator shaft wall. Typically, a custom-fabricated steel face plate bracket is designed by the engineer of record (EOR) and mounted to the elevator cab guide-rail support. An opening is cut into the shaft wall gypsum wall board to fit flush around the custom fabricated steel face bracket to which the elevator guide-rail horizontal bracket is attached. The custom-fabricated steel face plate allows for some flexibility in locating the guide-rail support in the shaft wall.

The elevator cab guide rails themselves are offset inward, away from the elevator shaft walls by adjustable horizontal guide-rail brackets, which are spaced vertically over the height of the elevator cab guide rail. The guide-rail offset from the face of the elevator shaft wall typically ranges between 4 and 18 inches.

One style of elevator that has become popular is traction elevators, which eliminates the need for an elevator machine room, as the hoist machinery is now installed in the elevator shaft. Seismic horizontal forces for the attachment of the elevator cab guide rail can be in the range of 4000 to 6000 pounds for passenger elevators (greater for freight elevators) and need to be developed into the floor-framing system. The guide-rail support deflection criteria are stringent, typically limiting the allowable deflection to $\frac{1}{8}$ inch under normal elevator cab running loads, and not more than $\frac{1}{4}$ inch due to seismic forces.

The application of the elevator cab guide-rail horizontal design forces, being offset from the elevator shaft wall, results in a twist, or torque, on the guide-rail support in the shaft wall in addition to the direct forces. This torque force is often overlooked by the design engineers. Typically, the best type of framing members to support these horizontal design forces is either a square or rectangular hollow structural section (HSS) since each has a closed cross section, which is good for resisting torsion forces.

Currently in light-frame construction it is common for the designer to use wood rim beams on the four sides of the elevator floor opening and then just span the HSS guide-rail supports vertically between floor levels. This may not be acceptable to the elevator manufacturer since the connection of the guide-rail support is to the floor wood rim beam. The load path for transferring the guide-rail design forces needs to be evaluated, and the corners of the wood rim beam ring typically need to be mechanically connected to transfer the design forces between ring members. The floor sheathing nailed to the top of the wood beams should not be considered as being sufficient to transfer loads acting perpendicular to the wood beam as this puts the top of the wood beam in cross-grain bending. Also, an elevator cab guide-rail support attachment point often occurs at the floor line, requiring a bracket bolted to the wood rim beam, which may require an additional strut framing member behind it to extend back and away from the elevator shaft to transfer the design loads into the surrounding floor-framing system. A discussion with the elevator manufacturer is needed to determine acceptable floor connections.

If CFS joists are used around the elevator shaft floor opening, then struts extending back into the floor-framing system away from the elevator shaft will be required to transfer the elevator guide-rail support reactions into the surrounding floor framing.

It is probably best for the engineer to frame the four corners of the elevator shaft with hollow structural section (HSS) columns and with a ring of HSS beams around the elevator shaft floor opening at each floor level, including the elevator overrun above the roof. The elevator guide-rail supports in the shaft walls, set to align with the elevator cab guide rails, would then be erected to span vertically between HSS floor and roof ring beams. The steel rings provide a load path around the perimeter of the elevator shaft floor opening to transfer the guide-rail design forces into the floor framing. The steel beams are generally smaller than the wood member rings and can more easily resist the design forces causing bending in the floor beam, possibly leading to fewer strut members for transferring forces into the surrounding floor diaphragm.

A steel beam ring is more expensive than an all-wood rim beam ring at the floor levels. An all-wood rim beam ring, when acceptable to the elevator manufacturer, can lead to more complicated bolted connections to wood framing members, as well as additional strut members into the surrounding floor framing. If conventional 2× lumber is used for the floors, this can be an issue since the floor joists will shrink vertically and the steel framing of the elevator shaft will not shorten, which can lead to surrounding floors sloping upward to the elevator shaft, the worst being at the upper floor levels since the joist shrinkage is cumulative over the floor levels of the building.

Whether the elevator is framed with a steel ring or wood framing around the elevator shaft floor opening, the designer should provide separate structural drawings showing full-height building framing elevations of the elevator shaft vertical support framing and guide-rail support points. These drawings should include all required framing connections to transfer the guide-rail reaction forces into each floor level of the building for all elevators in the building. Elevators in multistory light-frame structures are complex, and additional detailing is required.

The design of the elevator is typically a deferred submittal to the building department, so something should be shown on the structural drawing regarding the elevator framing for the permit set (elevator guide-rail supports, roof hoist beam, floor-framing ring, corner steel columns [when used], etc.). This structural drawing can be revised/updated once the elevator manufacturer and type of elevator is selected, but in the meanwhile, the structural drawings provide references for initial pricing purposes by the building general contractor.

16.2 ELEVATOR SHAFT WALLS

Typically, CFS C studs are used for most stud wall framing. Shaft walls for mechanical ducts or elevators can be an exception where CFS J studs are utilized to allow for drywall placement from the opposite side of the stud wall, so no scaffolding has to be set up in the shaft to install the drywall sheathing. The fire rating of the shaft may introduce furring channels on the CFS studs as well. The designer needs to determine if the shaft wall of the elevator or mechanical shaft should be included as part of the shear wall system as there is no testing of a sheathed shear wall using J studs or C studs with furring channels between the sheathing and the C studs.

17. Items Not Addressed in This Example

The following items are not addressed in this example but are nevertheless necessary for a complete design of the building's lateral-resisting system:

1. Wind design to compare to seismic to determine which governs.

2. Design of the structural podium deck for shear wall overturning and uplift forces.

3. Design of shear wall continuous rod anchorages to a concrete podium deck.

4. Special Inspections and Structural Observation of building construction.

5. Distribution of lateral forces between light-frame sheathed shear walls along the same wall line.

6. Design of seismic joints.

7. Mixed systems (when used with light-frame sheathed shear walls):

   a. Rigidity of concrete/CMU walls with light-frame walls at the same floor level.

      i. Often there can be a couple of concrete or CMU shear walls that occur above the building's main podium level for supporting a structural slab at the floor level above. This can occur over a driveway leading to a subterranean parking level below the main podium located at grade level or a high bay for a first-floor retail space where the second floor is the main podium deck level for the residential framing above. The structural slab and concrete/CMU walls are used to provide required occupancy and fire separation between the residential level above and the parking level/retail space below.

      ii. The relative rigidity of the concrete and CMU walls relative to the light-frame sheathed shear walls needs to be addressed concerning how design forces are distributed between walls.

   b. Rigidity of structural steel moment frames\braced frames with light-frame walls at the same floor level.

      i. Where structural steel moment frames or structural steel-braced frames occur at the same floor level as the light-frame shear walls, the relative rigidity between moment frames, braced frames, and light-frame sheathed shear walls needs to be addressed concerning how design forces are distributed between frames and walls.

18. References

See the reference listing at the front of this design volume.

Design Example 4
Masonry Shear Wall Building

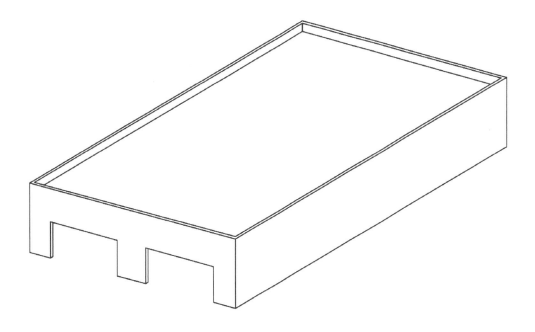

OVERVIEW

While masonry can be used to construct buildings of all types and sizes, it is most often used in low-rise construction, particularly for residential, retail, light commercial, and institutional buildings. This type of construction has generally had a good earthquake performance record. The warehouse building considered in this example is a typical one-story masonry "box building" with a wood-frame roof.

The design of masonry is based on the 2016 edition of TMS 402, *Building Code Requirements for Masonry Structures*, and TMS 602, *Specification for Masonry Structures,* which are developed by The Masonry Society (TMS). The code contains design provisions for structural design using both strength-design and allowable stress design procedures. This example will focus only on strength-design procedures.

OUTLINE

1. Building Geometry and Loads

2. Calculation of the Design Base Shear and Load Combinations

3. Design of Walls to Resist In-Plane Seismic Loads

4. Design of Walls to Resist Out-of-Plane Seismic Loads

5. Out-of-Plane Wall Anchorage

1. Building Geometry and Loads

1.1 GIVEN INFORMATION

- 60 feet × 90 feet in plan with typical floor and roof framing shown in Figures 4-1 and 4-2. An elevation of the wall on line A is shown in Figure 4-3.

- Walls consist of 8-inch-thick (nominal), solid-grouted, medium-weight concrete masonry units (CMU) laid in running bond with Type S mortar. Masonry has a specified compressive strength, f'_m, of 2000 psi with units laid in running bond. Steel reinforcement is Grade 60 ($f_y = 60$ ksi). Figure 4-4 shows a section through the walls on lines 1 and 3.

- The self-weight of the roof and roof framing is 17 psf, and the roof live load is 20 psf.

- The building is located in Oakland, California, on a site that is classified as Site Class D.

1.2 BUILDING WEIGHTS

Since the building has masonry shear walls and a roof with wood structural panel (WSP) sheathing, the roof diaphragm may be idealized as flexible as permitted by Section 12.3.1.1 of ASCE 7, Minimum Design Loads and Associated Criteria for Buildings and Other Structures. This means that the diaphragm spans between the load-resisting walls, which resist lateral load from the diaphragm in proportion to tributary width. Inertial forces generated by walls perpendicular to the direction of loading are transferred to the foundations and to the diaphragm, which spans between walls parallel to the applied loads. In addition to the seismic load from the diaphragm and out-of-plane walls, walls parallel to the direction of loading also resist the inertial loads generated by their self-weight.

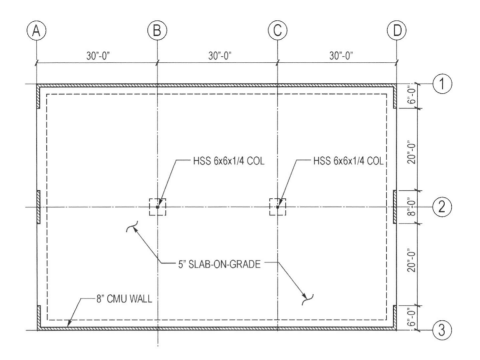

Figure 4-1. Floor plan

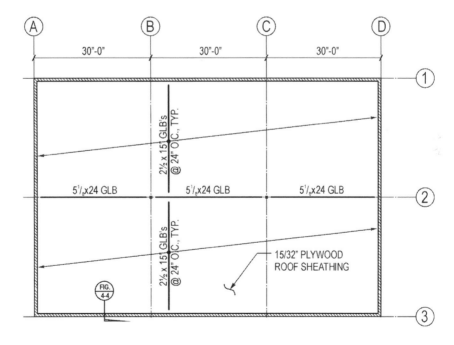

Figure 4-2. Roof framing plan

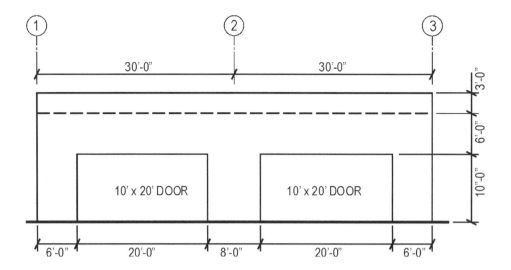

Figure 4-3. Elevation on line A

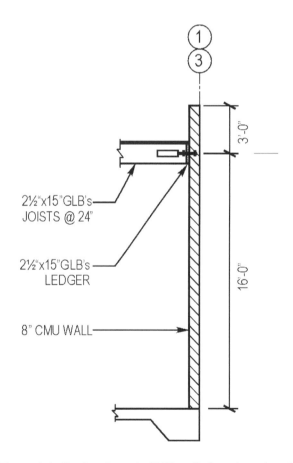

Figure 4-4. Section through CMU wall along lines 1 and 3

The seismic weight of the roof is equal to

$$W_{roof} = \frac{17 \text{ psf}(60 \text{ ft} \times 90 \text{ ft})}{1000} = 92 \text{ kips}$$

The masonry wall is constructed with 8-inch-thick, solid-grouted, medium-weight CMU, which has a self-weight of 78 psf. Therefore, for earthquake loads in the north-south direction, the seismic weight of perpendicular walls is equal to the weight of the east-west walls and parapets that are tributary to the roof diaphragm. Conservatively ignoring any openings in the walls on lines 1 and 3:

$$W_{walls, \text{ lines } 1 \& 3} = 78 \text{ psf} \left(\frac{19^2}{2} \right) \left(\frac{1}{16} \right) 90 \text{ ft} \times 2 = 158 \text{ kips}$$

Taking into account the fact that 35 percent of the walls in the north-south direction consists of openings, which can be assumed to have a weight of 10 psf:

$$W_{walls, \text{ lines } A \& D} = [0.35(10 \text{ psf}) + 0.65(78 \text{ psf})](60 \text{ ft} \times 19 \text{ ft})2 = 124 \text{ kips}$$

Therefore, the total seismic weight in the north-south direction is equal to:

$$W_{roof} + W_{walls, \text{ lines } 1 \& 3} + W_{walls, \text{ lines } A \& D} = 92 + 158 + 124 = 374 \text{ kips}$$

2. Calculation of the Design Base Shear and Load Combinations   ASCE 7

2.1 DESIGN SPECTRAL ACCELERATIONS

The spectral accelerations to be used in design are equal to

$S_{DS} = 1.00g$	$S_{D1} = 0.60g$

2.2 CLASSIFY THE STRUCTURAL SYSTEM AND DETERMINE SEISMIC DESIGN PARAMETERS

From ASCE 7 Tables 11.6-1 and 11.6-2, the building is assigned to Seismic Design Category (SDC) D. ASCE 7 Table 12.2-1 indicates that only special reinforced masonry walls are permitted in SDC D, E, and F. The design coefficients for special reinforced shear walls in bearing wall systems are as follows:

$R = 5.0$	$\Omega_0 = 2.5$	$C_d = 3.5$

2.3 RESPONSE SPECTRUM

Determine the approximate fundamental building period using Section 12.8.2.1:

$$C_t = 0.02 \text{ and } x = 0.75 \qquad\qquad \text{T 12.8-2}$$

$$T_a = C_t h_n{}^x = 0.02 \times 16^{0.75} = 0.16 \text{ sec} \qquad\qquad \text{Eq 12.8-7}$$

$$T_o = 0.2 \frac{S_{D1}}{S_{DS}} = 0.2 \frac{0.60}{1.00} = 0.12 \text{ sec} \qquad\qquad \text{\S11.4.6}$$

$$S_a = S_{DS}\left(0.4 + 0.6 \frac{T}{T_o}\right) = \left(0.4 + 0.6 \frac{T}{0.12}\right) = 0.4 + 5.0T \text{ for } T < T_o \qquad\qquad \text{Eq 11.4-5}$$

$$T_s = \frac{S_{D1}}{S_{DS}} = \frac{0.60}{1.00} = 0.60 \text{ sec} \qquad\qquad \text{\S11.4.6}$$

$$S_a = \frac{S_{D1}}{T} = \frac{0.60}{T} \text{ for } T > T_s \qquad\qquad \text{Eq 11.4-6}$$

The long-period equation for S_a does not apply here because the long-period transition occurs at 12 seconds (from Figure 22-16).

2.4 HORIZONTAL IRREGULARITIES   T 12.3-1

1a.   Torsional irregularity—does not apply to diaphragms that can be idealized as flexible.

1b. to 5.   By inspection, the building does not have any of these horizontal structural irregularities.

> NO HORIZONTAL STRUCTURAL IRREGULARITIES

2.5 VERTICAL IRREGULARITIES   T 12.3-2

1a. to 5b.   By inspection, the one-story building does not qualify for any of the vertical structural irregularities.

> NO VERTICAL STRUCTURAL IRREGULARITIES

2.6 LATERAL FORCE PROCEDURE   T 12.6-1

1. Simplified alternative structural design criteria—The building satisfies the requirements of Section 12.14.1.1—PERMITTED

2. Equivalent lateral force analysis—According to Table 12.6-1, since $T < 3.5T_s$ (0.16 sec < 2.10 sec) and the building is regular and is Occupancy Category II—PERMITTED

3. Modal response spectrum analysis—PERMITTED

4. Seismic response history procedures—PERMITTED

> USE EQUIVALENT LATERAL FORCE ANALYSIS

2.7 BASE SHEAR

$$C_s = \frac{S_{DS}}{\left(\dfrac{R}{I_e}\right)} = \frac{1.00}{\left(\dfrac{5.0}{1.0}\right)} = 0.20 \le \left[\frac{S_{D1}}{T\left(\dfrac{R}{I_e}\right)} = \frac{0.60}{0.16\left(\dfrac{5.0}{1.0}\right)} = 0.75\right] \qquad \text{Eq 12.8-2 and Eq 12.8-3}$$

Also,

$$C_s \ge 0.01, \text{ and } C_s \ge \frac{0.5S_1}{\left(\dfrac{R}{I_e}\right)} = \frac{0.5 \times 0.6}{\left(\dfrac{5.0}{1.0}\right)} = 0.06 \qquad \text{Eq 12.8-5 and Eq 12.8-6}$$

$$\boxed{C_s = 0.20}$$

$$V = C_s W = 0.20 \times 374 = 75 \text{ kips} \qquad \text{Eq 12.8-1}$$

$$\boxed{V = 75 \text{ kips}}$$

2.8 REDUNDANCY FACTOR

According to Section 12.3.4, the redundancy factor should be calculated for each principal axis. The redundancy factor is 1.3 unless either Section 12.3.4.2(a) or 12.3.4.2(b) is satisfied, in which case the redundancy factor can be taken as 1.0. The wall segments in the north-south building have a height-to-length ratio of greater than 1.0. By inspection, the removal of any wall segment does not result in more than a 33 percent reduction in story strength. Removal of any wall segment also does not result in an extreme torsional irregularity since the building has a flexible diaphragm. Therefore, from Table 12.3-3, the redundancy factor is 1.0 in the north-south direction. In the east-west direction, the length of shear wall on each side of the structure consists of more than two bays, where the number of bays is equal to the length of shear wall divided by the story height. Therefore, from Section 12.3.4.2(b), the redundancy factor is 1.0 in the east-west direction.

$$\rho = 1.0 \text{ FOR EAST-WEST DIRECTION}$$

$$\rho = 1.0 \text{ FOR NORTH-SOUTH DIRECTION}$$

2.9 LOAD COMBINATIONS

For the one-story building, the applicable load combinations for earthquake design are as follows (Section 2.3.6):

$$(1.2 + 0.2S_{DS})D + \rho Q_E = (1.2 + 0.2 \times 1.0)D + 1.0Q_E = 1.4D + Q_E \qquad \text{Load Comb. 6 (modified)}$$

$$(0.9 - 0.2S_{DS})D + \rho Q_E = (0.9 - 0.2 \times 1.0)D + 1.0Q_E = 0.7D + Q_E \qquad \text{Load Comb. 7 (modified)}$$

3. Design of Walls to Resist In-Plane Seismic Loads   TMS 402

The procedures for designing to resist in-plane loads will be illustrated using the 8-foot-long wall segment on line A. Since the roof diaphragm can be idealized as flexible, the lateral load in the north-south direction is resisted equally by the walls on lines A and D. Figures 4-5 and 4-6 show the results of a computer analysis of the wall on line A.

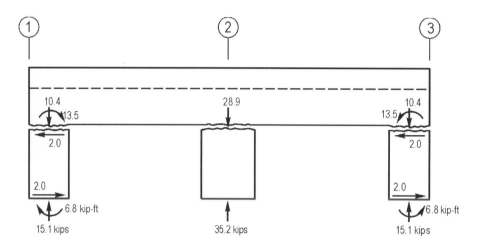

Figure 4-5. Dead loads on wall along line A

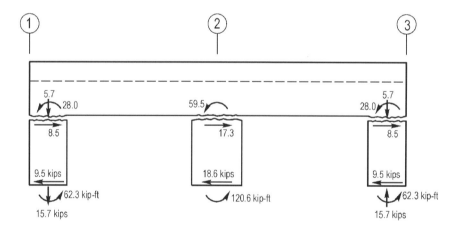

Figure 4-6. Earthquake loads on wall along line A

3.1 PRELIMINARY REINFORCEMENT LAYOUT

Figure 4-7 shows a preliminary layout of reinforcement for the 8-foot-long wall segment.

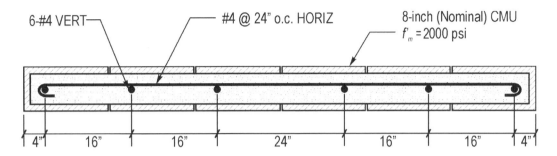

Figure 4-7. Layout of reinforcement for 8-foot-long wall segment line A

In accordance with TMS 402 Section 7.3.2.6, the maximum spacing (s_{max}) of vertical reinforcement in special reinforced masonry shear walls shall be the smallest of one-third the length (L_w) of the shear wall, one-third the height (H) of the shear wall, and 48 inches (24 inches for masonry not laid in running bond).

$$s_{max} = 24 \text{ in} < 48 \text{ in} \ \ldots \text{ OK}$$

$$< \frac{H}{3} = \frac{10 \text{ ft}(12)}{3} = 40 \text{ in} \ \ldots \text{ OK}$$

$$< \frac{L}{3} = \frac{8 \text{ ft}(12)}{3} = 32 \text{ in} \ \ldots \text{ OK}$$

Horizontal reinforcement (A_s) shall be at least 0.2 in² and have maximum spacing of the smallest of one-third the length of the shear wall, one-third the height of the shear wall, and 48 inches (24 inches for masonry not laid in running bond).

$$A_s = 0.20 \text{ in}^2 = 0.20 \text{ in}^2 \ \ldots \text{ OK}$$

$$s_{max} = 24 \text{ in} < 48 \text{ in} \ \ldots \text{ OK}$$

$$< \frac{H}{3} = \frac{10 \text{ ft}(12)}{3} = 40 \text{ in} \ \ldots \text{ OK}$$

$$< \frac{L}{3} = \frac{8 \text{ ft}(12)}{3} = 32 \text{ in} \ \ldots \text{ OK}$$

The minimum cross-sectional area of reinforcement in each direction shall be not less than 0.0007 multiplied by the gross cross-sectional area of the wall:

$$\left(\frac{\Sigma A_s}{tL_w} \right) = \frac{6(0.20 \text{ in}^2)}{7.63 \text{ in}(96 \text{ in})} = 0.0016 > 0.0007 \ \ldots \text{ OK}$$

$$\left(\frac{A_v}{st} \right)_{hor} = \frac{0.20 \text{ in}^2}{24 \text{ in}(7.63 \text{ in})} = 0.0011 > 0.0007 \ \ldots \text{ OK}$$

where t is the wall thickness. The sum of the vertical and horizontal reinforcements shall exceed 0.002 times the gross cross-sectional area of the wall:

$$\left(\frac{\Sigma A_s}{tL_w}\right) + \left(\frac{A_v}{st}\right) = 0.0016 + 0.0011 = 0.0027 > 0.002 \ \ldots \text{ OK}$$

The vertical reinforcement must also be at least one-third the shear reinforcement:

$$\left(\frac{\Sigma A_s}{tL_w}\right) = 0.0016 > \frac{1}{3}\left(\frac{A_s}{tL_w}\right) = \frac{0.0011}{3} = 0.0004 \ \ldots \text{ OK}$$

3.2 IN-PLANE AXIAL AND FLEXURAL LOADS

The most effective way to evaluate the ability of a masonry wall to resist axial and flexural loads is to develop an interaction diagram. An interaction diagram is a plot of the change in flexural strength of a member with axial load that is developed using the basic assumptions for strength design. Combinations of factored axial load and bending moment that fall within the interaction diagram are acceptable, and the member can adequately resist such loads. If any combination of axial load and bending moment falls outside the interaction diagram, the cross section is inadequate, and the member must be redesigned.

To obtain an accurate interaction diagram, the designer determines the moment capacity for several values of applied axial load to obtain the smooth curve. Such an analysis is best determined with a specialized computer program. However, an approximate interaction diagram curve can be developed using selected points on the interaction diagram:

   a. The axial load capacity when there is no bending moment on the member.

   b. The flexural strength when there is no axial load.

   c. The balanced strain condition when the strain in the extreme compression fiber is equal to the maximum usable strain, and the strain in the extreme tension steel is equal to the steel yield strain.

The strength-reduction factor, ϕ, for all combinations of axial and flexural load is equal to 0.9. From Figures 4-5 and 4-6, the loads for the three applicable load combinations are as follows:

   1. $1.2D + 1.6L_r$
      $P_u = 49.1$ kips; $M_u = 0$ kip-ft; $V_u = 0$ kips (at the top of the wall segment)
      $P_u = 56.6$ kips; $M_u = 0$ kip-ft; $V_u = 0$ kips (at the bottom of the wall segment)

   2. $1.2D + E = 1.4D + E_h$
      $P_u = 40.5$ kips; $M_u = 59.5$ kip-ft; $V_u = 17.3$ kips (at the top of the wall segment)
      $P_u = 49.3$ kips; $M_u = 120.6$ kip-ft; $V_u = 18.7$ kips (at the bottom of the wall segment)

   3. $0.9D + E = 0.7D + E_h$
      $P_u = 20.2$ kips; $M_u = 59.5$ kip-ft; $V_u = 17.3$ kips (at the top of the wall segment)
      $P_u = 24.6$ kips; $M_u = 120.6$ kip-ft; $V_u = 18.7$ kips (at the bottom of the wall segment)

Check the capacity with axial loads alone and no flexural loads.

The effective height for compression loads, h, is equal to the full story height, H, since lateral support in the out-of-plane direction occurs only at the ground and roof levels. As specified in TMS 402 Section 9.3.2, reinforcing steel is not used to resist compression because it is not supported by lateral ties.

$$r = \frac{t}{\sqrt{12}} = \frac{7.63 \text{ in}}{\sqrt{12}} = 2.20 \text{ in}$$

$$\frac{h}{r} = \frac{16 \text{ ft}(12)}{2.20} = 87.3 < 99$$

The nominal axial strength, P_n, is therefore equal to:

$$P_n = 0.8 \left[0.8 f'_m (A_n - A_{st}) + f_y A_{st} \right] \left[1 - \left(\frac{h}{140r} \right)^2 \right] \qquad \text{TMS 402 Eq 9-15}$$

$$= 0.8 \left[0.8(2 \text{ ksi})(7.63 \text{ in} \times 96 \text{ in} - (0)) + 60 \text{ ksi}(0) \right] \left[1 - \left(\frac{87.3}{140} \right)^2 \right] = 573 \text{ kips}$$

where A_n is the net area of the cross section and A_{st} is the area of laterally tied longitudinal reinforcement (which is equal to 0 for the wall).

In accordance with TMS 402 Section 9.1.4, the strength reduction factor, ϕ, for combinations of axial and flexural load in reinforced masonry is equal to 0.9. Therefore,

$$\phi P_n = 0.9(573) = 516 \text{ kips} > P_u \ \ldots \ \text{OK}$$

For a given axial load (P_u), the corresponding moment (M_u) on the interaction diagram is determined by setting the masonry strain in the extreme compression fiber at ε_{mu} (which is equal to 0.0025 for concrete masonry; see TMS 402 Section of 9.3.2) and selecting a neutral axis depth (c). The compression force in the masonry is given by:

$$C_m = 0.64 c b f'_m$$

where b is width of the compression block, which is equal to the wall thickness, t in this case.

Using similar triangles, the strain in each reinforcing steel bar (ε_{si}) is given by:

$$\varepsilon_{si} = \varepsilon_{mu} \left(\frac{d_i - c}{c} \right)$$

where d_i is the distance from the extreme compression fiber to the reinforcing bar. The force in each reinforcing bar (T_{si}) is then given by:

$$T_{si} = \varepsilon_{si} E_s A_{si} = \varepsilon_{mu} \left(\frac{d_i - c}{c} \right) E_s A_{si} \le f_y A_{si}$$

where E_s is the steel modulus of elasticity, A_{si} is the area of each reinforcing bar, and f_y is the steel yield stress. If the selected neutral axis location does not result in equilibrium of forces on the cross section, the location of the neutral axis is modified until equilibrium exists within acceptable limits:

$$\Sigma T_{si} + P_u = C_m$$

Table 4-1 shows the forces on the cross section after iterations have determined the depth of the neutral axis to be 6.14 inches when there is no axial load.

$$\phi M_{n0} = 0.9 \left(\frac{3206.6}{12} \right) = 240 \text{ kip-ft}$$

Table 4-1. Equilibrium calculations for flexural strength with no axial load (c = 6.14 in)

	A_{si} (in^2)	d_i (in)	ε_{si} (in/in)	f_{si} (ksi)	P_{n0} (kips)	M_{n0} (kip-in)
Masonry		2.457			60.0	2732.6
Steel						
Bar 1	0.20	4.00	0.0009	—	—	—
Bar 2	0.20	20.00	−0.0056	−60.0	−12.0	−336.0
Bar 3	0.20	36.00	−0.0121	−60.0	−12.0	−144.0
Bar 4	0.20	60.00	−0.0219	−60.0	−12.0	144.0
Bar 5	0.20	76.00	−0.0284	−60.0	−12.0	336.0
Bar 6	0.20	92.00	−0.0349	−60.0	−12.0	528.0
Total	1.2				−0.0	3260.6

A balanced strain condition occurs when the strain in the extreme compression fiber is equal to the maximum usable strain, ε_{mu} (which is equal to 0.0025 for concrete masonry; see TMS 402 Section 9.3.2), and the strain in the extreme tension steel is equal to the steel yield strain. The depth of the neutral axis at the balanced strain condition, c_b, can therefore be determined from:

$$c_b = \frac{d}{\left(\dfrac{f_y}{E_s \varepsilon_{mu}} + 1 \right)} = \frac{d}{\left(\dfrac{60 \text{ ksi}}{29,000 \text{ ksi} \times 0.0025} + 1 \right)} = 0.547d = 0.547(92 \text{ in}) = 50.3 \text{ in}$$

Table 4-2 shows the forces on the cross section at the balanced condition:

$$\phi P_b = 0.9(469 \text{ kips}) = 422 \text{ kips}$$

$$\phi M_b = 0.9 \left(\frac{14,467 \text{ kip-in}}{12} \right) = 1085 \text{ kip-ft}$$

Figure 4-8 shows the interaction diagram and applied loads, indicating the wall has sufficient flexural strength.

Table 4-2. Equilibrium calculations for flexural strength at balanced condition (c = 50.3 in)

	A_i (in^2)	d_i (in)	ε_{si} (in/in)	f_{si} (ksi)	P_b (kips)	M_b (kip-in)
Masonry		20.13			491.5	13,697.5
Steel						
Bar 1	0.20	4.00	0.0023	—	—	—
Bar 2	0.20	20.00	0.0015	—	—	—
Bar 3	0.20	36.00	0.0007	—	—	—
Bar 4	0.20	60.00	−0.0005	−13.9	−2.8	33.5
Bar 5	0.20	76.00	−0.0013	−37.0	−7.4	207.1
Bar 6	0.20	92.00	−0.0021	−60.0	−12.0	528.0
Total	1.2				469.3	14,466.5

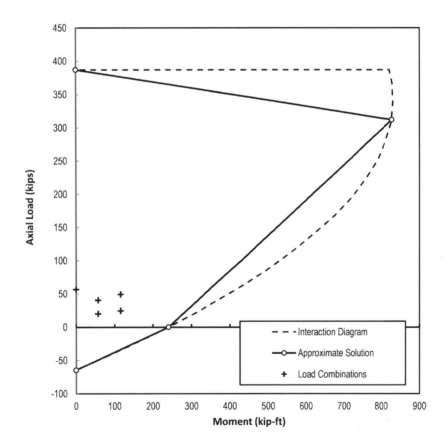

Figure 4-8. Layout of reinforcement for 8-foot-long wall segment

3.3 MAXIMUM REINFORCEMENT

TMS 402 §9.3.3.2

The ductility of a shear wall or its ability to deform in the nonlinear range is highly dependent on the amount of reinforcement in the wall. Thus, TMS 402 limits wall flexural reinforcement to levels that are consistent with the ductility inherent in the design parameters (R and C_d) specified in ASCE 7.

The maximum flexural reinforcement is limited by ensuring that the strain in the extreme tensile reinforcement exceeds steel yield strain by a specified amount, depending on the required ductility capacity. Table 4-3 shows the minimum required strain at the ultimate state, as a function of the steel yield strain, where d_v is the total depth of the cross section in the direction of shear being considered.

The verification of the maximum reinforcement is performed using the load combination $D + 0.75L + 0.525Q_E$, where Q_E is the effect of the horizontal component of earthquake load. Reinforcement in compression may be used in evaluating equilibrium of the cross section when calculating the maximum reinforcement even if it is not laterally supported by ties.

The provisions for maximum reinforcement may be superseded by using TMS 402 Section 9.3.6.6, which provides an alternative approach to ensure that walls have sufficient ductility. Walls of short or moderate height with relatively low axial loads and shear stresses are assumed to possess sufficient ductility. Otherwise, the use of confined boundary elements is required to increase the masonry compression strain capacity. Where special boundary elements are required, their effectiveness must be confirmed by testing to verify the strain capacity of the confined masonry.

Table 4-3. Minimum strain required for satisfying maximum reinforcement ratio

Basic Seismic-Force-Resisting System	R	$\dfrac{M_u}{V_u d_v}$	$\alpha_{min} = \dfrac{\varepsilon_s}{\varepsilon_y}$
Special Reinforced Masonry Shear Walls	5	>1.0	4.0
		< 1.0	1.5
Intermediate Reinforced Masonry Shear Walls	3.5	>1.0	3.0
		< 1.0	1.5
Walls Loaded Out-of-Plane	—	—	1.5
All Others	All	>1.0	1.5
	>1.5	< 1.0	1.5
	<1.5	< 1.0	None

At the base of the wall, the axial load for checking the maximum reinforcement is equal to:

$$P_{umr} = P_D + 0.75P_L + 0.525P_{Q_E} = 35.2 + 0.75(0) + 0.525(0) = 35.2 \text{ kips}$$

Table 4-4 shows the equilibrium calculations for determining the neutral axis and steel strain for the above axial load. From the table, the strain in the extreme tension fiber is equal to:

$$\varepsilon_{s,max} = 0.0223 = 10.8\varepsilon_y > 4\varepsilon_y \ \ldots \ \text{OK}$$

Table 4-4. Equilibrium calculations for maximum reinforcement (c = 8.93 in)

	A_i (in²)	d_i (in)	ε_{si} (in/in)	f_{si} (ksi)	P_{umr} (kips)	M_{umr} (kip-in)
Masonry		3.57			87.2	3873.7
Steel						
Bar 1	0.20	4.00	0.0014	40.0	8.0	352.1
Bar 2	0.20	20.00	−0.0031	−60.0	−12.0	−336.0
Bar 3	0.20	36.00	−0.0076	−60.0	−12.0	−144.0
Bar 4	0.20	60.00	−0.0143	−60.0	−12.0	144.0
Bar 5	0.20	76.00	−0.0188	−60.0	−12.0	336.0
Bar 6	0.20	92.00	−0.0233	−60.0	−12.0	528.0
	1.2				35.19	4753.8

3.4 IN-PLANE SHEAR STRENGTH   TMS 402 §9.3.4.1.2

In order to reduce the possibility of a non-ductile shear failure, TMS 402 Section 7.3.2.6.1.1 stipulates that shear strength, ϕV_n, of special reinforced masonry shear walls must exceed the shear corresponding to the development of 1.25 times the nominal moment strength, M_n. However, the nominal shear strength, V_n, need not exceed $2.5V_u$. For shear, $\phi = 0.8$ per TMS Section 9.1.4.5.

From the interaction diagram in Figure 4-8, the moment strength increases with axial load in the range of axial load considered. The nominal moment strength at the maximum axial load combination ($P_u = 49.3$ kips for $1.2D + E$) is equal to 411 kip-ft. Therefore, 1.25 times the nominal moment strength is given by:

$$1.25M_n = 1.25\left(\frac{411 \text{ kip-ft}}{0.9}\right) = 571 \text{ kip-ft}$$

Then the shear demand corresponding to 1.25 times the wall flexural strength is equal to:

$$V_{1.25M_n} = V_u\left(\frac{1.25M_n}{M_u}\right) = 18.7 \text{ kips}\left(\frac{571 \text{ kip-ft}}{120.6 \text{ kip-ft}}\right) = 88.5 \text{ kips}$$

However, since ϕV_n need not exceed $\phi 2.5V_u$:

$$\phi 2.5V_u = 0.8(2.5)(18.7) = 37.4 \text{ kips} \quad \rightarrow \text{Governs.}$$

The shear strength of masonry members is a combination of the shear resistance provided by the masonry, V_{nm}, and the shear resistance provided by shear reinforcement, V_{ns}. The nominal shear strength is therefore equal to:

$$V_n = (V_{nm} + V_{ns})\gamma_g \qquad \text{TMS 402 Eq 9-17}$$

where γ_g is a grouted shear wall factor that is equal to 1.0 for fully grouted walls (γ_g is equal to 0.75 for partially grouted walls). Shear strength is highly dependent on the shear span-to-depth ratio of the member, which is defined by the term $M_u/V_u d_v$ in which M_u is the moment demand corresponding to the factored shear demand, V_u, and d_v is the actual depth of the masonry cross section in the direction the shear is being considered. The value of $M_u/V_u d_v$ must be positive and need not exceed 1.0. From Figures 4-5 and 4-6, the shear span ratio of the wall segment is equal to:

$$\frac{M}{V d_v} = \frac{120.6 \text{ kip-ft}}{18.7 \text{ kips}(8 \text{ ft})} = 0.81 < 1.0$$

Conservatively using the load combination with the smallest axial load at the base of the wall, the shear strength provided by the masonry is given by:

$$V_{nm} = \left[4 - 1.75\left(\frac{M_u}{V_u d_v}\right) \right] A_n \sqrt{f'_m} + 0.25 P_u \qquad \text{TMS 402 Eq 9-20}$$

$$= \frac{[4 - 1.75(0.81)](7.63 \text{ in})(96 \text{ in})\sqrt{2000} \text{ psi}}{1000} + 0.25(24.6 \text{ kips}) = 90.7 \text{ kips}$$

The shear strength contributed by the steel is equal to:

$$V_{ns} = 0.5\left(\frac{A_v}{s}\right) F_y d_v = 0.5\left(\frac{0.2 \text{ in}}{24 \text{ in}^2}\right)(60 \text{ ksi})(96 \text{ in}) = 24 \text{ kips} \qquad \text{TMS 402 Eq 9-21}$$

Therefore,

$$V_n = (V_{nm} + V_{ns})1.0 = 90.7 + 24 = 115 \text{ kips}$$

When $M_u/V_u d_v < 0.25$, the nominal shear strength is limited by the following equation:

$$V_n \leq 6\left(A_n \sqrt{f'_m}\right)\gamma_g \qquad \text{TMS 402 Eq 9-18}$$

and when $M_u/V_u d_v > 1.0$,

$$V_n \leq 4\left(A_n \sqrt{f'_m}\right)\gamma_g \qquad \text{TMS 402 Eq 9-19}$$

For values of $M_u/V_u d_v$ between 0.25 and 1.0, the maximum value of V_n is determined by interpolation between Equations 9-18 and 9-19. The maximum shear strength of the wall is thus given by:

$$V_{n,\max} \leq \left(4 + \frac{(1-0.81)(6-4)}{(1-0.25)} \right) A_n \sqrt{f'_m} = 4.51 A_n \sqrt{f'_m} = \frac{4.51(7.63 \text{ in} \times 96 \text{ in})\sqrt{2000 \text{ psi}}}{1000}$$

$$= 148 \text{ kips} > 115 \text{ kips} \; \ldots \; \text{OK}$$

In accordance with TMS 402 Section 9.1.4.5, the strength reduction factor for masonry subjected to shear is equal to 0.80. The design shear strength of the wall segment is therefore equal to:

$$\phi V_n = 0.8(115) = 92 \text{ kips} > \phi 2.5 V_u = 37.4 \text{ kips} \; \ldots \; \text{OK}$$

The wall segment has sufficient shear strength to resist the shear demands at the base of the wall. By inspection, the wall segment is also capable of resisting the shear at the top of the segment.

3.5 SHEAR FRICTION STRENGTH

Masonry walls with low axial loads and low shear span ratios are susceptible to shear sliding when subjected to in-plane lateral loads. TMS 402 Section 9.3.6.5 provides procedures for the design of walls to resist shear sliding. The nominal shear friction strength, V_{nf}, is obtained as follows:

For $M_u/(V_u d_v) \leq 0.5$:

$$V_{nf} = \mu(A_{sp}f_y + P_u) \geq 0 \qquad\qquad \text{TMS 402 Eq 9-33}$$

where μ is the coefficient of friction, which is equal to 1.0 for masonry on concrete with an unfinished surface or a finished surface that has been intentionally roughened, and is equal to 0.70 for all other conditions. A_{sp} is the area of steel (only web reinforcement in flanged walls) that is adequately anchored above and below the horizontal shear plane to develop the yield strength of the reinforcement. P_u is the axial load on the wall and is positive for compression.

For $M_u/(V_u d_v) \geq 1.0$:

$$V_{nf} = 0.42 f'_m A_{nc} \qquad\qquad \text{TMS 402 Eq 9-34}$$

where A_{nc} is the net area of the wall cross section (including applicable portions of effective flange widths) between the neutral axis and the fiber of maximum compressive strain, calculated at the nominal moment strength of the cross section.

For values of $M_u/(V_u d_v)$ between 0.5 and 1.0, V_{nf} shall be determined by linear interpolation between the values given by Equations 9-33 and 9-34.

The load combination $0.9D + E(0.7D + E_h)$ governs for the 8-foot wall because it provides the minimum axial load to resist sliding:

$$P_u = 24.6 \text{ kips}; M_u = 120.6 \text{ kip-ft}; V_u = 18.7 \text{ kips}$$

$$\frac{M_u}{V_u d_v} = \frac{120.6}{18.7(8)} = 0.81$$

From Equation 9-33:

$$V_{nf} = \mu(A_{sp}f_y + P_u) = 1.0\big[(0.2 \times 6)60 + 24.6\big] = 96.6 \text{ kips}$$

And from Equation 9-34, conservatively using the neutral axis depth with no axial load in Table 4-1 ($c = 6.14$ inches):

$$V_{nf} = 0.42 f'_m A_{nc} = 0.42 f'_m ct = 0.42(2.0)(6.14)(7.63) = 39.4 \text{ kips}$$

By interpolating:

$$V_{nf} = 96.6 + \frac{(39.4 - 96.6)}{(1.0 - 0.5)}(0.81 - 0.5) = 61.1 \text{ kips}$$

$$\phi V_{nf} = 0.8(61.1) = 48.9 \text{ kips} < V_u = 18.7 \text{ kips} \;\ldots\; \text{OK}$$

4. Design of Walls to Resist Out-of-Plane Seismic Loads   TMS 402

A major consideration in the strength design of masonry walls to resist out-of plane loads is the fact that the lateral displacement is often comparable to the wall thickness. This means that secondary effects (also known as *P*-delta effects), which exist as a result of the application of loads on the wall's deformed shape, can be a significant part of the wall demand and must be considered in the analysis.

TMS 402 requirements for out-of-plane design provide procedures for walls that satisfy one of the following requirements:

1. $P_u \le 0.05 f'_m A_g$

2. $0.05 f'_m A_g < P_u \le 0.20 f'_m A_g$; $\dfrac{h}{t} \le 30$ Eq 9-22

where P_u is the factored axial load at the location of maximum moment, A_g is the gross cross-sectional area, and f'_m is the masonry compressive strength. h is the effective height and t is the wall thickness. There are no design requirements for walls with axial loads greater than $0.2 f'_m A_g$ since there is no experimental data on the out-of-plane response of masonry walls with such large axial loads.

The out-of-plane demand may be determined either by a second-order analysis or by an alternative first-order analysis that utilizes a moment magnifier to incorporate *P*-delta effects. The alternative procedure is applicable to walls with different boundary conditions and loading.

4.1 DESIGN OF WALL ON LINE 1 (NO OPENINGS)   TMS 402 §9.3.5.4.2

The wall on line 1, which has no openings, will be designed as a simple span between the floor and roof levels. This is consistent with computer analyses of out-of-plane wall response, which indicate that during dynamic loading, the presence of a relatively short parapet does not reduce the moment in the wall span as much as during static loading. The procedure for a second-order analysis provided in TMS 402 is applicable to pinned-pinned boundary conditions and uniformly distributed lateral loads and will be used to evaluate the wall.

From Figure 4-2, the roof dead and live loads on the wall on line 1 are equal to:

$P_{fD} = 17(15) = 255$ lb/ft

$P_{fL_R} = 20(15) = 300$ lb/ft

At the wall mid-height, which is the critical section, the self-weight of the wall is equal to:

$$P_w = 78\left(3 + \frac{16}{2}\right) = 858 \text{ lb/ft}$$

Figure 4-4 shows the connection of the roof to the wall. The eccentricity of the roof reaction, which occurs at the face of the glulam ledger, is given by:

$$e = \frac{t}{2} + 2.5 = \frac{7.63}{2} + 2.5 = 6.3 \text{ in}$$

From ASCE 7 Section 12.11.1, the out-of-plane earthquake load on the structural wall is equal to:

$$F_p = 0.4 S_{DS} I_e W_p = 0.4(1.0)(1.0)(78) = 31.2 \text{ psf}$$

For the load combination $0.9D + E = 0.7D + E_h$:

$$P_{uf} = 0.7(255) = 179 \text{ lb/ft}$$

$$P_{uw} = 0.7(858) = 601 \text{ lb/ft}$$

$$P_u = P_{uf} + P_{uw} = 179 + 601 = 780 \text{ lb/ft}$$

$$\frac{P_u}{A_g} = \frac{780}{12(7.63)} = 8.5 \text{ psi} < 0.05 f'_m = 100 \text{ psi} \ \dots \ \text{OK}$$

Try #4 bars spaced at 24 inches on center ($A_s = 0.10 \text{ in}^2/\text{ft}$, $d = 3.82$ in) and determine the wall properties. The gross moment of inertia is equal to:

$$I_g = \frac{b(t)^3}{12} = \frac{12(7.63)^3}{12} = 444 \text{ in}^4/\text{ft}$$

From TMS 402 Table 9.1.9.2, the modulus of rupture, f_r, for fully grouted masonry with Type S mortar with flexural stresses normal to bed joints is 163 psi. The cracking moment is thus given by:

$$M_{cr} = \left(f_r + \frac{P_u}{A_g} \right) S_n = (163 + 8.5)\frac{12(7.63)^2}{6} = 19{,}968 \text{ lb-in/ft} = 1664 \text{ lb-ft/ft}$$

The depth of the neutral axis, c, is given by:

$$c = \frac{A_s f_y + P_u}{0.64 f'_m b} = \frac{0.10 \text{ in}^2/\text{ft}(60{,}000 \text{ psi}) + 780 \text{ lb/ft}}{0.64(2000 \text{ psi})12 \text{ in}} = 0.44 \text{ in} \qquad \text{TMS 402 Eq 9-31}$$

From TMS 402 Table 4.2.2, the elastic moduli of steel and concrete masonry are given by:

$$E_s = 29{,}000 \text{ ksi}$$

$$E_m = 900 f'_m = \frac{900(2000 \text{ psi})}{1000} = 1800 \text{ ksi}$$

The modular ratio is therefore equal to:

$$n = \frac{E_s}{E_m} = \frac{29{,}000 \text{ ksi}}{1800 \text{ ksi}} = 16.1$$

and the cracked moment of inertia is given by:

$$I_{cr} = n\left(A_s + \frac{P_u t_{sp}}{f_y 2d} \right)(d-c)^2 + \frac{bc^3}{3} \qquad \text{TMS 402 Eq 9-30}$$

$$= 16.1\left(0.10 \text{ in}^2/\text{ft} + \frac{780 \text{ lb/ft} \times 7.63 \text{ in}}{60{,}000 \text{ psi} \times 2 \times 3.81 \text{ in}} \right)(3.81 - 0.44 \text{ in})^2 + \frac{12(0.44 \text{ in})^3}{3} = 21.0 \text{ in}^4$$

The wall deflection can be calculated directly (assuming the wall is uncracked) with the following equation:

$$\delta_u = \frac{\dfrac{wh^2}{8} + \dfrac{P_{uf}e}{2}}{\dfrac{48 E_m I_g}{5h^2} - (P_{uw} + P_{uf})} = \frac{\left(\dfrac{31.2 \text{ psf}(16 \text{ ft} \times 12)^2}{8(12 \text{ in})} + \dfrac{179 \text{ lb/ft}(6.3 \text{ in})}{2} \right)}{\dfrac{48(1{,}800{,}000 \text{ psi})(444 \text{ in}^4/\text{ft})}{5(16 \times 12)^2} - 780 \text{ lb/ft}} = 0.06 \text{ in}$$

Therefore, the moment demand, including *P*-delta effects, is equal to:

$$M_u = \frac{w_u h^2}{8} + \frac{P_{uf}e}{2} + (P_{uf} + P_{uw})\delta_u \qquad \text{TMS 402 Eq 9-23 and Eq 9-24}$$

$$= \frac{31.2 \text{ psf}(16 \text{ ft})^2}{8} + \frac{179 \text{ lb/ft}}{2}\left(\frac{6.3 \text{ in}}{12}\right) + 780 \text{ lb/ft}\left(\frac{0.06 \text{ in}}{12}\right) = 1049 \text{ lb-ft/ft}$$

M_u is less than M_{cr}, so the assumption of an uncracked wall is correct. The flexural strength of the wall is given by (see commentary for TMS 402 Section 9.3.5.2):

$$M_n = \left(A_s f_y + \frac{P_u}{\phi}\right)\left(\frac{t_{sp} - a}{2}\right) + A_s f_y \left(d - \frac{t_{sp}}{2}\right)$$

where:

$$a = \frac{A_s f_y + P_u/\phi}{0.8 f'_m b} = \frac{0.10 \text{ in}^2/\text{ft}(60,000 \text{ psi}) + \dfrac{780 \text{ lb/ft}}{0.9}}{0.8(2000 \text{ psi})12 \text{ in}} = 0.36 \text{ in} \qquad \text{Comm §9.3.5.2}$$

Therefore,

$$\phi M_n = 0.9\left[\begin{array}{l}\left(0.10 \text{ in}^2/\text{ft} \times 60,000 \text{ psi} + \dfrac{780 \text{ lb/ft}}{0.9}\right)\left(\dfrac{7.63 \text{ in} - 0.36 \text{ in}}{2}\right) \\[3mm] + 0.10 \text{ in}^2/\text{ft} \times 60,000 \text{ psi}\left(3.81 \text{ in} - \dfrac{7.63 \text{ in}}{2}\right)\end{array}\right]\frac{1}{12}$$

$$= 1870 \text{ lb-ft/ft} > M_u = 1049 \text{ lb-ft/ft} \ \dots \ \text{OK}$$

The above procedure can be repeated to show the wall reinforcement is satisfactory for other applicable load combinations. The wall reinforcement needs to be checked against the maximum limits in TMS 402 Section 9.3.3.2. From Table 4-3, the tensile strain in the extreme steel fiber must be at least 1.5 times the yield strain ($\alpha = 1.5$) for the following load combination:

$$P_{umr} = P_D + 0.75 P_L + 0.525 P_{Q_E} = [858 + 255] + 0.75(0) + 0.525(0) = 1113 \text{ lb}$$

From the commentary of TMS 402 Section 9.3.3.2, the maximum reinforcement ratio for a fully grouted member with only concentrated tension reinforcement is:

$$\rho_{max} = \frac{0.64 f'_m \left(\dfrac{\varepsilon_{mu}}{\varepsilon_{mu} + \alpha\varepsilon_y}\right) - \dfrac{P}{bd}}{f_y}$$

$$= \frac{0.64(2000 \text{ psi})\left(\dfrac{0.0025}{0.0025 + 1.5 \times 0.0021}\right) - \dfrac{1113 \text{ lb/ft}}{12 \text{ in} \times 3.81 \text{ in}}}{60,000 \text{ psi}} = 0.009$$

The wall reinforcement ratio is:

$$\rho = \frac{A_s}{bd} = \frac{0.10 \text{ in}^2}{12 \text{ in}(3.81 \text{ in})} = 0.0022 < 0.009 \ \dots \ \text{OK}$$

The wall horizontal deflection at mid-height under allowable stress design load combinations, δ_s, must satisfy the following equation:

$$\delta_s \leq 0.007h \qquad \text{TMS 402 Eq 9-32}$$

For the allowable stress load combination $0.6D + 0.7E$:

$$w_s = 0.7(31.2) = 21.8 \text{ psf}$$
$$P_{sf} = 0.6(255) = 153 \text{ lb/ft}$$
$$P_s = 0.6(255 + 601) = 514 \text{ lb/ft}$$

And since the designer can assume the wall is not cracked because it was uncracked under strength-level loads, the deflection at mid-height is equal to:

$$\delta_s = \frac{\dfrac{w_s h^2}{8} + \dfrac{P_s e}{2}}{\dfrac{48 E_m I_g}{5h^2} - (P_s)} = \frac{\left(\dfrac{21.8 \text{ psf}(16 \text{ ft} \times 12)^2}{8(12)} + \dfrac{153 \text{ lb/ft}(6.3 \text{ in})}{2} \right)}{\dfrac{48(1{,}800{,}000 \text{ psi})(444 \text{ in}^4)}{5(16 \text{ ft} \times 12)^2} - 514 \text{ lb/ft}}$$

$$= 0.04 \text{ in} < 0.007h = 1.34 \text{ in} \ \ldots \ \text{OK}$$

As with the determination of the strength of the wall, the wall can be checked for the other allowable stress design load combination to verify that the deflection is acceptable.

4.2 DESIGN OF WALL SEGMENT ON LINE A   TMS 402 §9.3.5.4.3

The 8-foot wall segment on line A is adjacent to openings. Therefore, as shown in Figure 4-9, the segment supports out-of-plane loads over a tributary width larger than its width. A conservative approach is to ignore the openings and design the 8-foot segment to resist a uniformly distributed load that corresponds to a 28-foot tributary width over its entire height. With this approach, the equations for pinned-pinned boundary conditions and uniformly distributed loads, which were described in the previous section, can be used.

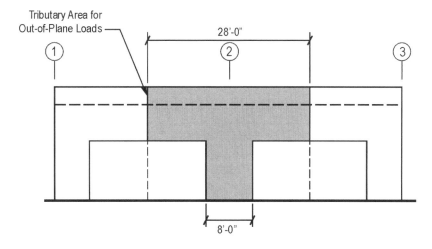

Figure 4-9. Tributary width for out-of-plane loads for an 8-foot-long wall segment

An alternative, less conservative approach is to use the moment magnification procedure, which is included in TMS 402. The moment magnification procedure can be used for walls with all boundary conditions and loading and is not subject to the limitations of provisions used in the previous section. To account for P-delta effects, the factored moment from a first order analysis, $M_{u,0}$, is modified by the following equation:

$$M_u = \psi M_{u,0}$$ TMS 402 Eq 9-27

where

$$\psi = \frac{1}{1 - \dfrac{P_u}{P_e}}$$ TMS 402 Eq 9-28

and

$$P_e = \frac{\pi^2 E_m I_{eff}}{h^2}$$ TMS 402 Eq 9-29

When M_u is less than M_{cr}, I_{eff} shall be taken as 0.75 times the gross moment of inertia. Otherwise, the wall is considered cracked, and I_{eff} is equal to I_{cr}. The value of P_u/P_e must not exceed 1.0.

Figure 4-10 shows the load and maximum moment on the wall segment. Figure 4-5 shows that the axial load at the top of the wall segment is equal to 28.9 kips. For the load combination with the lowest axial load (which results in the smallest moment strength):

$$P_u = 0.7(28.9) = 20.2 \text{ kips}$$

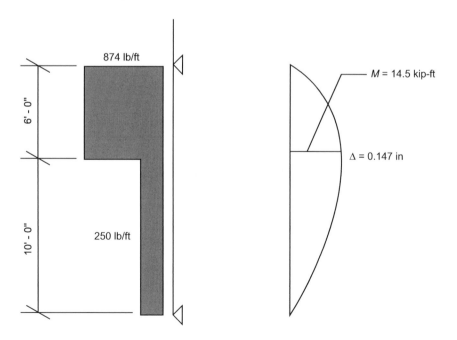

Figure 4-10. Out-of-plane loads for an 8-foot-long wall segment

The cracking moment is equal to:

$$M_{cr} = \left(f_r + \frac{P_u}{A_g} \right) S_n = \left(\frac{163 \text{ psi}}{1000} + \frac{20.2 \text{ kips}}{7.63 \text{ in} \times 96 \text{ in}} \right) \frac{96 \text{ in}(7.63 \text{ in})^2}{6} = 178 \text{ kip-in}$$

From Figure 4-7, $A_s = 1.2 \text{ in}^2$ and $b = 96$ in. Assuming the wall is cracked, the moment of inertia is calculated as follows:

$$c = \frac{A_s f_y + P_u}{0.64 f'_m b} = \frac{1.2 \text{ in}^2 (60 \text{ ksi}) + 20.2}{0.64(2.0 \text{ ksi})96 \text{ in}} = 0.75 \text{ in}$$ TMS 402 Eq 9-31

$$I_{cr} = n \left(A_s + \frac{P_u t}{f_y 2d} \right) (d - c)^2 + \frac{bc^3}{2}$$ TMS 402 Eq 9-30

$$= 16.1 \left(1.2 \text{ in}^2 + \frac{20.2 \text{ kips} \times 7.63 \text{ in}}{60 \text{ ksi} \times 2 \times 3.81 \text{ in}} \right) (3.81 \text{ in} - 0.75 \text{ in})^2 + \frac{12(0.75 \text{ in})^3}{3} = 233.4 \text{ in}^4$$

The second order moment is equal to:

$$M_u = \Psi M_{u,0} = \frac{M_{u,0}}{1 - \frac{P_u h^2}{\pi^2 E_m I_{eff}}} = \frac{14.5 \text{ kip-ft}(12)}{1 - \frac{20.2 \text{ kips}(16 \text{ ft} \times 12)^2}{\pi^2 (1800 \text{ psi})(233.4 \text{ in}^4)}}$$

$$= 1.22(14.5 \text{ kip-ft} \times 12) = 212 \text{ kip-in}$$

$M_u > M_{cr}$, so the assumption of a cracked wall is correct.

$$a = \frac{A_s f_y + \frac{P_u}{\phi}}{0.8 f'_m b} = \frac{1.2 \text{ in}^2 (60 \text{ ksi}) + \frac{20.2 \text{ kips}}{0.9}}{0.8(2 \text{ ksi})96 \text{ in}} = 0.61 \text{ in}$$

$$\phi M_n = \phi \left[\left(A_s f_y + \frac{P_u}{\phi} \right) \left(\frac{t - a}{2} \right) + A_s f_y \left(d - \frac{t}{2} \right) \right]$$

$$= 0.9 \left[\left(1.2 \text{ in}^2 \times 60 \text{ ksi} + \frac{20.2 \text{ kips}}{0.9} \right) \left(\frac{7.63 \text{ in} - 0.61 \text{ in}}{2} \right) + 1.2 \times 60 \text{ ksi}(0) \right]$$

$$= 298 \text{ kip-in} > M_u = 217 \text{ kip-in} \ \ldots \ \text{OK}$$

Conservatively checking the wall deflection at strength-level loads (instead of service-level loads):

$$\delta_u = \Psi \delta_{ui} = 1.22(0.147) = 0.18 \text{ in} < 0.007h = 1.34 \text{ in} \ \ldots \ \text{OK}$$

5. Out-of-Plane Wall Anchorage   TMS 402

The out-of-plane anchorage of walls is a critical aspect in the design of many masonry buildings. During past earthquakes, the separation of walls from diaphragms has resulted in severe damage and the partial or complete collapse of several buildings. ASCE 7 Section 12.11.2 provides provisions for the anchorage of walls and transfer of the anchorage forces into diaphragms. In addition to resisting the prescribed forces, continuous ties or struts must be provided between diaphragm chords to distribute the anchorage forces into the diaphragms in SDC C, D, E, and F. Added chords may be used to create subdiaphragms with a maximum length-to-width ratio of 2.5 to 1 to transmit the anchorage forces to the main continuous cross-ties. Walls must be designed to span between anchors if the spacing between anchors exceeds 4 feet.

5.1 CALCULATION OF ANCHORAGE FORCES   ASCE 7

The anchorage force is given by:

$$F_p = 0.4 S_{DS} k_a I_e W_p$$ ASCE 7 Eq 12.11-1

where k_a is the amplification factor for diaphragm flexibility, which is given by:

$$k_a = 1.0 + \frac{L_f}{100}$$ ASCE 7 Eq 12.11-2

L_f is the span between vertical elements that provide lateral support to the diaphragm in the direction considered. For the wall on line 1:

$$k_a = 1.0 + \frac{90}{100} = 1.9$$

The weight of wall tributary to the diaphragm is equal to:

$$W_p = 78\left(\frac{16}{2} + 3\right) = 858 \text{ lb/ft}$$

Therefore:

$$F_p = 0.4 S_{DS} k_a I_e W_p = 0.4(1.0)(1.9)(1.0)(858) = 652 \text{ lb/ft}$$

The anchorage force must exceed the following:

$$F_p \geq 0.2 k_a I_e W_p = 0.2(1.9)(1.0)(858) = 326 \text{ lb/ft} \ \ldots \ \text{OK}$$

5.2 DESIGN OF ANCHORAGE CONNECTION   TMS 402

Figure 4-11 shows the out-of-plane anchorage connection for the wall on line 1. For headed anchor bolts, tensile strength is determined by either masonry breakout or yield and fracture of the bolt steel. For masonry breakout, the anchor bolt strength is given by:

$$\phi B_{anb} = \phi 4 A_{pt} \sqrt{f'_m}$$ TMS 402 Eq 9-1

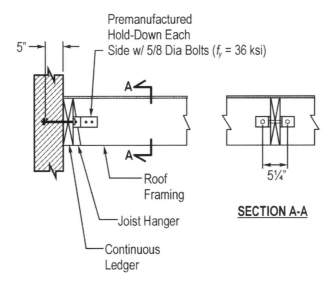

Figure 4-11. Out-of-plane anchorage connection

The strength reduction factor for masonry breakout is equal to 0.5, and A_{pt} is the projected tension area on the masonry surface, which is equal to:

$$A_{pt} = \pi l_b^2 = \pi(5)^2 = 78.5 \text{ in}^2$$

where l_b is the effective embedment length. The projected tension area must be reduced to account for the overlap of the areas of adjacent bolts so that no portion of masonry is included more than once.

From Figure 4-12, the central angle of the overlapping segment is given by:

$$\theta = 2\cos^{-1}\left(\frac{s}{2l_b}\right) = 2\cos^{-1}\left(\frac{5.25}{2 \times 5}\right) = 2.036 \text{ radians}$$

and the modified projected area is equal to:

$$A'_{pt} = \pi l_b^2 - \frac{1}{2} l_b^2(\theta - \sin\theta) = 78.5 - \frac{1}{2}(5)^2(2.036 - \sin 2.036) = 64.2 \text{ in}^2$$

The masonry tensile breakout strength of each bolt is therefore equal to:

$$\phi B_{anb} = \phi 4 A_{pt}\sqrt{f'_m} = 0.5(4)(64.2 \text{ in}^2)\sqrt{2000} = 5742 \text{ lb}$$

For steel tensile yield, the strength of each bolt is given by:

$$\phi B_{ans} = \phi A_b f_y = 0.9(0.31 \text{ in}^2)36,000 \text{ psi} = 10,044 \text{ lb} \qquad \text{TMS 402 Eq 9-2}$$

The strength of the bolts is determined by masonry breakout. If the two bolts are spaced at 8 feet on center:

$$\frac{F_p}{\phi B_{anb}} = \frac{8 \text{ ft}(652 \text{ lb/ft})}{2(5742 \text{ lb})} = 0.45 < 1.0 \ \ldots \text{ OK}$$

Verify that the wall can span 8 feet horizontally between the anchors. If the engineer assumes a beam width of 6 feet (3-foot high parapet plus an additional 3 feet of wall below the roof) with #4 bars at 24 inches on center:

$$M_u \approx \frac{w_u l^2}{8} = \frac{(652 \text{ lb/ft})(8 \text{ ft})^2}{8} = 5216 \text{ lb-ft}$$

$$\phi M_n = \phi f_y A_s \left(d - \frac{f_y A_s}{1.6 f'_m b} \right)$$

$$= 0.9(60,000)(0.2 \text{ in}^2 \times 3) \left(3.81 \text{ in} - \frac{60,000 \text{ psi} \times 0.2 \text{ in}^2 \times 3}{1.6 \times 2000 \text{ psi} \times 72 \text{ in}} \right) \frac{1}{12} = 9865 \text{ lb-ft} \ \ldots \text{ OK}$$

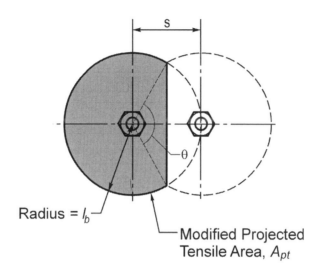

Radius = l_b

Modified Projected
Tensile Area, A_{pt}

Figure 4-12. Overlap of projected tensile areas

Design Example 5
Tilt-Up Building

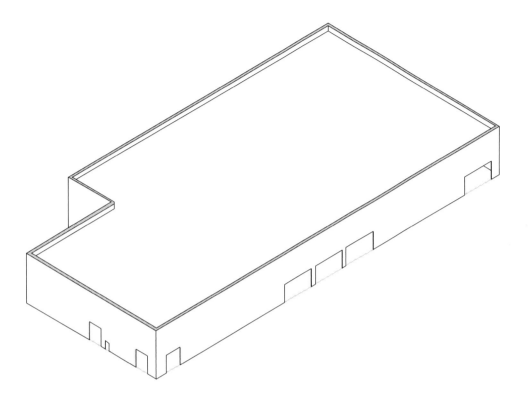

OVERVIEW

This example presents the seismic design of major components of a tilt-up building. Many tilt-up buildings have suffered severe structural damage in past earthquakes, particularly during the 1971 San Fernando and 1994 Northridge events. The most common problem has been wall-roof separations, with subsequent partial collapse of the roof. Since those events, the building codes have significantly improved, yet a major earthquake has yet to test the current tilt-up code provisions.

The example building is a warehouse, which has tilt-up concrete walls and a panelized hybrid roof system. The hybrid roof, common in California, Nevada, Arizona, and Oregon, consists of a panelized wood structural panel (plywood or oriented strand board) system supported on open-web steel joists. The building's roof framing plan is shown in Figure 5-1, and a typical section through the building is given in Figure 5-2. The emphasis in this design example is on the seismic design of the slender wall panel loaded out-of-plane and the wall-to-roof anchorage, with a discussion on shear wall design and computing base shear in tilt-up buildings. A more complete example illustrating general concrete shear wall design may be found in the *2018 IBC Structural/Seismic Design Manual* Volume 3.

OUTLINE

1. Building Geometry and Loads

2. Overview of ACI Slender Wall Design

3. Out-of-Plane Lateral Design Wall Forces

4. Primary Moment from the Out-of-Plane Forces

5. Primary Moment from the Vertical Load Eccentricity

6. Total Factored Moment Including *P*-Delta Effects

7. Nominal Moment Strength ϕM_n

8. Service-Load Deflection Considerations

9. Wall Anchorage at Roof Purlins (North-South Loading)

10. Wall Anchorage at Subpurlins (East-West Loading)

11. Subdiaphragm Design (East-West Loading)

12. Continuity Ties across the Main Diaphragm (East-West Loading)

13. Shear Wall Design Loads

14. References

1. Building Geometry and Loads   ASCE 7

1.1 GIVEN INFORMATION

Seismic-force-resisting system

> A bearing-wall system consisting of intermediate precast concrete shear walls supporting a flexible diaphragm of wood structural panels (WSP).

Seismic and site data

> Mapped spectral accelerations for the site:
>
> $S_s = 1.5$ (short period)
>
> $S_1 = 0.6$ (1-second period)
>
> Risk Category II
>
> Site Class D
>
> $S_{DS} = 1.0$

Wind

> Assumed not to govern

Roof loading onto walls

Dead load = 12 psf

Live load (roof) = 20 psf (reducible)   IBC T 1607.1

No snow load

Uniform loading from roof assumed

Roof load eccentricity = 5 inches from inside face of panel

Walls

Thickness = 9.25 inches with periodic ¾-inch narrow horizontal reveals

Height = 32 feet (top of wall)

Height = 28 feet (roof line)

Normal weight concrete = 150 pcf

$f_c' = 3000$ psi

A615, Grade 60 steel reinforcing ($F_y = 60$ ksi)

Roof structure

Structural-I sheathing [oriented strand board (OSB) WSP]

Pre-engineered/premanufactured open-web steel joists and joist girders with full-width wood nailers

All wood is Douglas Fir-Larch (DFL)

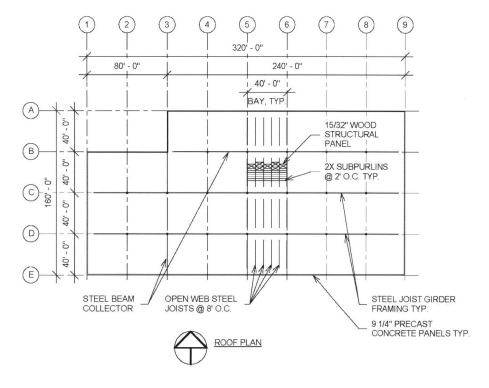

Figure 5-1. Roof framing plan

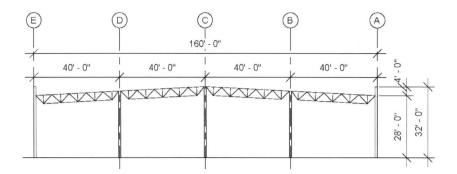

Figure 5-2. Building section

2. Overview of ACI Slender Wall Design

Concrete walls under combined axial and out-of-plane lateral forces may be designed under ACI 318 Chapter 6 by accounting for slenderness effects using Section 6.6.4, 6.7, or 6.8. An alternative wall design procedure is provided in ACI 318 Section 11.8, which allows very slender concrete walls with certain restrictions. This section made its debut in ACI 318-99, and it is generally based on the 1997 *Uniform Building Code*, which incorporated the equations, concepts, and full-scale testing developed by the Structural Engineers Association of Southern California and published in the *Report of the Task Committee on Slender Walls* in 1982 (SCCACI/SEAOSC, 1982).

Walls designed under the alternative slender wall method of ACI 318-14 Section 11.8 are typically tilt-up concrete panels that are site-cast, cured, and tilted into place. They are designed to withstand out-of-plane forces and carry vertical loads at the same time. These slender walls differ from concrete walls designed under the simplified design method (ACI 318 Section 11.5.3) and walls designed as compression members (ACI 318 Section 11.5.2) in that slender walls have greater restrictions on axial loads and must be a tension-controlled design when subjected to combined bending and axial load. In addition, secondary effects of eccentricities and *P*-delta moments play an important role in analysis and design of these slender tilt-up panels.

In this example, the out-of-plane lateral design forces for a one-story tilt-up concrete slender wall panel are determined, and the adequacy of a proposed reinforced concrete section is checked. The example wall panel has two door openings, as shown in Figure 5-3. The pier between the two openings is analyzed using the slender wall design method of ACI 318 Section 11.8, as adopted by reference through IBC Section 1901.2. Analysis of the wall panel for lifting stresses or other erection loads is not a part of this example and is usually completed by the subcontractor's specialty engineer.

3. Out-of-Plane Lateral Design Wall Forces

The concrete wall panels may be loaded out-of-plane by wind or seismic forces. For ease of analysis, the wall panel is subdivided into a design strip. Typically, a solid panel is subdivided into 1-foot-wide design strips for out-of-plane design. However, for simplicity, where wall openings are involved, the entire pier width between openings is generally used as the design strip. The distributed loading accounts for the strip's self-weight as well as the tributary loading from above each opening. Figure 5-4 illustrates the horizontal load distribution on the wall's profile.

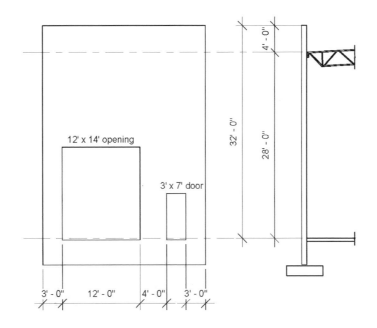

Figure 5-3. Elevation view of wall panel

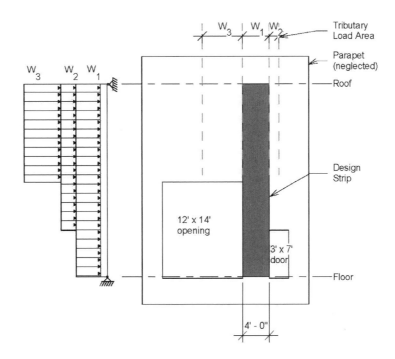

Figure 5-4. Wall-loading diagram

3.1 SEISMIC COEFFICIENT OF WALL ELEMENT

The wall panel is considered a bearing wall and a shear wall; thus, ASCE 7 Section 12.11.1 applies in determining the lateral seismic force.

$$F_p = 0.4S_{DS}I_e w_w$$

but not less than $0.1w_w$

$$I_e = 1.0$$
$$S_{DS} = 1.0g$$
$$F = 0.4(1.0)(1.0)w_w = 0.4w_w$$

3.2 LOAD COMBINATIONS FOR STRENGTH DESIGN   ASCE 7

For this example, the use of IBC load combination Equation 16-5 of Section 1605.2 is applicable and governs for concrete strength design under seismic loading. Because the axial load will create significant secondary *P*-delta moments later in the analysis, Equation 16-7 will not govern over Equation 16-5. With *F* = 0 and *H* = 0, the load combination becomes

$$1.2D + 1.0E + f_1L + f_2S \hspace{3cm} \text{IBC Eq 16-5}$$

where

D = self-weight of wall and dead load of roof and equipment

$L = 0$ (floor live load)

$S = 0$ (snow load)

$E = E_h + E_v = \rho Q_E + 0.2S_{DS}D$ Eq 12.4-1, Eq 12.4-2 and Eq 12.4-3

where

$\rho = 1.0$ for wall elements   §12.3.4.1

IBC load combination (Equation 16-5) reduces to

$$(1.2 + 0.2S_{DS})D + 1.0Q_E \text{ or } (1.2 + 0.2)D + 1.0Q_E$$
$$\text{or simply } 1.4D + 1.0Q_E$$

3.3 LATERAL OUT-OF-PLANE WALL FORCES

The lateral wall forces Q_E are determined by multiplying the wall's tributary weight by the lateral force coefficient. Three different uniformly distributed loads are determined because of the presence of two door openings of differing heights. See Figure 5-4.

$$\text{Wall weight} = w_w = \frac{9.25}{12}(150 \text{ lb/ft}^3) = 116 \text{ lb/ft}^2$$

$$F_{P \, wall} = 0.4(116 \text{ lb/ft}^2) = 46 \text{ lb/ft}^2$$
$$W_1 \quad = 46 \text{ lb/ft}^2 \times 4 \text{ ft} = 184 \text{ plf}$$
$$W_2 \quad = 46 \text{ lb/ft}^2 \times 3/2 \text{ ft} = 69 \text{ plf}$$
$$W_3 \quad = 46 \text{ lb/ft}^2 \times 12/2 \text{ ft} = 276 \text{ plf}$$

4. Primary Moment from the Out-of-Plane Forces

The objective is to check $\phi M_n \geq M_u$ where $M_u = M_{ua} + P_u \Delta_u$ (ACI 318 Equation 11.8.3.1a). M_{ua} is the maximum moment (usually at mid-height) due to applied factored loads and consists of two components: an out-of-plane loading moment ($M_{u\,oop}$) and a vertical eccentricity loading moment ($M_{u\,ecc}$). $P_u \Delta_u$ is a secondary moment created by *P*-delta effects and is investigated in Part 6.

To determine $M_{u\,oop}$, the loading diagram in Figure 5-5 should be used.

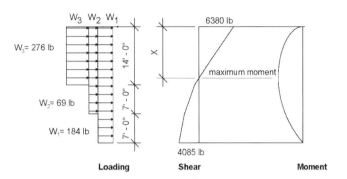

Figure 5-5. Loading diagram

ACI 318 Section 11.8.2.1 states, "The wall shall be analyzed as a simply supported, axially loaded member subject to an out-of-plane uniformly distributed lateral load, with maximum moments and deflections occurring at mid-height." As evident from Figure 5-5, a pier between openings has neither a uniform lateral load nor a maximum moment occurring at mid-height. In this situation, it is acceptable to compute an equivalent distributed load and the more accurate maximum moment $M_{u\,oop}$ located slightly away from mid-height. This is then combined with $M_{u\,ecc}$ and $P_u \Delta_u$ as computed at mid-height.

The designer then locates the point of zero shear for maximum moment $M_{u\,oop}$. They ignore the parapet's negative moment benefits in reducing the positive moment for simplicity of analysis. If the designer decides to use the parapet's negative moment to reduce the positive moment, special care should be taken to use the shortest occurring parapet height. For this approach, the seismic coefficient for the parapet shall be the same as that for the wall below using forces based on ASCE 7 Section 12.11.1. The parapet should be checked separately under Section 13.3.1, but is not a part of this example.

This example conservatively assumes the maximum moment occurs at a critical section width of 4 feet. In cases where the maximum moment occurs well above the doors, a more comprehensive analysis could consider several critical design sections, which would account for a wider design section at the location of maximum moment and for a narrower design section with reduced moments near the top of the doors. ACI 318 Section 11.8.1.1a states that the "cross section is constant over the height of the wall." Therefore, the use of a comprehensive analysis to account for a nonuniform design section width is beyond the scope of Section 11.8.

4.1 DETERMINE THE SHEAR REACTIONS AT TOP AND BOTTOM WALL SUPPORTS

R_{grade} = shear reaction at grade level of design strip

R_{roof} = shear reaction at roof level of design strip

$$R_{grade} = \left[184\left(\frac{28^2}{2}\right) + 69\left(\frac{21^2}{2}\right) + 276\left(\frac{14^2}{2}\right)\right]\frac{1}{28} = 4085 \text{ lb}$$

$$R_{roof} = \left[184(28) + 69(21) + 276(14)\right] - 4085 = 6380 \text{ lb}$$

Determine the distance of the maximum moment $M_{u\,oop}$ as measured from the roof elevation downward (Figure 5-5):

$$X = \frac{6380}{184 + 69 + 276} = 12.1 \text{ ft to point of zero shear (maximum moment)}$$

4.2 DETERMINE $M_{U\,OUT\text{-}OF\text{-}PLANE\,(OOP)}$

This is the primary moment due to factored out-of-plane forces, which excludes *P*-delta effects and vertical load eccentricity effects. Using Figure 5-5, the following is obtained:

$$M_{u\,oop} = 6380(12.1) - (184 + 69 + 276)\frac{(12.1)^2}{2} = 38{,}473 \text{ lb-ft}$$

$$M_{u\,oop} = 38.5 \text{ kip-ft}$$

5. Primary Moment from the Vertical Load Eccentricity

Any vertical loads that act at an eccentric distance from the wall's center also apply a moment to the design wall section. In this example only the roof loads are applied to the wall with an eccentricity.

P_{roof} = gravity loads from the roof acting on the design strip

P_{roof} = (roof dead load) × (tributary width of pier) × (tributary length of roof)

$$P_{roof} = (12 \text{ psf})\left(4 + \frac{3}{2} + \frac{12}{2}\right)\frac{40}{2} = 2760 \text{ lb}$$

Note: When concentrated gravity loads, such as from a girder, are applied to slender walls, the loads are assumed to be distributed over an increasing wall width at a slope of 2 units vertical to 1 unit horizontal down to the flexural design section height (ACI 318 Section 11.8.2.2).

The applicable load combination determined in Part 3 is $1.4D + 1.0Q_E$ for seismic considerations. Roof live load is not combined with seismic loads in the IBC strength design-load combinations. However, when investigating load combinations including wind design, a portion of the roof live load is included.

$$P_{u\,roof} = 1.4(2760) = 3864 \text{ lb}$$

The eccentric load places an applied moment at the roof level. With the base of the wall considered pinned, the resulting moment at mid-height is approximately half of the applied moment. Assuming a 5-inch ledger and ¾-inch reveals, the following is obtained:

$$M_{u\,ecc} = P_{u\,roof}\,\frac{e}{2}$$

where

$$e = 5\text{ in} + \frac{9.25 - 0.75}{2} = 9.25\text{ in}$$

$$M_{u\,ecc} = 3864\left(\frac{9.25}{2}\right) = 17{,}871\text{ lb-in}$$

$$M_{u\,ecc} = 1.5\text{ kip-ft}$$

6. Total Factored Moment Including *P*-Delta Effects

The total factored moment M_u is the applied moment M_{ua} with an increase for *P*-delta effects. From Parts 4.2 and 5:

$$M_{ua} = M_{u\,oop} + M_{u\,ecc}$$
$$= 38.5 + 1.5 = 40.0\text{ kip-ft}$$

M_{ua} is magnified using ACI 318 Equation 11.8.3.1d

$$M_u = \frac{M_{ua}}{1 - \dfrac{5P_u l_c^2}{(0.75)48E_c I_{cr}}}$$

The calculation for M_u using ACI Equation 11.8.3.1d provides a direct solution for second-order effects, including *P*-delta moments, instead of the iterative process of ACI Section 11.8.3.1(a). Various software programs on the market today still use an iterative second-order approach or, in some cases, have no second-order analysis. Software program results can have significant errors when improper input assumptions are made. The designer is cautioned to ensure a proper second-order analysis is utilized with proper wall stiffness assumptions.

To use ACI Equation 11.8.3.1d, the wall's vertical loading and section properties must be calculated.

6.1 DETERMINE THE TOTAL VERTICAL LOAD

P_{total} = P_{roof} + $P_{wall\ top}$

P_{roof} = 2760 lb (from Part 5)

$P_{wall\ top}$ = the portion of the wall's self weight above the flexural design section. It is acceptable to assume the design section is located midway between the floor and roof levels.

$$P_{wall\ top} = (116\ psf)\left(4 + \frac{3}{2} + \frac{12}{2}\right)\left(\frac{28}{2} + 4\right) = 24{,}012\ lb$$

P_{total} = P_{roof} + $P_{wall\ top}$ = 2760 + 24,012 = 26,772 lb

P_u = 1.4(26,772) = 37,481 lb

= 37.5 kips

6.2 DETERMINE NECESSARY SECTION PROPERTIES   ACI 318

For this pier, a trial double-curtain reinforcing arrangement of six #5 bars for each face will be assumed, as shown in Figure 5-6. The location of the reinforcing around the pier is controlled by the necessary concrete cover dimensions. For tilt-up concrete, the reinforcing depth *d* can be based on ACI Section 20.6.1.3.3 for precast cover dimensions, provided that the construction is similar to that normally expected under plant controlled conditions. With the wall panels normally cast on the building's concrete floor slab, reinforcement placement on chairs, and short-edge forms, tighter construction tolerances can be met compared with traditional monolithically poured concrete walls. For wall panels with #11 bars and smaller, the minimum cover dimension is ¾ inch,

d = thickness − reveal − cover − tie diameter − ½ bar diameter

d = 9¼ − ¾ − ¾ − ⅜ − (½)(⅝) = 7.06 in

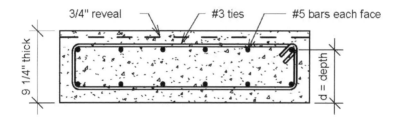

Figure 5-6. Cross section

The cracked moment of inertia I_{cr} is necessary to determine the *P*-delta effects, and ACI Equation 11.8.3.1c provides

$$I_{cr} = \frac{E_s}{E_c}\left(A_s + \frac{P_u}{f_y}\frac{h}{2d}\right)(d - c)^2 + \frac{l_w c^3}{3}$$

where

$$E_s = 29,000 \text{ ksi}$$

$$E_c = 57\sqrt{f_c'} = 3122 \text{ ksi} \qquad \text{§19.2.2.1}$$

$$a = \frac{P_u + A_s f_y}{0.85 f_c' b} = \frac{37,500 + 6(0.31)(60,000)}{0.85(3000)(48)} = 1.22 \text{ in}$$

and thus per ACI 318 Section 22.2.2.4,

$$c = \frac{a}{\beta_1} = \frac{1.22}{0.85} = 1.44 \text{ in} \qquad \text{Eq 22.2.2.4.1}$$

and the effective steel area per ACI 318 Section R11.8.3.1 considering the compression load is

$$A_{se,w} = \left(A_s + \frac{P_u}{f_y} \frac{h}{2d} \right) = 6(0.31) + \left(\frac{37,500}{60,000} \right) \frac{9.25}{2(7.06)} = 2.27 \text{ in}^2$$

Therefore,

$$I_{cr} = \frac{29,000}{3122} \times 2.27(7.06 - 1.44)^2 + \frac{48(1.44)^3}{3} = 714 \text{ in}^4$$

The $h/2d$ term for $A_{se,w}$ modifies the impact of compression force P_u for conditions where the reinforcing steel is not a single curtain at the center of the wall's thickness.

6.3 DETERMINE THE TOTAL FACTORED MOMENT MAGNIFIED FOR *P-Δ* EFFECTS

Using ACI 318 Equation 11.8.3.1d:

$$M_u = \frac{M_{ua}}{1 - \dfrac{5 P_u l_c^2}{(0.75) 48 E_c I_{cr}}} = \frac{40.0}{1 - \dfrac{5(37.5)(28 \times 12)^2}{(0.75) 48 (3122)(714)}} = 54.3 \text{ kip-ft}$$

7. Nominal Moment Strength φ*M*ₙ

The nominal moment strength ϕM_n is given by the following equation:

$$M_n = A_{se} f_y \left(d - \frac{a}{2} \right) = 2.27(60,000)\left(7.06 - \frac{1.22}{2} \right) = 878 \text{ kip-in}$$

$$M_n = 73.2 \text{ kip-ft}$$

$$\phi = 0.90 \text{ per ACI 318 Table 21.2.2}$$

$$\phi M_n = 0.90(73.2) = 65.9 \text{ kip-ft}$$

$$M_u = 54.3 \text{ kip-ft} < 65.9 \text{ kip-ft}$$

$$M_u < \phi M_n \ldots \text{ OK}$$

7.1 CHECK FLEXURAL CRACKING MOMENT

Verify that $\phi M_n \geq M_{cr}$ to determine the acceptability of the slender wall design method (ACI 318 Section 11.8.1.1c). M_{cr} is defined in ACI 318 Section 24.2.3.5 with this use of f_r defined in Section 19.2.3.1.

$$M_{cr} = f_r \frac{I_g}{y_t} = 7.5\sqrt{3000} \frac{\frac{48(9.25)^3}{12}}{\frac{9.25}{2}} = 281{,}187 \text{ lb-in} = 23.4 \text{ kip-ft} \qquad \text{Eq 24.2.3.5a}$$

$$M_{cr} = 23.4 \text{ kip-ft} \leq \phi M_n = 65.9 \text{ kip-ft} \; \ldots \; \text{OK}$$

Using the alternative slender wall method, the reinforcing is sufficient to provide adequate strength.

Note: For the purposes of ACI 318 Section 11.8.1.1c, I_g and y_t are conservatively based on the gross thickness without consideration for architectural reveal depth. This approach creates a worst-case comparison of M_{cr} to ϕM_{cr}. In addition, the exclusion of the reveal depth in the M_{cr} calculation likely produces a more accurate deflection value when the reveals are narrow, shallow, and few in number.

7.2 CHECK SECTION FOR TENSION-CONTROLLED RESTRICTION

ACI 318 Section 11.8.1.1b requires walls that are designed using the alternative design of slender walls provisions to be tension controlled. ACI 318 Section R21.2.2 defines tension-controlled sections as those whose net tensile strain $\varepsilon_t > 0.005$ when the concrete in compression reaches its assumed strain limit of 0.003. The net tensile strain limits can also be stated in terms of the ratio c/d_t, where c is the depth of the neutral axis at nominal strength and d_t is the distance from the extreme compression fiber to the extreme tension steel. A net tensile strain limit of $\varepsilon_t > 0.005$ is equivalent to $c/d_t < 0.375$ for Grade 60 reinforcement (ACI 318 Figure R21.2.2a).

$$c/d_t = 1.44/7.06 = 0.204 < 0.375 \; \ldots \; \text{OK}$$

Therefore, the slender wall method is acceptable.

7.3 CHECK THE MAXIMUM VERTICAL STRESS AT MIDHEIGHT

Check the factored vertical stress at the mid-height section to determine whether the alternative slender wall design method is acceptable (ACI 318 Section 11.8.1.1d). With only dead load D and roof live load L_r contributing to P_u, the IBC load combinations of Section 1605.2 with ASCE 7 Section 12.4.2 reduce to the following:

IBC Equation 16-1: $1.4D$

IBC Equation 16-2: $1.2D + 0.5L_r$

IBC Equation 16-3: $1.2D + 1.6L_r + 0.5W$

IBC Equation 16-4: $1.2D + 1.0W + 0.5L_r$

IBC Equation 16-5: $(1.2 + 0.2S_{DS})D + 1.0Q_E = 1.4D + 1.0Q_E$

IBC Equation 16-6: $0.9D + 1.0W$

IBC Equation 16-7: $(0.9 - 0.2S_{DS})D + 1.0Q_E = 0.7D + 1.0Q_E.$

From inspection of the load combinations previously listed, only combinations 16-1, 16-3, and 16-5 can govern the vertical load. As determined in Part 6.1, the total vertical dead load D is 26,772 pounds. The reduced roof live load L_r is determined from ASCE 7 Section 4.8 as follows:

$$A_T = \frac{40 \text{ ft}}{2}\left(4 + \frac{3}{2} + \frac{12}{2}\right) = 230 \text{ ft}^2$$

$$L_r = L_o R_1 R_2$$

where

$L_o = 20$ psf, $R_2 = 1.0$ (flat roof) and

$R_1 = 1.2 - 0.001A_T = 0.97$

$L_r = 19.4$ psf

$P_{Lr} = 19.4 \text{ psf} \times 230 \text{ ft}^2 = 4462$ lb

Load combinations 16-1, 16-3, and 16-5 result in the following P_u vertical loads:

IBC Equation 16-1 $1.4D = 1.4(26{,}772) = 37{,}481$ lb

IBC Equation 16-3 $1.2D + 1.6L_r + 1.0W = 1.2(26{,}772) + 1.6(4462) = 39{,}266$ lb (governs)

IBC Equation 16-5 $1.4D + Q_E = 1.4(26{,}772) = 37{,}481$ lb

Vertical load $P_u = 39{,}266 < 0.06(3000)(48 \times (9.25 - 0.75)) = 73{,}440$ lb . . . OK

The compression load P_u is low enough to use the alternative slender wall method; otherwise a different method, such as the simplified design method (ACI 318 Section 11.5.3) or the compression member method (ACI 318 Section 11.5.2), would be required along with their restrictions on wall slenderness.

8. Service-Load Deflection Considerations   ACI 318

Out-of-plane deflections are limited under service-level loading to prevent permanent wall deformations under frequent wind and earthquake events. Based on the full-scale slender wall tests conducted by SEAOSC in the 1980s (SCCACI/SEAOSC, 1982), it was observed that permanent set could occur prior to theoretical yield of the reinforcing, and thus a service-level deflection limit of $l_c/150$ was adopted by the *Uniform Building Code* and later the IBC. In addition, the full-scale testing revealed that cracking initiated at $f_r = 5\sqrt{f'_c}$ instead of at $f_r = 7.5\sqrt{f'_c}$ as given in ACI Equation 19.2.3.1, and thus ACI Table 11.8.4.1 has included a two-thirds adjustment factor on Δ_{cr} and M_{cr}. This conflict between observed behavior and the ACI equation for modulus of rupture f_r is associated with reinforcing restraint to concrete shrinkage (Lawson, 2007).

Another departure between the observed behavior and traditional ACI equations is the load-deflection graph. The full-scale testing program revealed a load-deflection relationship that was clearly bilinear instead of following Branson's effective moment of inertia I_e (ACI Equation 24.2.3.5a). The reason behind this deviation in slender wall panels is associated with the unique flexural stiffness of thin bending members (Lawson, 2007). Therefore, the following bilinear approach is provided by ACI Table 11.8.4.1.

If the moment M_a (including P-delta effects) does not exceed $(2/3)M_{cr}$:

$$\Delta_s = \frac{M_a}{M_{cr}} \Delta_{cr}$$

Otherwise,

$$\Delta_s = (2/3)\Delta_{cr} + \frac{(M_a - (2/3)M_{cr})}{(M_n - (2/3)M_{cr})}(\Delta_n - (2/3)\Delta_{cr})$$

where

$$\Delta_{cr} = \frac{5M_{cr}l_c^2}{48E_c I_g} \qquad\qquad \text{Eq 11.8.4.3a}$$

$$\Delta_n = \frac{5M_n l_c^2}{48E_c I_{cr}} \qquad\qquad \text{Eq 11.8.4.3b}$$

Because M_a must include P-delta effects based on Δ_s, and Δ_s depends upon M_a, an iterative process will be necessary. To determine M_a, service-level loads are utilized using the appropriate load combinations in ACI Section R11.8.4.1.

The service-level seismic load combination equals $D + 0.5L + 0.7E$ where $E = \rho Q_E + 0.2S_{DS}D$ per ASCE 7 Section 12.4.2. Thus, $D + 0.5L + 0.7(\rho Q_E + 0.2S_{DS}D)$ or $(1 + 0.14S_{DS})D + 0.5L + 0.7\rho Q_E$. With $L = 0$, $\rho = 1.0$, and $S_{DS} = 1.0$, the applicable load combination for service-level seismic loads reduces to the following:

$$1.14D + 0.7Q_E$$

8.1 DETERMINE THE APPLIED SERVICE-LEVEL MOMENT

Initially, M_a is the applied service-level moment and comprises $M_{a\,oop}$ (out-of-plane) and $M_{a\,ecc}$ (eccentricity).

$$M_a = M_{a\,oop} + M_{a\,ecc}$$

Because $M_{a\,oop}$ is solely caused by the seismic loads Q_E in this example,

$$M_{a\,oop} = 0.7M_{u\,oop} = 0.7(38.5) = 27.0 \text{ kip-ft}$$

Additionally, in an approach similar to Part 5,

$$M_{a\,ecc} = P_{roof}(e/2) = 1.14(2760)9.25/2 = 14{,}552 \text{ lb-in} = 1.2 \text{ kip-ft}$$
$$M_a = 27.0 + 1.2 = 28.2 \text{ kip-ft (without } P\text{-}\Delta \text{ effects)}$$

8.2 COMPUTE THE INITIAL SERVICE-LOAD DEFLECTION

The initial M_a is used to compute the first iteration of P-delta effects.

Initial M_a = 28.2 kip-ft (without P-Δ effects)

M_{cr} = 23.4 kip-ft (from Part 7.1)

$(2/3)M_{cr}$ = 15.6 kip-ft

$M_a > (2/3)M_{cr}$, so the cross section is initially assumed to be a cracked section

Using ACI Table 11.8.4.1 for Δ_s:

$$\Delta_s = (2/3)\Delta_{cr} + \frac{(M_a - (2/3)M_{cr})}{(M_n - (2/3)M_{cr})}(\Delta_n - (2/3)\Delta_{cr})$$

where:

$$\Delta_{cr} = \frac{5M_{cr}l_c^2}{48E_c I_g} = \frac{5(23.4 \times 12)(28 \times 12)^2}{48(3122)\left(\dfrac{48(9.25)^3}{12}\right)} = 0.33 \text{ in}$$

$$\Delta_n = \frac{5M_n l_c^2}{48E_c I_{cr}} = \frac{5(73.2 \times 12)(28 \times 12)^2}{48(3122)(714)} = 4.63 \text{ in}$$

$(2/3)M_{cr} = (2/3)23.4 = 15.6$ kip-ft

$$\Delta_s = (2/3)0.33 + \frac{(28.2 - 15.6)}{(73.2 - 15.6)}(4.63 - (2/3)0.33)$$

$\Delta_s = 1.18$ in (without P-Δ effects)

8.3 DETERMINE THE SERVICE-LOAD MOMENT M_a, INCLUDING P-DELTA EFFECTS

For service loads including the effects of the vertical load eccentricity and P-delta effects:

$$M_a = M_{a\,oop} + M_{a\,ecc} + M_{a\,P\Delta}$$

Use Figures 5-7 and 5-8 to determine $M_{a\,ecc}$ and $M_{a\,P\Delta}$ for a deflected shape.

Determine the force component H from statics summing moments about the base of the wall. From Figure 5-7, and assuming a parabolic deflected shape:

$$H = \frac{(P_{wall\,top} + P_{wall\,bottom})\dfrac{2\Delta_s}{3} - P_{roof}e}{l_c}$$

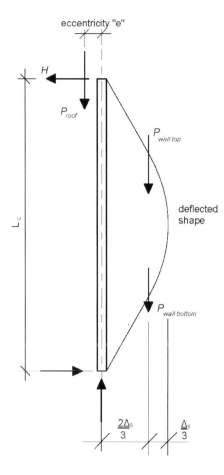

Figure 5-7. Vertical loading diagram

Because the panel's openings are not positioned symmetrically with the panel's mid-height, $P_{wall\,bottom}$ will be less than $P_{wall\,top}$. For ease of calculation, conservatively assume $P_{wall\,bottom} = P_{wall\,top}$, which is similar to panels without openings. Sum moments about the base:

$$H = \frac{4P_{wall\,top}\Delta_s}{3l_c} - \frac{P_{roof}e}{l_c}$$

Using Figure 5-8, and substituting for H, compute the moment component M from statics to account for eccentricity and P-delta effects:

$$M = P_{roof}(\Delta_s + e) + P_{wall\,top}\frac{\Delta_s}{3} + H\frac{l_c}{2}$$

$$M = P_{roof}\frac{e}{2} + (P_{wall\,top} + P_{roof})\Delta_s$$

Therefore,

$$M_a = M_{a\,oop} + P_{roof}\frac{e}{2} + (P_{wall\,top} + P_{roof})\Delta_s$$

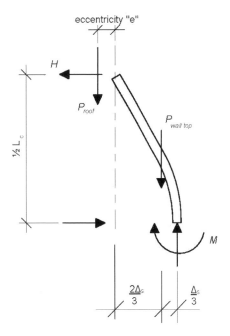

Figure 5-8. Free-body diagram

First iteration

$$M_a = 27.0 + 1.2 + 1.14(24.012 + 2.76)\frac{1.18 \text{ in}}{12}$$

$$M_a = 31.2 \text{ kip-ft}$$

Plug into Equation 11.8.4.1b for a new Δ_s:

$$\Delta_s = (2/3)0.33 + \frac{(31.2 - 15.6)}{(73.2 - 15.6)}(4.63 - (2/3)0.33)$$

$$\Delta_s = 1.41 \text{ in (first iteration with } P\text{-}\Delta \text{ effects)}$$

Second iteration

$$M_a = 27.0 + 1.2 + 1.14(24.012 + 2.76)\frac{1.41 \text{ in}}{12}$$

$$M_a = 31.8 \text{ kip-ft}$$

Plug into Equation 11.8.4.1b for a new Δ_s:

$$\Delta_s = (2/3)0.33 + \frac{(31.8 - 15.6)}{(73.2 - 15.6)}(4.63 - (2/3)0.33)$$

$$\Delta_s = 1.46 \text{ in (second iteration with } P\text{-}\Delta \text{ effects)}$$

Third iteration

$$M_a = 27.0 + 1.2 + 1.14(24.012 + 2.76)\frac{1.46\text{ in}}{12}$$

$$M_a = 31.9 \text{ kip-ft}$$

Plug into Equation 11.8.4.1b for a new Δ_s:

$$\Delta_s = (2/3)0.33 + \frac{(31.9 - 15.6)}{(73.2 - 15.6)}(4.63 - (2/3)0.33)$$

$$\Delta_s = 1.47 \text{ in}$$

Fourth iteration

$$M_a = 27.0 + 1.2 + 1.14(24.012 + 2.76)\frac{1.47\text{ in}}{12}$$

$$M_a = 31.9 \text{ kip-ft (converged with } P\text{-}\Delta \text{ effects)}$$

$$\Delta_s = 1.47 \text{ in} \leq \frac{l_c}{150} = 2.24 \text{ in} \ \dots \ \text{OK}$$

Therefore, the proposed slender wall section is acceptable using the alternative slender wall method.

Commentary

Instead of the lengthy iterative approach, the designer could simply have assumed a trial $\Delta_s = l_c/150 = 2.24$ inches as a worst case to compute M_a, then use ACI Equation 11.8.4.1b for a new Δ_s. If the new Δ_s satisfies the $l_c/150$ limit, the slender wall section is acceptable.

An example of the reinforcing layout for the entire wall panel is shown in Figure 5-9.

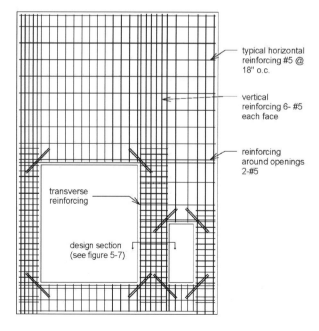

typical horizontal
reinforcing #5 @
18" o.c.

vertical
reinforcing 6- #5
each face

reinforcing
around openings
2-#5

transverse
reinforcing

design section
(see figure 5-7)

Figure 5-9. Typical panel reinforcing

9. Wall Anchorage at Roof Purlins (North-South Loading)

In single-story buildings, tilt-up wall panels typically are supported out-of-plane at the roof structure and floor slab. While failures of the concrete wall section itself out of plane are extremely rare, wall anchorage failures at the roofline have frequently occurred during earthquakes. In response to these failures, the current anchorage design forces and detailing requirements are significantly more stringent than they were under older codes (Lawson et al., 2018).

From a historical perspective, the most critical element in tilt-up engineered buildings is the wall anchorage. In the 1960s and up until the 1971 San Fernando, California, earthquake, engineers in the west typically provided no positive direct tie anchoring the perimeter concrete wall panels to the supporting wood roof structure. Instead, the roof plywood sheathing was simply nailed to a wood ledger that was bolted to the inside face of the wall panels. The roof's glued-laminated timber beams (glulams) were supported on top of concrete pilasters and had tie connections with minimal capacity. This indirect tie arrangement relied on the wood ledger in cross-grain bending, a very weak material property of wood.

In the 1971 San Fernando earthquake, many wood ledgers split in half due to cross-grain bending loads, and plywood edge nailing pulled through plywood panel edges as the result of tension loads. Partial roof collapses and wall collapses were common in the areas of strong ground motion.

Beginning with the 1973 UBC, cross-grain bending in wood was expressly prohibited, and specific wall anchorage requirements were established. Over the years since then, the wall-anchorage design forces have increased in response to continuing poor performance of wall anchorage during earthquakes and additional information learned from instrumented tilt-up buildings.

The current wall-anchorage code requirements are a result of the 1994 Northridge earthquake. The unexpected wall-anchorage damage to newer buildings was primarily attributed to inadequate connection overstrength for the roof accelerations. Research has shown that roof-top accelerations may be three to four times the ground acceleration. IBC Section 1604.8.2 specifies the need for wall anchorage in these structures. ASCE 7 Section 12.11.2.1 determines the anchorage design forces for the structural walls of tilt-up buildings, including the requirements of Section 12.11.2.2, to transfer wall-anchorage forces into the diaphragm in seismically active areas (Seismic Design Categories C through F). The wall-anchorage forces in flexible diaphragms are amplified by the k_a factor, which varies from 1.0 to 2.0, depending on the diaphragm's span between lateral-resisting walls and frames. Flexible diaphragms with spans in excess of 100 feet have wall-anchorage loads that are double the normal wall design force and three to four times the typical tilt-up building base shear to account for the expected roof-top amplification associated with flexible diaphragms.

The requirements of ASCE 7 Section 13.4 associated with anchorage of nonstructural concrete components do not apply here because all bearing walls and shear walls are classified as structural walls under Section 11.2. In addition, all nonstructural walls supported by flexible diaphragms are also anchored per Section 12.11.2 per Table 13.5-1 Footnote c. The design forces associated with the concrete and masonry wall anchorage at structural walls have already been factored up to maximum expected levels in comparison with material overstrengths.

9.1 FORCES ON WALL-ANCHORAGE TIES   ASCE 7

In this example, the structural concrete wall-anchorage forces to the flexible diaphragm are governed by ASCE 7 Equation 12.11-1:

$$F_p = 0.4S_{DS}k_aI_eW_p$$

where F_p shall not be taken less than $0.2k_aI_eW_p$ and flexible diaphragm amplification factor k_a is

$$k_a = 1.0 + \frac{L_f}{100}$$

where k_a need not be greater than 2.0. L_f is the flexible diaphragm's span in feet between the walls or frames that provide lateral support in the direction being considered.

In this example building, the reentrant corner provides diaphragm support reactions with the attached collectors, and thus the following diaphragm spans are recognized:

North-south seismic forces:

Grid lines 1 to 3	$L_f = 80$ ft	$k_a = 1.8$
Grid lines 3 to 9	$L_f = 240$ ft	$k_a = 2.0$

East-west seismic forces:

Grid lines A to B	$L_f = 40$ ft	$k_a = 1.4$
Grid lines B to E	$L_f = 120$ ft	$k_a = 2.0$

In both the north-south and east-west orthogonal directions, the majority of the wall anchorages require $k_a = 2.0$. To simplify the repetitive wall anchorage, $k_a = 2.0$ for all designs in this example.

With $S_{DS} = 1.0$, $k_a = 2.0$, and $I_e = 1.0$,

$$F_p = 0.4S_{DS}k_aI_eW_p = 0.80W_p \qquad \text{Eq 12.11-1}$$

For this building's 9¼-inch-thick concrete wall panels (150 lb/ft³), the unit wall load is

$$F_p = W_p = 0.8(116 \text{ psf}) = 92.8 \text{ psf}$$

Check this unit load with the minimum wall-roof anchorage force per ASCE 7 Section 1.4.4 and Section 12.11.2.1.

5 psf < 92.8 psf . . . OK

0.2(116 psf) = 23.2 psf < 92.8 psf . . . OK

$0.2k_aI_eW_p = 0.2(2.0)1.0(116 \text{ psf}) = 46.4$ psf < 92.8 psf . . . OK

Use $F_p = 92.8$ psf

While this building has a combination of solid wall panels and panels with penetrations, the solid panel condition will produce the worst-case wall-anchorage forces and will be used for design here. Using statics to sum moments about the wall's base, the following calculation for the wall anchorage force per foot of roof line includes the parapet's cantilever effects (see Figure 5-10).

$$F_p = 92.8 \text{ psf}(32 \text{ ft})\left(\frac{32 \text{ ft}}{2}\right)\frac{1}{28 \text{ ft}} = 1697 \text{ plf along the roofline}$$

The anchorage force per joist is

$$F_p = (8 \text{ ft})(1697 \text{ lb/ft}) = 13,576 \text{ lb}$$

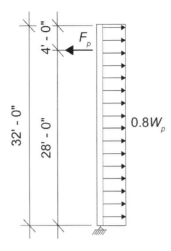

Figure 5-10. Wall section with loading

Commentary

When tie spacing exceeds 4 feet, Section 12.11.2.1 requires that structural walls be designed to resist bending between anchors. Instead of using ASCE 7 Equation 12.11-1, the designer may elect to use the out-of-plane force for the wall itself; per Section 12.11.1, $F_p = 0.4S_{DS}I_eW$. The reasoning behind this approach is that the wall's out-of-plane bending is expected to have a more ductile behavior than the connections and thus are designed for lower forces. This design force also has a lower bound of $0.20W_p$ per Section 1.4.4.

9.2 CHECK CONCRETE ANCHORAGE OF TYPICAL WALL-ROOF TIE   ACI 318

Concrete anchorage design is in accordance with Chapter 17 of ACI 318 as modified by IBC Section 1905.1.8.

ACI's Table 17.3.1.1 lists the various failure modes that must be considered in determining the required anchor strength.

The first step is to determine the resulting design loads acting on the wall-roof anchorage system. The wall-roof anchorage along the north and south walls consists of a steel joist seat welded to an embedded plate with headed-weld studs (see Figure 5-11). Because the embed resists both the wall tie force and the vertical gravity reaction of the steel joist, several loads must be combined.

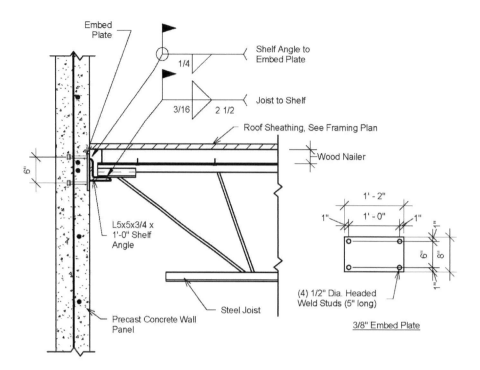

Figure 5-11. Steel joist to wall-tie detail

The vertical gravity end reaction from the steel joist creates a prying force on the embedded plate's anchors. It will be assumed a force couple at the headed-weld studs will resist the eccentric gravity load.

Calculate the joist end reaction R:

$$R = (12\text{ psf} + 20\text{ psf})(8\text{ ft})\left(\frac{40\text{ ft}}{2}\right) = 1920\text{ lb }(dead) + 3200\text{ lb }(live)$$

Conservatively assuming the vertical joist reaction is acting at the edge of the shelf angle, the reaction eccentricity is 5 inches, which matches the panel design assumption in Part 5. With the 6-inch vertical spacing between the two pairs of headed-weld studs, the following stud forces are determined using the load combinations of IBC Section 1605.2 and ASCE 7 Section 12.4.2.

Load Combination IBC Equation 16-3

$$1.2(D + F) + 1.6(L_r \text{ or } S \text{ or } R) + 1.6H + (f_1L \text{ or } 0.5W)$$

Given $S = 0$, $R = 0$, $L = 0$, $F = 0$, $H = 0$, and wind is not being considered, this load combination reduces to

$$1.2D + 1.6L_r$$

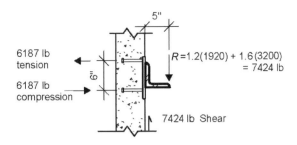

Figure 5-12. Load on embed

Load Combination IBC Equation 16-5 with ASCE 7 Section 12.4.2

$$(1.2D + 0.2S_{DS})D + \rho Q_E + L + 0.2S$$

Given $S_{DS} = 1.0$, $L = 0$, $S = 0$, and $\rho = 1.0$, this load combination reduces to $1.4D + Q_E$.

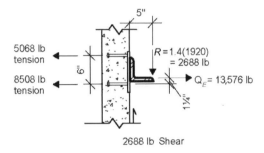

Figure 5-13. Load on embed

Load Combination IBC Equation 16-7 with ASCE 7 Section 12.4.2

$$(0.9 - 0.2S_{DS})D + \rho Q_E + 1.6H$$

Given $S_{DS} = 1.0$, $H = 0$, and $\rho = 1.0$, this load combination reduces to $0.7D + Q_E$.

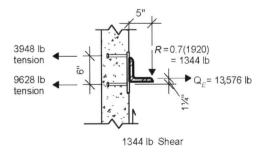

Figure 5-14. Load on embed

The load combination from IBC Equation 16-3 results in only two weld studs loaded in tension, while the other two load combinations result in all four weld studs tension loaded. The load combination from IBC Equation 16-3 is considered first.

Load Combination Equation 16-3 Analysis

Steel strength in tension N_{sa}   **ACI §17.4.1**

The nominal steel strength for a ½-inch-diameter steel headed stud anchor is computed using ACI Equation 17.4.1.2:

$$N_{sa} = A_{se,N} f_{uta}$$
$$A_{se,N} = 0.196 \text{ in}^2 \text{ (½-in-diameter smooth shaft)}$$
$$f_{uta} = 65,000 \text{ psi (AWS D1.1, Type B)}$$

Thus, $N_{sa} = 12.74$ kips.

Steel headed stud anchors conforming to AWS D1.1 Type B qualify as a ductile steel element, and thus the strength reduction factor ϕ is 0.75 per Section 17.3.3:

$$\phi N_{sa} = 0.75(12.74 \text{ kips}) = 9.56 \text{ kips}$$

The most highly stressed anchors in this group are the top two headed stud anchors. The design tension force for an individual anchor in this group is $N_{ua,i} = 6187/2 = 3094$ lb.

$$\phi N_{sa} = 9.56 \text{ kips} > 3.094 \text{ kips} \ldots \text{OK}$$

Concrete breakout strength in tension N_{cbg}   **ACI §17.4.2**

The ½-inch-diameter studs have an after-weld length of 5 inches, and considering their ⁵⁄₁₆-inch-thick heads, they have an effective embedment of $h_{ef} = 4.688$ inches. The plate's thickness may be added to h_{ef} because the failure surface extends out past the outline of the embed plate. This results in $h_{ef} = 4.688 + 0.375 = 5.06$ inches, rounded to $h_{ef} = 5$ inches. For the different possible failure modes being evaluated, ACI Section 17.2.1.1 is consulted to determine whether group action is occurring. For concrete breakout in tension, the critical spacing is $3h_{ef} = 15$ inches, which is greater than the actual spacing and therefore group action is occurring.

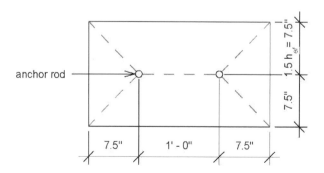

Figure 5-15. Projected failure area

ACI Equation 17.4.2.1b:

$$N_{cbg} = \frac{A_{Nc}}{A_{Nco}}(\psi_{ec,N})(\psi_{ed,N})(\psi_{c,N})(\psi_{cp,N})N_b$$

$$A_{Nc} = 2(7.5 \text{ in})[2(7.5 \text{ in}) + 12 \text{ in}] = 405 \text{ in}^2 \qquad \text{F 5-15}$$

$$A_{Nco} = 9h^2_{ef} = 9(5)^2 = 225 \text{ in}^2 \qquad \text{Eq 17.4.2.1c}$$

Per ACI Section 17.4.2.1, A_{Nc} shall not exceed nA_{Nco}.

$$nA_{Nco} = 2(9h^2_{ef}) = 450 \text{ in}^2 > A_{Nc} \ \ldots \text{ OK}$$

The modification for any possible loading eccentricity is per Equation 17.4.2.4:

$$\psi_{ec,N} = \frac{1}{\left(1 + \dfrac{2e'_N}{3h_{ef}}\right)} \le 1.0 \text{ max}$$

where e'_N is the eccentricity of the resultant tensile force from the centroid of the bolt group acting in tension. Because there is only one row of anchors acting in tension in this load combination, the anchor group's resultant tension force aligns with the anchor row and thus

$$e'_N = 0 \text{ in}$$

$$\psi_{ec,N} = \frac{1}{\left(1 + \dfrac{2(0)}{3(5)}\right)} = 1.0 \text{ max}$$

$\psi_{ed,N} = 1.0$ (no adjacent edge effects) §17.4.2.5

$\psi_{c,N} = 1.25$ (uncracked section due to short parapet) §17.4.2.6

$\psi_{cp,N} = 1.0$ (cast-in-place anchor) §17.4.2.7

$$N_b = k_c \lambda_a \sqrt{f'_c} h_{ef}^{1.5} = 24(1.0)\sqrt{3000}(5)^{1.5} = 14.7 \text{ kips} \qquad \text{Eq 17.4.2.2a}$$

$$N_{cbg} = \frac{405}{225}(1.0)(1.0)(1.25)(1.0)14.7 = 33.1 \text{ kips}$$

The strength reduction factor ϕ is 0.70 per Section 17.3.3 because no supplementary reinforcing is provided, and thus

$$\phi N_{cbg} = 0.70(33.1 \text{ kips}) = 23.2 \text{ kips} > 6.19 \text{ kips} \ \ldots \text{ OK}$$

Pullout strength in tension   ACI §17.4.3

$N_{pn} = \psi_{c,p}N_p$ Eq 17.4.3.1

$\psi_{c,P} = 1.4$ (assume uncracked section due to short parapet height) §17.4.3.6

$N_p = 8A_{brg} f'_c$ (where headed studs or bolts are used)   Eq 17.4.3.4

$A_{brg} = $ (head area) − (shank area) = 0.785 − 0.196 = 0.589 in^2

$N_{pn} = 1.4[8(0.589)(3000 \text{ psi})] = 19.8 \text{ kips}$

$nN_{pn} = 2(19.8) = 39.6 \text{ kips}$

The strength reduction factor ϕ is 0.70 per Section 17.3.3 because no supplementary reinforcing is provided, and thus

$$\phi N_{pn} = 0.70(39.6 \text{ kips}) = 27.7 \text{ kips} > 6.19 \text{ kips } \ldots \text{ OK}$$

Concrete side-face blowout strength in tension   ACI §17.4.4

In this example, it will be assumed that the concrete anchorage is not located near an edge; thus, N_{sb} will not control the design. However, the purlin layout is often not well coordinated with the concrete panel joint layout, and therefore conflicts between the two can occur. Where purlin anchorage is located near panel joints, N_{sb} must be evaluated. This is true also for roof anchorage to wall panels with no parapet.

Governing tensile strength

For this gravity-only load combination, the steel tensile strength at 19.0 kips for the top pair of anchors is less than the other various concrete tensile failure modes checked, and this strength is greater than the design tensile load of 6.19 kips. However, acceptability is pending the combined tensile and shear interaction check presented below.

Steel strength in shear V_{sa} ACI §17.5.1

The nominal steel strength for a ½-inch-diameter steel headed stud anchor is computed using ACI Equation 17.5.1.2a. Bolts if present use ACI Equation 17.5.1.2b.

$$V_{sa} = A_{se,V} f_{uta} \qquad \text{Eq 17.5.1.2a}$$
$$A_{se,V} = 0.196 \text{ in}^2 \text{ (½-in diameter smooth shaft)}$$
$$f_{uta} = 65,000 \text{ psi (AWS D1.1, Type B)}$$
$$V_{sa} = 12.7 \text{ kips per anchor}$$

Steel headed stud anchors conforming to AWS D1.1 Type B qualify as a ductile steel element, and thus the strength reduction factor ϕ is 0.70 per Section 17.3.3. In addition, four anchors are present to evenly provide shear strength:

$$\phi V_{sa} = 0.70(4)(12.7 \text{ kips}) = 35.6 \text{ kips}$$

From Figure 5-12, the design shear force is 7.42 kips.

$$\phi V_{sa} = 35.6 \text{ kips} > 7.42 \text{ kips } \ldots \text{ OK}$$

Concrete breakout strength in shear V_{cb} ACI §17.5.2

As previously mentioned, it is assumed in this example that the embed plate is not located near an edge of the panel. In this situation, V_{cb} will not govern (ACI Section R17.5.2.1). Where purlin embeds are located near panel joints, V_{cb} must be evaluated.

Concrete pryout strength in shear V_{cpg}   **ACI §17.5.3**

For a group of cast-in-place anchors, the nominal pryout strength in shear V_{cpg} is a function of the concrete breakout strength N_{cbg} determined earlier.

$$V_{cpg} = k_{cp}N_{cbg}$$ Eq 17.5.3.1b

$k_{cp} = 2.0$ for anchor embedments $h_{ef} \geq 2.5$ in

$N_{cpg} = N_{cbg} = 33.1$ kips

$V_{cpg} = 2(33.1) = 66.2$ kips

The strength reduction factor ϕ is 0.70 per Section 17.3.3 because no supplementary reinforcing is provided, and thus

$$\phi V_{cpg} = 0.70(66.2 \text{ kips}) = 46.3 \text{ kips} > 7.42 \text{ kips} \ \ldots \ \text{OK}$$

Governing shear strength

For this gravity-only load combination, the steel strength at 35.6 kips for the four anchors is less than the other various concrete shear failure modes checked, and this strength is greater than the design shear load of 7.42 kips. However, acceptability is pending the combined tensile and shear interaction check presented below.

Interaction of tensile and shear forces   **ACI §17.6**

An interaction equation check (ACI Equation 17.6.3) is required unless either the shear V_{ua} or tension N_{ua} does not exceed 20 percent of their design strengths ϕV_n or ϕN_n, respectively. The following shear and tension checks are made for this load combination:

Check if $V_{ua}/\phi V_n \leq 0.20$

   7.42 kips/35.6 kips $= 0.21 > 0.20 \ \ldots$ Not satisfied

Check if $N_{ua}/\phi N_n \leq 0.20$

   6.19 kips/19.0 kips $= 0.33 > 0.20 \ \ldots$ Not satisfied

Thus, interaction ACI Equation 17.6.3 is required to be checked.

$$\frac{N_{ua}}{\phi N_n} + \frac{V_{ua}}{\phi V_n} \leq 1.2$$

For the four-headed stud anchorage configuration

   $0.33 + 0.21 = 0.54 \leq 1.2 \ \ldots$ OK

In summary, the headed studs under the gravity load combination (3) are acceptable.

Load Combination Equation 16-5 Analysis

This load combination contains contributions from earthquake loading *E*. Because the design strengths will be compared with design loads that include earthquake forces within Seismic Design Category C or a higher structure, the provisions of ACI Section 17.2.3 are applicable.

The seismic anchorage provisions of ACI 318 Section 17.2.3 aim to prevent sudden brittle failures when subjected to high seismic loads because design earthquake forces are normally less than those thought to potentially occur during the design life of the structure. More specifically, ACI 318 Sections 17.2.3.4.3 (for tension) and 17.2.3.5.3 (for shear) require ductile anchor behavior or alternatively a seismic anchor design force with overstrength Ω. However, for anchorage connections with less than 20 percent of the factored total design force coming from a seismic component, the ductility and/or overstrength requirements are eliminated (ACI 318 Sections 17.2.3.4.1 and 17.2.3.5.1). Observing Figure 5-13, more than 20 percent of the anchor's tension force is from *E* triggering the ductility/overstrength requirements for the tension design, but less than 20 percent of its shear force is from *E*, allowing those requirements to be ignored for shear design.

Overriding this discussion is 2018 IBC Section 1905.1.8, which modifies the requirements of ACI Section 17.2.3.4.2 (tension design). In response to brittle connection failures observed after the 1994 Northridge earthquake, the wall-anchorage loads from ASCE 7 Equation 12.11-1 already approximate maximum expected force levels and include an embedded overstrength factor to eliminate the need for a connector's ductility in tension (*SEAOC Blue Book*, 1999). With this in mind, the IBC eliminates ACI's requirement for anchorage ductility or additional overstrength for tension design when forces are determined from Equation 12.11-1. Thus in this example, the connection design will not consider ductility or additional overstrength requirements for either tension or shear.

An additional requirement to consider is ACI 318 Section 17.2.3.4.4, which employs a 0.75 factor on the concrete strength limit states based on a cracked concrete assumption, unless it can be demonstrated that the concrete will remain uncracked at the anchor. In this example, the bending moment at the wall-anchorage location is minimal due to the very short parapet, and cracking due to shrinkage is unlikely due to the minimal in-plane panel restraint at the roof line; thus, it can be demonstrated that the modulus of rupture will not be exceeded.

Steel strength in tension N_{sa}   **ACI §17.4.1**

As was determined for the previous load combination, N_{sa} = 12.74 kips per anchor and

$$\phi N_{sa} = 0.75(12.74 \text{ kips}) = 9.56 \text{ kips}$$

The most highly stressed anchors in this group are the bottom two headed stud anchors. The design tension force for an individual anchor in this group is $N_{ua,i}$ = 8508/2 = 4254 lb.

$$\phi N_{sa} = 9.56 \text{ kips} > 4.25 \text{ kips} \dots \text{OK}$$

Concrete breakout strength in tension N_{cbg}   **ACI §17.4.2**

With all four anchors in tension, the projected failure area has increased. The ½-inch-diameter headed studs have an after-weld length of 5 inches, and considering their ⁵⁄₁₆-inch-thick heads, they have an effective embedment of h_{ef} = 4.688 inches. The plate's thickness may be added to h_{ef} because the failure surface extends out past the outline of the embed plate. This results in h_{ef} = 4.688 + 0.375 = 5.06 inches, rounded to h_{ef} = 5 inches. For the different possible failure modes being evaluated, ACI Section 17.2.1.1 is consulted to determine whether group action is occurring. For concrete breakout in tension, the critical spacing is $3h_{ef}$ = 15 inches, which is greater than the actual spacing and therefore group action is occurring.

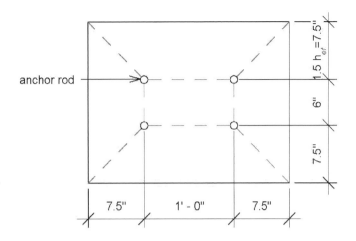

Figure 5-16. Projected failure area

ACI Equation 17.4.2.1b:

$$N_{cbg} = \frac{A_{Nc}}{A_{Nco}} (\psi_{ec,N})(\psi_{ed,N})(\psi_{c,N})(\psi_{cp,N})N_b$$

$A_{Nc} = [2(7.5 \text{ in}) + 6 \text{ in}] [2(7.5 \text{ in}) + 12 \text{ in}] = 567 \text{ in}^2$ F 5-16

$A_{Nco} = 9h_{ef}^2 = 9(5)^2 = 225 \text{ in}^2$ Eq 17.4.2.1c

Per ACI Section 17.4.2.1, A_{Nc} shall not exceed nA_{Nco}.

$$nA_{Nco} = 4(9h_{ef}^2) = 900 \text{ in}^2 > A_{Nc} \ \ldots \ \text{OK}$$

The modification for any possible loading eccentricity is per Equation 17.4.2.4:

$$\psi_{ec,N} = \frac{1}{\left(1 + \dfrac{2e'_N}{3h_{ef}}\right)} \leq 1.0 \text{ max}$$

where e'_N is the eccentricity of the resultant tensile force from the centroid of the anchor group acting in tension. Using statics, e'_N is computed for this load combination (see Figure 5-13):

$$e'_N = \frac{6 \text{ in}}{2} - \frac{6 \text{ in}(5068 \text{ lb})}{13,576 \text{ lb}} = 0.76 \text{ in}$$

$$\psi_{ec,N} = \frac{1}{\left(1 + \dfrac{2(0.76)}{3(5.0)}\right)} = 0.91$$

$\psi_{ed,N} = 1.0$ (no adjacent edge effects)   §17.4.2.5

$\psi_{c,N} = 1.25$ (uncracked section due to short parapet)   §17.4.2.6

$\psi_{cp,N} = 1.0$ (cast-in-place anchor)   §17.4.2.7

$N_b = k_c \lambda_a \sqrt{f'_c} h_{ef}^{1.5} = 24(1.0)\sqrt{3000}(5)^{1.5} = 14.7 \text{ kips}$ Eq 17.4.2.2a

$N_{cbg} = \dfrac{567}{225}(0.91)(1.0)(1.25)(1.0)14.7 = 42.1 \text{ kips}$

The strength reduction factor ϕ is 0.70 per Section 17.3.3 because no supplementary reinforcing is provided and thus

$$\phi N_{cbg} = 0.70(42.1 \text{ kips}) = 29.5 \text{ kips}$$

In conditions where the concrete in the vicinity of the anchor could crack, ACI 318 Section 17.2.3.4.4 requires the concrete design strength to be taken as $0.75\phi N_n$. However, in the case of this tilt-up wall panel, the concrete is not expected to crack as mentioned previously.

The total tension force on the embed per Figure 5-13 is

$$N_{ua} = 5068 \text{ lbs} + 8508 \text{ lbs} = 13{,}576 \text{ lbs} < 29.5 \text{ kips} \ \ldots \ \text{OK}$$

Pullout strength in tension **ACI §17.4.3**

As was determined for the previous load combination, $N_{pn} = 19.8$ kips per anchor. The most highly stressed anchors in this group are the bottom two headed studs.

$$nN_{pn} = 2(19.8) = 39.6 \text{ kips}$$

The strength reduction factor ϕ is 0.70 per Section 17.3.3 because no supplementary reinforcing is provided. In addition, as was mentioned previously, the concrete remains uncracked; thus,

$$\phi N_{pnn} = 0.70(39.6 \text{ kips}) = 27.7 \text{ kips} > 8.51 \text{ kips} \ \ldots \ \text{OK}$$

Concrete side-face blowout strength in tension **ACI §17.4.4**

As stated previously, it will be assumed in this example that the concrete anchorage is not located near an edge; thus, $N_{sb} = 1.0$.

Steel strength in shear V_{sa} **ACI §17.5.1**

As determined in the previous load combination analysis, the four headed stud group has a design strength of

$$\phi V_{sa} = 0.70(4)(12.7 \text{ kips}) = 35.6 \text{ kips}$$

From Figure 5-13, the design shear force is 2.69 kips.

$$\phi V_{sa} = 35.6 \text{ kips} > 2.69 \text{ kips} \ \ldots \ \text{OK}$$

Concrete breakout strength in shear V_{cb} **ACI §17.5.2**

As previously mentioned, it is assumed in this example that the embed plate is not located near an edge of the panel. In this situation, V_{cb} will not govern (ACI Section R17.5.2.1).

Concrete pryout strength in shear V_{cpg}   **ACI §17.5.3**

For cast-in-place anchors, the nominal pryout strength in shear, V_{cpg}, is a function of the concrete breakout strength N_{cbg} determined earlier.

$V_{cpg} = k_{cp} N_{cpg}$ **ACI Eq 17.5.3.1b**

$k_{cp} = 2.0$ for anchor embedments where $h_{ef} \geq 2.5$ in

$N_{cpg} = N_{cbg} = 42.1$ kips

$V_{cpg} = 2(42.1) = 84.2$ kips

The strength reduction factor ϕ is 0.70 per Section 17.3.3 because no supplementary reinforcing is provided. In addition, as was mentioned previously, the concrete remains uncracked; thus

$\phi V_{cpg} = 0.70(84.2 \text{ kips}) = 58.9 \text{ kips} > 2.69 \text{ kips} \ldots$ OK

Governing shear strength

For this load combination, the steel shear strength at 35.6 kips for the four anchors is less than the other various concrete shear failure modes checked, and this design strength is greater than the design shear load of 2.69 kips.

Interaction of tensile and shear forces   **ACI §17.6**

An interaction equation check (ACI Equation 17.6.3) is required unless either the shear V_{ua} or tension N_{ua} does not exceed 20 percent of their design strengths ϕV_n or ϕN_n, respectively. The following shear and tension checks are made for this load combination.

Check if $V_{ua}/\phi V_n \leq 0.20$

2.69 kips/35.6 kips $= 0.08 < 0.20 \ldots$ Satisfied

Thus, the interaction Equation 17.6.3 need not be checked, and the full strength in tension is permitted as has been already checked above. In summary, the steel headed stud anchors under this load combination are acceptable.

Load Combination Equation 16-7 Analysis

Similar to load combination Equation 16-5, this loading also contains contributions from earthquake loading E, and IBC Section 1905.1.8 again is applicable by modifying the requirements of ACI Section 17.2.3.4.2. As stated previously, IBC Section 1905.1.8 contains explicit exceptions to the ACI ductility and overstrength requirements for wall-anchorage design if ASCE 7 Equation 12.11-1 or 12.14-10 is utilized.

Steel strength in tension N_{sa}   **ACI §17.4.1**

As was determined for the previous load combination, $N_{sa} = 12.74$ kips per anchor and

$\phi N_{sa} = 0.75(12.74 \text{ kips}) = 9.56$ kips

The most highly stressed anchors in this group are the bottom two headed studs. The design tension force for an individual anchor in this group is $N_{ua,i} = 9628/2 = 4814$ lb.

$\phi N_{sa} = 9.56 \text{ kips} > 4.81 \text{ kips} \ldots$ OK

Concrete breakout strength in tension N_{cbg} **ACI §17.4.2**

The projected failure area involves all four anchors, which are in tension, similar to the previous load combination checked.

ACI Equation 17.4.2.1b:

$$N_{cbg} = \frac{A_{Nc}}{A_{Nco}}(\psi_{ec,N})(\psi_{ed,N})(\psi_{c,N})(\psi_{cp,N})N_b$$

$$A_{Nc} = [2(7.5 \text{ in}) + 6 \text{ in}][2(7.5 \text{ in}) + 12 \text{ in}] = 567 \text{ in}^2$$

$$A_{Nco} = 9h_{ef}^2 = 9(5)^2 = 225 \text{ in}^2 \qquad \qquad \textbf{ACI Eq 17.4.2.1c}$$

Per ACI Section 17.4.2.1, A_{Nc} shall not exceed nA_{Nco}.

$$nA_{Nco} = 4(9h_{ef}^2) = 900 \text{ in}^2 > A_{Nc} \ \dots \ \text{OK}$$

The modification for any possible loading eccentricity is per Equation 17.4.2.4:

$$\psi_{ec,N} = \frac{1}{\left(1 + \dfrac{2e_N'}{3h_{ef}}\right)} \le 1.0 \text{ max}$$

where e_N' is the eccentricity of the resultant tensile force from the centroid of the anchor group acting in tension. Using statics, e_N' is computed for this load combination (see Figure 5-14):

$$e_N' = \frac{6 \text{ in}}{2} - \frac{6 \text{ in}(3948 \text{ lb})}{13{,}576 \text{ lb}} = 1.26 \text{ in}$$

$$\psi_{ec,N} = \frac{1}{\left(1 + \dfrac{2(1.26)}{3(5.0)}\right)} = 0.86$$

$\psi_{ed,N} = 1.0$ (no adjacent edge effects) §17.4.2.5

$\psi_{c,N} = 1.25$ (uncracked section due to short parapet) §17.4.2.6

$\psi_{cp,N} = 1.0$ (cast-in-place anchor) §17.4.2.7

$N_b = k_c \lambda_a \sqrt{f_c'} h_{ef}^{1.5} = 24(1.0)\sqrt{3000}(5)^{1.5} = 14.7 \text{ kips}$ Eq 17.4.2.2a

$N_{cbg} = \dfrac{567}{225}(0.86)(1.0)(1.25)(1.0)14.7 = 39.8 \text{ kips}$

The strength reduction factor ϕ is 0.70 per Section 17.3.3 because no supplementary reinforcing is provided. In addition, as was mentioned previously, the concrete remains uncracked; thus

$$\phi N_{cbg} = 0.70(39.8 \text{ kips}) = 27.9 \text{ kips}$$

The total tension force on the embed per Figure 5-14 is

$$N_{ua} = 3948 \text{ lb} + 9628 \text{ lb} = 13{,}576 \text{ lb} < 27.9 \text{ kips} \ \dots \ \text{OK}$$

Pullout strength in tension ACI §17.4.3

As was determined for the previous load combination, $N_{pn} = 19.8$ kips per anchor. The most highly stressed anchors in this group are the bottom two headed studs.

$$nN_{pn} = 2(19.8) = 39.6 \text{ kips}$$

The strength reduction factor ϕ is 0.70 per Section 17.3.3 because no supplementary reinforcing is provided. In addition, as was mentioned previously, the concrete remains uncracked; thus

$$\phi N_{pn} = 0.70(39.6 \text{ kips}) = 27.7 \text{ kips} > 9.63 \text{ kips} \ \ldots \ OK$$

Concrete side-face blowout strength in tension ACI §17.4.4

As stated previously, it will be assumed in this example that the concrete anchorage is not located near an edge; thus, $N_{sb} = 1.0$.

Steel strength in shear V_{sa} ACI §17.5.1

As determined in the previous load combination analysis, the four headed stud group has a design strength of

$$\phi V_{sa} = 0.70(4)(12.7 \text{ kips}) = 35.6 \text{ kips}$$

From Figure 5-14, the design shear force is 1.34 kips.

$$\phi V_{sa} = 35.6 \text{ kips} > 1.34 \text{ kips} \ \ldots \ OK$$

Concrete breakout strength in shear V_{cb} ACI §17.5.2

As previously mentioned, it is assumed in this example that the embed plate is not located near an edge of the panel. In this situation, V_{cb} will not govern (ACI Section R17.5.2.1).

Concrete pryout strength in shear V_{cpg} ACI §17.5.3

For cast-in-place anchors, the nominal pryout strength in shear V_{cpg} is a function of the concrete breakout strength N_{cbg} determined earlier.

$$V_{cpg} = k_{cp}N_{cpg}$$ ACI Eq 17.5.3.1b
$$k_{cp} = 2.0 \text{ for anchor embedments where } h_{ef} \geq 2.5 \text{ in}$$
$$N_{cpg} = N_{cbg} = 39.8 \text{ kips}$$
$$V_{cpg} = 2(39.8) = 79.6 \text{ kips}$$

The strength reduction factor ϕ is 0.70 per Section 17.3.3 because no supplementary reinforcing is provided. In addition, as was mentioned previously, the concrete remains uncracked; thus

$$\phi V_{cpg} = 0.70(79.6 \text{ kips}) = 55.7 \text{ kips} > 1.34 \text{ kips} \ \ldots \ OK$$

Governing shear strength

For this load combination, the steel shear strength at 35.6 kips for the four anchors is less than the other various concrete shear failure modes checked, and this design strength is greater than the design shear load of 1.34 kips.

Interaction of tensile and shear forces   **ACI §17.6**

An interaction equation check (ACI Equation 17.6.3) is required unless either the shear V_{ua} or tension N_{ua} does not exceed 20 percent of their design strengths ϕV_n or ϕN_n, respectively. The following shear and tension checks are made for this load combination.

Check if $V_{ua}/\phi V_n \le 0.20$

> 1.34 kips/35.6 kips = 0.04 < 0.20 . . . Satisfied

Thus, the interaction Equation 17.6.3 need not be checked, and the full strength in tension is permitted and has already been checked above. In summary, the steel headed stud anchors under this load combination are acceptable.

Check requirements to preclude splitting failure   **ACI §17.7**

For the cast-in-place headed studs, the following limits are checked:

Minimum center-to-center spacing = 4 diameters = 2 inches < 6 inches
Minimum edges distance = Concrete cover per ACI Section 20.6.1 . . . OK

In summary, the four ½-inch-diameter × 5-inch headed studs are acceptable.

9.3 CHECK SHELF ANGLE AT TYPICAL WALL-ROOF TIE   ASCE 7

In this example, the steel joist purlin sits on a steel shelf angle (L5 × 5 × ¾ in × 1 ft). Without additional information, it is assumed the load acts at the tip of the leg. The horizontal leg is subject to bending and seismic tension stresses. Evaluating the array of load combinations from IBC Section 1605.2 and ASCE 7 Section 12.4.2 for strength design forces, combinations (3) and (5) potentially govern.

Simplified load combination IBC Equation 16-3

> $1.2D + 1.6L_r$

Joist reaction = 1.2(1920 lb) + 1.6(3200 lb) = 7424 lb

Moment arm to critical section = leg − k dimension = 5 − 1.25 = 3.75 in

> $M_r = 7424$ lb(3.75 in) = 27,840 in-lb

Plastic section modulus:

$$Z = \frac{12 \text{ in}(0.75)^2}{4} = 1.69 \text{ in}^3$$

Per AISC Section F11.1, the nominal flexural strength, M_n, may be checked as follows:

$$M_n = M_p = F_y Z \leq 1.6 M_y \qquad\qquad\qquad\qquad \text{AISC Eq F11-1}$$
$$M_p = 36{,}000 \text{ ksi}(1.69 \text{ in}^3) = 60{,}840 \text{ in-lb}$$
$$1.6 M_y = 1.6 F_y S = 1.6(36{,}000)\left(\frac{12 \text{ in}(0.75)^2}{6}\right) = 64{,}800 \text{ in-lb}$$

Thus, $M_n = 60{,}840$ in-lb.

The design flexural strength is checked as follows:

$$\phi_b M_n = 0.90(60{,}840) = 54{,}756 \text{ in-lb} \geq 27{,}840 \text{ in-lb} \ \ldots \ \text{OK}$$

Simplified load combination IBC Equation 16-5

$$1.4D + Q_E$$

A combination of gravity forces with horizontal tie forces will be evaluated.

Joist gravity reaction = 1.4(1920 lb) = 2688 lb (dead load).

Moment arm to critical section = leg $- k$ dimension = 5 $-$ 1.25 = 3.75 in.

$$M_r = 2688 \text{ lb}(3.75 \text{ in}) = 10{,}080 \text{ in-lb}$$
$$Z = \frac{12 \text{ in}(0.75)^2}{4} = 1.69 \text{ in}^3$$
$$M_n = M_p = F_y Z \leq 1.6 M_y \qquad\qquad\qquad\qquad \text{AISC Eq F11-1}$$
$$M_p = 36{,}000 \text{ ksi}(1.69 \text{ in}^3) = 60{,}840 \text{ in-lb}$$
$$1.6 M_y = 1.6 F_y S = 1.6(36{,}000)\left(\frac{12 \text{ in}(0.75)^2}{6}\right) = 64{,}800 \text{ in-lb}$$

Thus, $M_n = 60{,}840$ in-lb.

The design flexural strength is checked as follows:

$$\phi_b M_n = 0.90(60{,}840) = 54{,}756 \text{ in-lb} \geq 10{,}080 \text{ in-lb} \ \ldots \ \text{OK}$$

Joist horizontal tie force = 13,576 lb (from Part 9.1).

Per ASCE 7 Section 12.11.2.2.2, steel elements of the structural wall anchorage system (SDC C and above) are designed for strength forces with an additional 1.4 multiplier. This material-specific multiplier is based on the observed poor performance of steel straps during the 1994 Northridge earthquake. It was determined that an inadequate overstrength range existed in various steel elements to accommodate the maximum expected rooftop accelerations. This 1.4 force multiplier is applied to all steel elements resisting the wall-anchorage forces of Section 12.11.2.1 (SDC C and above), including wall connectors, subdiaphragm strapping, continuous cross-ties, and their connections. Reinforcing steel, anchor rods and steel headed studs, wood bolting, and nailing are not subject to this force multiplier.

$$\text{Required tie force } P_r = 1.4(13{,}576 \text{ lb}) = 19{,}006 \text{ lb} \qquad\qquad \text{ASCE 7 §12.11.2.2.2}$$

The tie force is applied across a Whitmore section width at the end of the joist seat. Assuming a 5-inch joist bearing seat width and a 2-inch weld length (SJI minimum), the Whitmore section width is as follows:

$$W = 5 \text{ in} + 2(2 \text{ in} \tan 30°) = 7.3 \text{ in}$$

Tensile area $A_g = 7.3 \text{ in} \times 0.75 \text{ in} = 5.48 \text{ in}^2$

Determine the design tensile strength for checking combined forces per AISC Section H1.2:

$$P_c = \phi_t P_n = \phi_t F_y A_g = 0.90(36,000)5.48 = 177,552 \text{ lb} \qquad \text{AISC Eq D2-1}$$

$$\frac{P_r}{P_c} = \frac{19,006}{177,552} = 0.11 < 0.2$$

Therefore, AISC Equation H1-1b is applicable for checking the combined forces of tension and bending flexure.

$$\frac{P_r}{2P_c} + \left(\frac{M_{rx}}{M_{cx}} + \frac{M_{ry}}{M_{cy}} \right) \leq 1.0$$

$$\frac{0.11}{2} + \frac{10,080}{54,756} = 0.24 \leq 1.0 \ \dots \ \text{OK}$$

Therefore, the shelf angle support is adequate.

9.4 CHECK THE SHELF-ANGLE WELD TO THE EMBED PLATE   **AISC 360**

Check the use of a ¼-inch fillet weld all around the shelf angle's perimeter. Per AISC Table J2.4, the ¼-inch fillet weld meets the minimum weld size limitations for the thinner plate joined (⅜-inch embed plate), and per AISC Section J2.2b, the ¼-inch fillet weld meets the maximum weld size limitations for the ¾-inch edge thickness of the shelf angle.

Similar to the process in Part 9.2, the force distribution to the shelf angle's upper and lower welds is shown in Figure 5-17 for the various potentially governing load combinations.

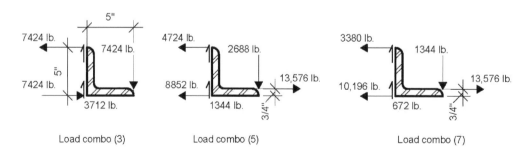

Figure 5-17. Factored loads on shelf angles

Because load combinations of IBC Equations 16-5 and 16-7 involve seismically induced wall-anchorage force to the weld, they are subject to the 1.4 force multiplier of ASCE 7 Section 12.11.2.2.2 (SDC C and above). The following lists the effective results of the worst vertical and horizontal force vectors acting on the fillet weld:

$$P_r = \sqrt{7424^2 + 3712^2} = 8300 \text{ lb}$$ 　　　　IBC Eq 16-3 Combination

$$P_r = \sqrt{(1.4 \times 8852)^2 + 1344^2} = 12{,}465 \text{ lb}$$ 　　　　IBC Eq 16-5 Combination

$$P_r = \sqrt{(1.4 \times 10{,}196)^2 + 672^2} = 14{,}290 \text{ lb}$$ 　　　　IBC Eq 16-7 Combination

In this example, the load combination of Equation 16-7 governs at 14,290 pounds. Where smaller wall-anchorage loads occur, often the gravity load combination of Equation 16-3 will govern.

Checking the strength of the ¼-inch × 12-inch-long fillet weld (AISC Section J2.2 and Table J2.5) gives

$$\phi R_n = \phi F_w A_w = 0.75(0.6 \times 70 \text{ ksi})\left(\frac{0.25 \text{ in}}{\sqrt{2}} \times 12 \text{ in}\right) = 66.8 \text{ kips} > 14.3 \text{ kips} \ \ldots \text{ OK}$$

Therefore, the shelf-angle weld to the embed plate is adequate.

9.5 CHECK JOIST-SEAT WELD AT TYPICAL WALL-ROOF TIE

The connection of the joist to the embed's shelf angle is through a fillet weld. Given its orientation, the steel shelf angle (L5 × 5 × ¾ in × 1 ft) has a flat run-out distance of 3¾ inches suitable for joist seat bearing.

Per the Steel Joist Institute's *Standard Specifications*, SJI 100-2015, the minimum weld at the joist seat attachments varies from ³⁄₁₆-inch × 2½-inch-long fillet on each side of the seat up to ¼-inch × 4-inch-long fillet (SJI, 2015 Section 5.7, LH-series joists), depending on how heavy the steel joist configuration is. Often the minimum size weld will be sufficient. In this example, the minimum ³⁄₁₆-inch × 2½-inch-long fillet on each side will be checked and upsized if necessary.

Checking the strength of the two rows of ³⁄₁₆-inch × 2½-inch-long fillet welds per AISC Section J2.4 is as follows:

$$\phi R_n = \phi F_w A_w = 0.75(0.6 \times 70 \text{ ksi})\left(\frac{0.1875 \text{ in}}{\sqrt{2}} \times 2.5 \text{ in}\right)2 = 20.9 \text{ kips}$$

Required tie force $P_r = 1.4(13{,}576 \text{ lb}) = 19{,}006 \text{ lb} < 20{,}900 \text{ lb} \ \ldots$ Mininum weld is adequate.

Therefore, this new joist seat weld to the shelf angle support is adequate. Because larger joists may require a larger weld to comply with the SJI *Standard Specifications*, this weld should be listed as a minimum, with a note that the joist designer may require a larger weld for installation.

9.6 DESIGN STEEL JOIST FOR TYPICAL WALL-ROOF ANCHORAGE FORCES　　　ASCE 7

Whether combined with a panelized WSP-sheathed roof or a metal deck roof, steel trusses or joists are the most common roof framing system now in tilt-up buildings. Specialty engineers in association with joist manufacturers typically design the steel joist members. As required by IBC Section 2207.2, the building's design engineer is responsible for providing axial wall-tie and continuity-tie forces to the manufacturer along with information stating which load factors, if any, have already been applied.

In this example, the designer should report to the joist manufacture that the unfactored wall tie axial force (tension and compression) acting through the joist top chord is $F_p = 13{,}576$ lb increased by the steel material overstrength factor 1.4 per ASCE 7 Section 12.11.2.2.2, resulting in $F_p = 13{,}576 \times 1.4 = 19{,}006$ lb. It is necessary to indicate to the joist manufacturer that this tie force is from seismic effects so that the joist's specialty engineer is able to apply the proper IBC load combinations with Section 12.4.2.

Though not shown in this example, the top chord axial effects of wind W must also be considered if it could lead to a governing design of the joist. Because the load combinations of IBC Section 1605.2 (strength design) and Section 1605.3 (allowable stress design) contain very different formulas when considering seismic E and wind W, the design engineer cannot simply compare E and W to determine which governs.

In conditions where axial loads are transferred through the joist seat at either the wall tie or at interior splices at joist girders, it must be made clear to the manufacturer so that the seat strength will be checked also. There are limits to the amount of load that manufacturers can transfer through these joist seats, so the designer must check with the manufacturer's specialty engineer.

Occasionally, the tail end of a collector line terminates at the wall and provides out-of-plane wall anchorage, similar to line 3 at line E (see Figure 5-1). In these situations, the building's design engineer must specify a higher collector load as well as an E wall-tie load for the joist. The joist manufacturer's specialty engineer will have to check both the basic IBC load combinations with Section 12.4.2 for E as well as the basic load combinations with the overstrength factor of Section 12.4.3 for E_m. Alternatively, some diaphragms and collectors are designed to Section 12.10.3 where a 1.5 multiplier is used instead of the overstrength factor E_m from Section 12.10.2.

For this example, the following is the type of information to be placed on the drawings for the steel joist manufacturer to properly design the joists for lateral loading. The wall anchorage force E shown should already include the 1.4 multiplier for steel elements.

Joist Axial Forces

> $E = 19.0$ kips (unfactored)
>
> $E_m = 0.0$ kips (unfactored per ASCE 7 Section 12.10.2) Applicable only at collectors.
>
> $W = 7.0$ kips (unfactored)

Forces shall be checked in both tension and compression.
Axial force shall be transferred through the joist seats where noted in the details.

9.7 CHECK JOIST-TO-JOIST SPLICE AT THE GIRDER LINES ASCE 7

The interconnection of elements within the building is required per ASCE 7 Sections 12.1.3 and 12.1.4. In addition, the joist axial load from the wall anchorage must be distributed across the building's main diaphragm from chord to chord per Section 12.11.2.2.1 using continuous cross-ties (SDC C and above). Seismic loading in the north-south direction utilizes the steel joists as the continuous ties, and thus the joist axial load must be spliced across the interior girder lines. See Figure 5-18 for a typical connection. In Part 9.6, the wall anchorage force and thus continuous cross-tie force for the steel joists is $P_r = 1.4(13{,}576 \text{ lb}) = 19{,}006$ lb.

Per Section 12.1.3, the minimum interconnection force is $0.133S_{DS}W = 0.133W$, but not less than $0.05W$, where W is the dead load of the smaller portion of the building being connected together. Unlike the wall-anchorage force, W in this case includes the diaphragm weight and thus could govern at the interior of buildings. In this case, the diaphragm weight has increased from 12 psf to 14 psf to account for the girder self-weight. The worst-case value for W is at grid line C with the following result:

$$P_r \text{ (min)} = 0.133(14 \text{ psf})(8 \text{ ft})(40 \text{ ft} + 40 \text{ ft}) + 0.133(116 \text{ psf})(8 \text{ ft})(32)(32/2)/28 = 3449 \text{ lb}$$

Per Section 12.1.4, the minimum support connection force is 5 percent of the dead and live load reactions.

$$P_r \text{ (min)} = 0.05(14 \text{ psf} + 20 \text{ psf})(8 \text{ ft})(40 \text{ ft}/2) = 272 \text{ lb}$$

Thus, the wall-anchorage continuous tie force $P_r = 1.4(13,576 \text{ lb}) = 19,006 \text{ lb}$ governs.

The splice can be accomplished with a welded cover plate from joist top chord to joist top chord (see Figure 5-18). Check the use of a $\frac{1}{4} \times 3$-inch-wide cover plate with $\frac{3}{16}$-inch fillet welds.

Check the design tensile strength per AISC Section D2:

$$\phi_t P_n = \phi_t F_y A_g = 0.90(36,000)(0.25)(3) = 24,300 \text{ lb} \qquad \text{AISC Eq D2-1}$$

Required tie force $P_r = 19,006 \text{ lb} < 24,300 \text{ lb} \ldots$ OK

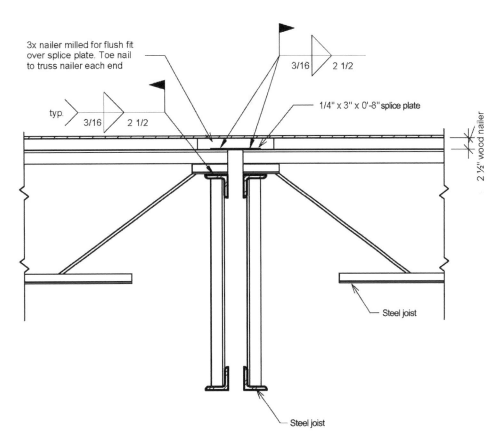

Figure 5-18. Joist to girder detail

Using two lines of $\frac{3}{16} \times 2\frac{1}{2}$-inch-long fillet welds, check the design weld strength per AISC Section J2.4:

$$\phi R_n = \phi F_w A_w = 0.75(0.6 \times 70 \text{ ksi}) \left(\frac{0.1875 \text{ in}}{\sqrt{2}} \times 2.5 \right) 2 = 20.9 \text{ kips}$$

Required tie force $P_r = 19.0$ kips < 20.9 kips $\ldots$ OK

Therefore, the steel joist splice across the interior girders is adequate.

Commentary

It is possible to splice the joist axial loads across the interior girders through their joist seats as is done at the wall-anchorage joist end. However, this requires added joist seat costs and requires the joist girder double-angle top chords to be joined together for this perpendicular force. If this is the design engineer's intent, it must be made clear to the joist manufacturer that the joist seats and joist-girder top chords are to be designed for these forces, including the 1.4 overstrength factor.

10. Wall Anchorage at Subpurlins (East-West Loading)   ASCE 7

On the east and west wall elevations, wall-roof ties are used to transfer out-of-plane seismic forces on the tilt-up wall panels to the subdiaphragms. Applicable requirements for connection of out-of-plane wall anchorages to flexible diaphragms are specified in ASCE 7 Section 12.11.2.1.

10.1 SEISMIC FORCE ON WALL-ROOF TIE

Seismic forces are determined using Equation 12.11-1 with $S_{DS} = 1.0$ and $I_e = 1.0$. Because the wall thickness and height are the same, these are the same forces as those determined in Part 9.1 for the north and south walls.

$F_p = 1697$ plf along the roof line

10.2 DESIGN TYPICAL WALL-ROOF TIE

Try ties at 4-foot spacing, and determine F_p:

$F_p = 4 \text{ ft} \times 1697 \text{ plf} = 6788 \text{ lb}$

Commentary

When tie spacing exceeds 4 feet, ASCE 7 Section 12.11.2.1 requires that walls be designed to resist bending between anchors.

Try prefabricated metal hold-downs with two $\frac{3}{4}$-inch bolts into a 3× subpurlin and two $\frac{5}{8}$-inch anchor rods connecting the hold-downs to the wall panel. This connection, illustrated in Figure 5-19, is designed to take both tension and compression as recommended by the SEAOSC/COLA Northridge Earthquake Tilt-up Building Task Force (SEAOSC/COLA 1994) and the 2008 *Blue Book* "Tilt-Up Buildings" article (SEAOC Seismology Committee 2008). Design of the hold-down hardware is not shown. Consult ICC-ES Evaluation Reports for the allowable load capacity of premanufactured hold-downs. Note that if a one-sided hold-down is used, stresses in the subpurlin due to eccentric loading should be considered per Section 12.11.2.2.6. Generally, one-sided wall-roof anchorage is not recommended in SDC C and above.

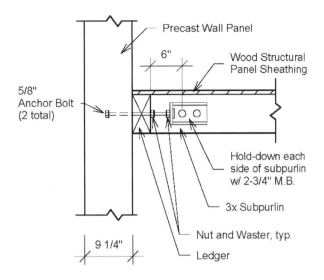

Figure 5-19. Wall-anchorage detail

Check the capacity of the two ¾-inch bolts in the Douglas Fir-Larch 3× subpurlin using 2018 AWC NDS Table 12G, where $C_D = 1.6$ and $C_g = 0.97$ and assuming ¼-inch steel side members.

$$(2630)(2 \text{ bolts})(1.6)(0.97) = 8164 \text{ lb} > 6788(0.7) = 4752 \text{ lb } \ldots \text{ OK}$$

Minimum required end distance $= 7D = 7(0.75) = 5.25$ in $\hfill$ NDS T 12.5.1A

A distance of 6 inches from the through-bolt in the hold-down to the ledger will be used. Often, there is a gap of ⅛ inch or more between the end of the subpurlin and the side of the ledger caused by panelized roof erection methods, and the use of a 6-inch edge distance will ensure compliance with the $7D$ requirement. A larger distance can be used to ensure that bolt row tear-out per NDS Appendix E does not occur in the 3× subpurlin, provided that the limits for compression buckling are checked.

Check the tension capacity of two ⅝-inch ASTM F1554 (Grade 36) anchor rods using LRFD:

$$F_t = 0.75F_u = 0.75(58) = 43.5 \text{ ksi} \hfill \text{AISC 360 T. J3.2}$$
$$\phi_t R_n = \phi_t F_t A_b = 0.75(43.5)(2)(0.307) = 20.0 \text{ kips } \ldots \text{ OK} \hfill \text{AISC 360 Eq J3-1}$$
$$R_u = F_p = 6788 \text{ lb} < 20.0 \text{ kips } \ldots \text{ OK}$$

Note: The 1.4 factor normally applied to steel elements of the wall anchorage system is not applied to anchor rods per ASCE 7 Section 12.11.2.2.2.

Check the compression capacity of two ⅝-inch ASTM F1554 Grade 36 anchor rods using LRFD:

$$P_n = F_{cr}A_g \hfill \text{AISC 360 Eq E3-1}$$
$$A_g = A_b = 0.307 \text{ in}^2$$

Radius of gyration of ⅝-in rod $= (0.625 \text{ in}/4) = 0.1563$

Assume $L = 4\frac{1}{2}$ inches and $K = 1.0$.

$$\frac{L_c}{r} = \frac{KL}{r} = \frac{1.0(4.5)}{0.1563} = 28.8$$

$$4.71\sqrt{\frac{E}{F_y}} = 4.71\sqrt{\frac{29,000}{36}} = 133.7 > \frac{L_c}{r}$$

Thus, AISC Equation E3-2 is applicable, so

$$F_{cr} = \left[0.658^{\frac{F_y}{F_e}}\right]F_y$$

where

$$F_e = \frac{\pi^2 E}{\left(\dfrac{L_c}{r}\right)^2} = 345 \text{ ksi} \qquad\qquad \text{AISC 360 Eq E3-4}$$

$$F_{cr} = \left[0.658^{\frac{F_y}{F_e}}\right]F_y = \left[0.658^{\frac{36}{345}}\right]36,000 = 34,462 \text{ psi}$$

$$P_n = 34,462(0.307)(2 \text{ rods}) = 21,160 \text{ lb}$$

$$\phi_c P_n = 0.90(21,160) = 19,044 \text{ lb} \geq 6788 \text{ lb } \dots \text{ OK}$$

Check the tension capacity of anchor rods in the wall panel considering concrete anchorage.

The tilt-up panels are exterior wall elements, but the requirements of ASCE 7 Sections 13.3 and 13.5.3 do not apply. This is because the tilt-up panels are structural walls instead of nonstructural architectural cladding. The requirements of Section 12.11 are the appropriate design rules in this situation. Section 12.11.2.2.5 requires that wall anchorage using straps be attached or hooked so as to transfer the forces to the reinforcing steel. In this case, cast-in-place bolts instead of straps are used, and the bolts are not required to be "hooked" around the wall reinforcement.

Recall that for wall anchorage, $F_p = 6788$ lb. Try a $\frac{5}{8}$-inch-diameter ASTM F1554 Grade 36 hex-headed bolt embedded in the concrete panel with 5 inches of embedment ($h_{ef} = 5$ inches). Because the anchorage spacing is only 48 inches, it is quite possible that the bolt embedment may be near an edge, unless the panel joints are specifically located to miss anchorage locations. Normally, special considerations are necessary for conditions where anchorage occurs near a panel joint. For this example, assume that the bolt embedment is not near a concrete edge and that the vertical shear load is negligible.

The wall's concrete anchorage needs to be checked using strength design under ACI 318-14 Chapter 17. The vertical shear load on the anchor is very low because of the small subpurlin tributary roof load. ACI Section 17.6.1 allows the full tension strength to be used without reduction when the factored shear load is less than 20 percent of the design shear capacity of the anchorage, as in this case.

ACI Table 17.3.1.1 requires the anchorage tensile design strength $\phi N_n > N_{ua}$ for the various failure modes. ϕN_n is determined by checking the steel strength in tension N_{sa} (ACI Section 17.4.1), the concrete breakout strength in tension N_{cbg} (ACI Section 17.4.2), the pullout strength in tension N_{pn} (ACI Section 17.4.3), and the concrete side-face blowout strength in tension N_{sb} (ACI Section 17.4.4). For anchorage forces involving seismic loads for structures in SDC C and above, ACI Section 17.2.3.4.4 requires the tension design strengths ϕN_n be multiplied by 0.75 unless it can be demonstrated that the concrete remains uncracked. The ductility and overstrength requirements of ACI Section 17.2.3.4.2 are not modified based on IBC Section 1905.1.8's exception for when ASCE 7 Equation 12.11-1 is used, as is the case here.

Steel Strength in Tension N_{sa}   **ACI §17.4.1**

The nominal steel strength for ⅝-inch-diameter ASTM F1554 Grade 36 headed anchor rods is as follows:

$N_{sa} = A_{se,N} f_{uta}$ Eq 17.4.1.2

$A_{se,N} = 0.226$ in^2 (net tensile area)   AISC *Steel Construction Manual* T 7-17

$f_{uta} = 58$ ksi   AISC *Steel Construction Manual* T 2-6

The specified tensile strength of the steel anchor f_{uta} shall be not greater than $1.9F_{ya} = 1.9(36) = 68$ ksi, per ACI Section 17.4.1.2. In this case, $f_{uta} = 58$ ksi governs.

Thus, $N_{sa} = (0.226)58 = 13.1$ kips per anchor.

Threaded bolts conforming to ASTM F1554 Grade 36 qualify as a ductile steel element and thus $\phi = 0.75$ for steel per ACI Section 17.3.3. Additionally, considering that two bolts are being provided, the design strength is

$\phi N_{sa} = 2(0.75)(13.1$ kips$) = 19.7$ kips > 6.79 kips ... OK

Concrete Breakout Strength in Tension N_{cbg}   **ACI §17.4.2**

For the different possible failure modes being evaluated, ACI Section 17.2.1.1 is consulted to determine whether group action is occurring. For concrete breakout in tension, the critical spacing is $3h_{ef} = 15$ inches, which is greater than the actual spacing of the two embedded anchors (one on each side of the subpurlin); therefore, they are spaced close enough to be considered acting as a group, as shown in Figure 5-20.

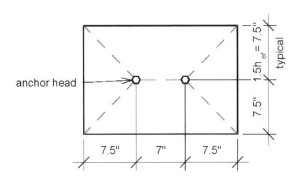

Figure 5-20. Projected area diagram

$N_{cbg} = \dfrac{A_{Nc}}{A_{Nco}} (\psi_{ec,N})(\psi_{ed,N})(\psi_{c,N})(\psi_{cp,N}) N_b$

$A_{Nc} = 2(7.5) \times (7.5 + 7.0 + 7.5) = 330$ in^2

$A_{Nco} = 9h^2_{ef} = 9(5)^2 = 225$ in^2 Eq 17.4.2.1b

Per ACI Section 17.4.2.1, A_{Nc} shall not exceed nA_{Nco}

$nA_{Nco} = 2(9h^2_{ef}) = 450 \text{ in}^2 > A_{Nc} \ldots$ OK

$\psi_{ec,N} = 1.0$ (no eccentric loading)   §17.4.2.4

$\psi_{ed,N} = 1.0$ (no adjacent edge effects)   §17.4.2.5

$\psi_{c,N} = 1.25$ (uncracked section due to short parapet)   §17.4.2.6

$\psi_{cp,N} = 1.0$ (cast-in-place anchor)   §17.4.2.7

$N_b = k_c \lambda_a \sqrt{f'_c} h_{ef}^{1.5} = 24(1.0)\sqrt{3000}(5)^{1.5} = 14.7$ kips   Eq 17.4.2.2a

$N_{cbg} = \dfrac{330}{225}(1.0)(1.0)(1.25)(1.0)14.7 = 27.0$ kips

The strength-reduction factor ϕ is 0.70 per ACI Section 17.3.3 because no supplementary reinforcing is provided, and thus

$\phi N_{cbg} = 0.70(27.0 \text{ kips}) = 18.9 \text{ kips} > 6.79 \text{ kips} \ldots$ OK

Pullout Strength in Tension   ACI §17.4.3

$N_{pn} = \psi_{c,p} N_p$ Eq 17.4.3.1

$\psi_{c,P} = 1.4$ (assume uncracked section due to short parapet height)   §17.4.3.6

$N_p = 8A_{brg} f'_c$ (where headed studs or bolts are used)   Eq 17.4.3.4

A_{brg} = bearing area of bolt head = (hex head area) − (shank area)

$A_{brg} = \dfrac{3F^2}{2\sqrt{3}} - (\text{shank area}) = 0.761 - 0.307 = 0.454 \text{ in}^2$

$N_{pn} = 1.4(8)(0.454)(3000 \text{ psi})(2 \text{ bolts}) = 30.5$ kips

The strength reduction factor ϕ is 0.70 per ACI Section 17.3.3 because no supplementary reinforcing is provided, and thus

$\phi N_{pn} = 0.70(30.5 \text{ kips}) = 21.4 \text{ kips} > 6.79 \text{ kips} \ldots$ OK

Concrete Side-Face Blowout Strength in Tension   ACI §17.4.4

Because it is assumed that this concrete anchor is not located near an edge, N_{sb} will not affect the design.

Check Requirements to Preclude Splitting Failure   ACI §17.7

For the cast-in-place headed studs, the following limits are checked:

Minimum center-to-center spacing = 4 diameters = 2.5 inches < 6 inches
Minimum edges distance = Concrete cover per ACI Section 20.6.1 ... OK

In summary, all applicable concrete anchorage failure modes have been checked and found satisfactory; thus, the two ⅝-inch-diameter × 5-inch embedded hex bolts are acceptable.

Compression Discussion

Wall anchorage forces act in compression as well as tension. Panelized wood roof systems by their very nature are not erected tight against the perimeter wall ledger, leaving a small gap to potentially close during seismic compression forces. Strap-type wall anchors that may have yielded and stretched under tensile forces are vulnerable to buckling and low-cycle fatigue as the gaps close. Cast-in-place anchor rods used in connectors can be checked for compression, but it is important to provide an additional nut against the interior wall surface to prevent the anchor punching through the wall. A common wall-roof tie connection shown in Figure 5-21 does not offer the same compression resistance as the anchor rod scheme presented in this example. Although there have been no failures of wall panels collapsing into the building, consideration of compressive forces will maintain the integrity of the wall anchorage tie and protect the diaphragm edge nailing under the reversible seismic forces.

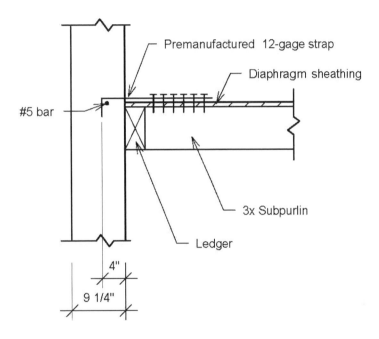

Figure 5-21. Wall-to-roof strap anchor

Anchorage Deformation Discussion

No prescriptive deformation limits of the wall tie system have been introduced into the IBC or ASCE 7; however, the compatibility of the anchorage system's flexibility and the diaphragm shear nailing along the ledger should be considered. Wall anchorage systems with too much flexibility will inadvertently load the WSP edge nailing and either pull the nails through the sheathing edge or place the wood ledgers in cross-grain bending or tension. Premanufactured strap-type wall ties are designed to limit the maximum deformation to ⅛ inch at their rated allowable load, and premanufactured hold-down devices using anchor rods also have inherent deformation. The designer should contact the device manufacturer for additional deformation information. This reported hold-down device flexibility is solely within the steel component itself and is additive to other sources of deformation. Additional deformation can be contributed by other anchorage components (e.g., bolts and nails) and installation practices (e.g., oversized holes).

10.3 DESIGN CONNECTION TO TRANSFER SEISMIC FORCE ACROSS FIRST ROOF TRUSS PURLIN

Under ASCE 7 Section 12.11.2.2.1 for SDC C and higher, continuity ties are provided in diaphragms and subdiaphragms to distribute wall anchorage loads. Consequently, the forces used to design the wall-roof ties must also be used to design the continuity ties within the subdiaphragm. From Part 10.2:

F_p = wall-roof tie load = 6788 lb

For this example, a subdiaphragm depth of 32 feet will be assumed to start with; and with steel joist purlins spaced at 8 feet, the connection at the first purlin from the wall must carry three-quarters of the wall-roof tie force. Some engineers use the full, unreduced force for all the cross-purlin connections, but this simplification is not required by rational analysis.

$$\frac{(32-8)}{32} \times F_p = \frac{3}{4} \times 6788 = 5091 \text{ lb}$$

At the second and third purlins from the wall, the force to be transferred is one-half and one-fourth, respectively, of the wall-roof tie force:

$\frac{1}{2} \times 6788 = 3394$ lb

$\frac{1}{4} \times 6788 = 1697$ lb

Try 12-gage metal strap with 10d common nails. Consult ICC-ES Evaluation Reports for allowable load capacity of premanufactured straps and ties.

The following calculation shows the determination of the number of 10d common nails into Douglas Fir-Larch required at the first connection using allowable stress design:

$$\frac{0.7(5091)}{1.6(127 \text{ lb})} = 17.5 < 18 \text{ nails}$$ NDS T 12P, T 11.3.1, and T 2.3.2

Therefore, use a 12-gage metal strap with 18-10d common nails (or equivalent) on each side.

The design of the 12-gage metal strap is not presented here, but the design is based on forces increased by 1.4 times the forces otherwise required under Section 12.11. This requirement of Section 12.11.2.2.2 is a result of the unexpected strap failures observed in the 1994 Northridge earthquake. It was found that many steel components lacked sufficient ductility and overstrength to adequately accommodate seismic overloads. It is the intent of the 1.4 steel-material multiplier to provide sufficient overstrength to resist maximum anticipated wall anchorage forces without relying on ductility. Both the gross and net sections shall be checked.

Where premanufactured and pre-engineered straps and ties are utilized using capacity values published in ICC-ES Evaluation Reports, the engineer should compare the published capacity with the 1.4 steel-increased force unless sufficient information is available to determine steel material values independently of other components.

Both subpurlins in Figure 5-22 likely would be 3× members because of the heavy strap nailing.

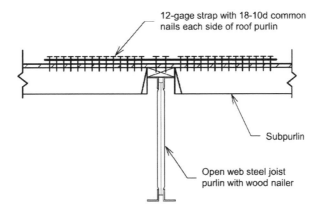

Figure 5-22. Strap detail

Designs of the second and third connections from the wall are similar to that shown above.

Note: Additional requirements for eccentric wall anchorage and walls with pilasters are provided in Sections 12.11.2.2.6 and 12.11.2.2.7.

11. Subdiaphragm Design (East-West Loading)

Subdiaphragms transfer forces from the individual wall anchorage ties to the main diaphragm's continuous cross-ties. To transfer seismic forces from the heavy perimeter walls into the main roof diaphragm, continuous cross-ties are necessary to drag the load uniformly across the diaphragm depth. Instead of creating a continuous cross-tie at every wall anchorage location, main continuous cross-ties can be placed at wider spacings using subdiaphragms. Subdiaphragms are portions of the main diaphragm that span between the continuous cross-ties and gather the wall-anchorage loads and transfer these loads to the cross-ties. Once the load is collected into the continuous cross-ties, it is distributed across the main diaphragm for further distribution to the building's shear walls and frames.

Subdiaphragms are provided for under ASCE 7 Section 12.11.2.2.1 as an analytical tool to provide a rational load path for wall anchorage. Consequently, subdiaphragms are considered part of the wall-anchorage system and are subject to loads per Section 12.11. Using this technique, the subdiaphragm shears are not combined with the global diaphragm shears. For SDC C and above, the subdiaphragm aspect ratios are limited to 2½ to 1, and it is assumed that this provides sufficient stiffness such that the independent deflection between the subdiaphragm and the main diaphragm may be ignored.

11.1 CHECK SUBDIAPHRAGM ASPECT RATIO

The maximum allowable subdiaphragm ratio is 2.5 to 1.   ASCE 7 §12.11.2.2.1

From Figures 5-1 and 5-23, the maximum north-south subdiaphragm span = 40 feet.

The minimum subdiaphragm depth = 40 feet/2.5 = 16 feet.

With the typical roof purlin spacing given as 8 feet, it is desirable for the engineer to keep the subdiaphragm depth dimension at increments of this 8-foot spacing. In this case, the 16-foot minimum subdiaphragm depth remains, which is less than the initial 32-foot depth assumed. This is acceptable.

11.2 FORCES ON SUBDIAPHRAGM

Because subdiaphragms are part of the out-of-plane wall anchorage system, they are also designed under the requirements of Section 12.11.2.1. Seismic forces on a typical east-west subdiaphragm are determined from Equation 12.11-1 with $S_{DS} = 1.0$ and $I_e = 1.0$.

As determined previously in Part 10.1, $F_p = 1697$ plf along the wall.

11.3 CHECK SUBDIAPHRAGM SHEAR

Assume a 32-foot-deep subdiaphragm, as shown in Figure 5-23. This is done for two reasons. First, the steel joist purlin along line 8 can be used as a subdiaphragm chord (see Figure 5-23). Second, the deeper-than-required subdiaphragm depth (32 feet vs. 16 feet) reduces the subdiaphragm shear to manageable levels.

Shear reaction to continuity cross-ties along lines C and D:

$$R = \frac{1697 \text{ plf}(40 \text{ ft})}{2} = 33,940 \text{ lb}$$

Maximum shear = 33,940/32 = 1061 plf

Applying the ASD load combination:

ASD shear = 0.7(1061 plf) = 742 plf

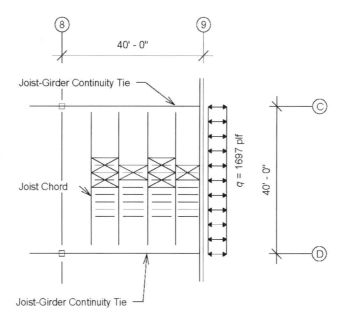

Figure 5-23. Subdiaphragm

Assume the main diaphragm is to be constructed with $^{15}\!/_{32}$-inch Structural-I OSB sheathing (WSP) with all edges supported (blocked), as is typical in a panelized hybrid roof system. Refer to the 2015 SDPWS Table 4.2A for nailing requirements of different assemblies. The sheathing arrangement (shown in Figure 5-1) for east-west seismic forces is Case 1 with the long panel direction of the sheathing parallel to supports. The sheathing edges are supported only by 2× subpurlin framing, and the strength is therefore limited by the nail spacings associated with 2-inch nominal framing width unless upgraded to 3× framing. Various nail spacings at sheathing panel edges and their respective seismic shear capacities are given in SDPWS Table 4.2A at nominal strength levels and need to be divided by 2 for allowable stress design (SDPWS Section 4.2.3). Considering the shear demand of 742 plf (ASD), determine the assembly acceptable in the subdiaphragm areas. Nominal capacity for use in SDPWS Table 4.2A = 2(742 plf) = 1484 plf. Per Table 4.2A, 3× framing at adjoining panel edges and boundaries is required based on:

$^{15}\!/_{32}$ in Structural-I OSB sheathing with the following common nailing:
10d × 1½ in penetration in framing at 2 in o.c. boundaries and continuous edges
10d × 1½ in penetration in framing at 3 in o.c. other edges
10d × 1½ in penetration in framing at 12 in o.c. intermediate areas
Nominal capacity = 1640 plf > 1484 plf . . . OK

11.4 CHECK STEEL JOIST AS SUBDIAPHRAGM CHORD

The steel joists 32 feet from the perimeter wall and the continuous horizontal reinforcement in the perimeter walls along lines 1 and 9 act as chords for the subdiaphragms.

Check to see if the steel joist can carry additional seismic force.

$$\text{Chord force} = \frac{1697 \text{ plf}(40)^2}{8(32)} = 10{,}606 \text{ lb}$$

Because the subdiaphragm chord is a steel element of the wall anchorage system, it is subject to a 1.4 force increase per Section 12.11.2.2.2.

$$\text{Chord force (steel)} = 10{,}606(1.4) = 14{,}848 \text{ lb}$$

This chord force (14.8 kips) is less than the wall-anchorage joist force (19.0 kips) found in Part 9.6, and thus does not govern.

Commentary

In reality, the steel joists acting as chords may not act in tension as a subdiaphragm chord as shown above. They will be loaded in tension only when compressive wall-anchorage forces act on the diaphragm. Under this loading, the seismic forces probably do not follow the subdiaphragm path shown above but are transmitted through the wood framing to other parts of the diaphragm. Even if subdiaphragm behavior does occur, the subdiaphragm may effectively be much deeper than shown. However, because it is necessary to demonstrate that there is a system to resist the out-of-plane forces on the diaphragm edge, the subdiaphragm system shown above is provided.

11.5 DETERMINE MINIMUM CHORD REINFORCEMENT AT EXTERIOR CONCRETE WALLS

This design example assumes that there is continuous horizontal reinforcement in the walls at the roof level that acts as a chord for both the main diaphragm and the subdiaphragms.

Subdiaphragm chord force $= P_u = 10{,}606$ lb

$$A_s = \frac{P_u}{\phi f_y} = \frac{10{,}606}{0.9(60{,}000)} = 0.20 \text{ in}^2$$

This is a relatively small amount of reinforcement. Generally, the main diaphragm chord reinforcement exceeds this amount. In present practice, the subdiaphragm chord steel requirement is not added to the chord steel requirement for the main diaphragm.

12. Continuity Ties across the Main Diaphragm (East-West Loading)

In a tilt-up building, continuous ties have two functions. The first is to transmit the heavy out-of-plane wall loads into the main diaphragm. The second function is that of "tying" the interior portions of the roof together. In this example, the continuity ties on lines C and D will be designed.

12.1 SEISMIC FORCES ON CONTINUITY CROSS-TIES ALONG LINES C AND D

A minimal interconnection of elements within the building is required per ASCE 7 Sections 12.1.3 and 12.1.4. Additionally, continuous cross-ties are required per Section 12.11.2.2.1 (SDC C and above) to transfer seismic forces from the heavy perimeter walls into the main diaphragm. In the east-west load direction, the subdiaphragm load is collected into the continuous cross-ties and then distributed across the main diaphragm for further distribution to the building's shear walls and frames.

The continuous cross-tie axial force at the line 8 connection is the sum of both subdiaphragm reactions. Because the continuous cross-ties are considered part of the wall-anchorage system, their design force is subject to the steel material overstrength multiplier 1.4 per Section 12.11.2.2.2.

$$P_r = \frac{1697 \text{ plf}(40 \text{ ft})}{2}(2)1.4 = 95{,}032 \text{ lb}$$

Per Section 12.1.3, the minimum interconnection force is $0.133 S_{DS} W = 0.133W$, but not less than $0.05W$, where W is the dead load of the smaller portions of the building being connected together. Unlike the wall-anchorage force, W in this case includes the diaphragm weight and thus could govern at the interior of buildings. In this case, the diaphragm weight is 14 psf to include the girder self-weight. The worst-case value for W for the continuous cross-tie is near the center of the building at grid line 5 (Figure 5-1) with the following result:

$$\begin{aligned} P_r \text{ (min)} &= 0.133(14 \text{ psf})(40 \text{ ft})(4)(40 \text{ ft}) + 0.133(116 \text{ psf})(40 \text{ ft})(32 \text{ ft})(32 \text{ ft}/2)/28 \\ &= 23{,}201 \text{ lb} \end{aligned}$$

Per Section 12.1.4, the minimum support connection force is 5 percent of the dead and live load reaction.

$$P_r \text{ (min)} = 0.05(14 \text{ psf} + 16 \text{ psf})(40 \text{ ft})(40 \text{ ft}/2) = 1200 \text{ lb}$$

Thus, the wall anchorage continuous cross-tie force is governed by the subdiaphragm design.

$$P_r = 93{,}032 \text{ lb}$$

Note: The continuous ties along lines C and D are not collector elements and thus are not subject to the special overstrength load combinations of Section 12.10.2.1 or the 1.5 multiplier of Section 12.10.3.4. The girder line along line B functions both as a continuous cross-tie and as a collector; therefore, both basic and higher collector load combinations must be considered. The collector design may govern at some locations, while cross-tie forces may govern at others.

12.2 DESIGN OF JOIST GIRDERS AS CONTINUITY TIES ALONG LINES C AND D

Whether combined with a WSP-sheathed hybrid roof or a metal deck roof, open-web steel joist girders are common roof girders in tilt-up buildings. Specialty engineers in association with the joist manufacturer typically design the steel joist-girder members. As required by IBC Section 2207.2, the building's design engineer is responsible for providing axial continuity cross-tie forces to the manufacturer along with information stating which load factors, if any, have already been applied.

In this example, the designer should report to the joist manufacturer that the unfactored wall anchorage axial force (tension and compression) acting on the joist-girder top chord is $P_r = 93,032$ lb. It is necessary to indicate to the joist manufacturer that this axial force is from seismic effects so that the joist-girder's specialty engineer is able to apply the proper IBC load combinations with ASCE 7 Section 12.4.2.

Though not shown in this example, the top chord axial effects of wind W must also be considered if the effects could lead to a governing design of the joist girder. Because the load combinations of IBC Section 1605.2 (strength design) and Section 1605.3 (allowable stress design) contain very different formulas when considering seismic E and wind W, the design engineer cannot simply compare E and W to determine which governs. For this reason, it is recommended that unfactored loads be reported.

With line B acting as a collector (Figure 5-1), any joist girders occurring there require an additional check of the higher collector loads of ASCE 7 Section 12.10.2 or 12.10.3.4 (SDC C and higher). In this situation, the structure's engineer must specify the higher collector load as well as an E continuous cross-tie load. The joist manufacturer's specialty engineer will have to check both the basic IBC load combinations with the cross-tie load E as well as the basic load combinations with the higher collector load.

The following is an example of the information to be placed on the drawings for the steel joist manufacturer to properly design the joist girders for lateral loadings at lines C and D. The wall-anchorage force E shown should already include the 1.4 multiplier for steel elements.

Joist-Girder Axial Forces

> $E = 93.0$ kips (unfactored)
>
> $E_m = 0.0$ kips (unfactored per ASCE 7 Section 12.10.2) Applicable only at collectors.
>
> $W = 18.4$ kips (unfactored)

Forces shall be checked in both tension and compression.

12.3 DESIGN OF JOIST-GIRDER SPLICES ALONG LINES C AND D

Splicing large axial loads between joist-girder top chords is best done with a knife plate between the top chords at the joist seat (Figure 5-24). Top chords have a 1-inch gap between them, and the joist-girder manufacturer will keep this space clear if it is known in advance that a knife plate will be installed here. To facilitate installation, the knife plate should be no thinner than $\frac{7}{8}$ inch. The height of the knife plate is that which is necessary to obtain splice welding access, and often the size of the knife plate is excessive just to accommodate installation.

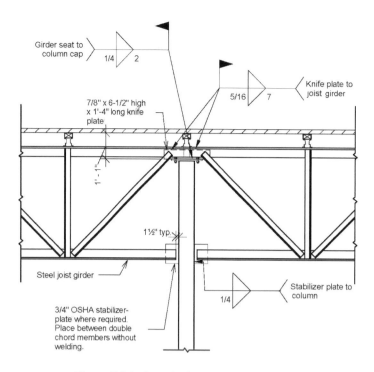

Figure 5-24. Detail of joist girder to column

Check the ⅞-inch × 6½-inch splice plate's design tensile strength per AISC Section D2:

$$\phi_t P_n = \phi_t F_y A_g = 0.90(36,000)(0.875)(6.5) = 184,275 \text{ lb}$$

Required tie force $P_r = 93,032$ lb < 184,275 lb ... OK

Using two lines of ⁵⁄₁₆-inch × 7-inch-long fillet welds, check the design weld strength per AISC §J2.4:

$$\phi R_n = \phi F_w A_w = 0.75(0.6 \times 70 \text{ ksi})\left(\frac{0.3125 \text{ in}}{\sqrt{2}} \times 7 \text{ in}\right)2 = 97.4 \text{ kips}$$

Required tie force $P_r = 93.0$ kips < 97.4 kips ... OK

Therefore, the joist-girder splice across the columns is adequate.

12.4 COMMENTS ON METAL DECK DIAPHRAGMS

Although less common in the southwestern United States than WSP sheathing, flexible metal deck diaphragms (without concrete fill) are still somewhat common in tilt-up construction in seismically active areas. When designed properly, metal decking can assist in providing wall anchorage and eliminate the need for subdiaphragms by acting itself as the continuous cross-tie. However, important detailing issues must be carefully considered.

Metal decks can only provide continuous cross-ties parallel to the deck span direction. ASCE 7 Section 12.11.2.2.4 specifically prohibits use of a metal deck perpendicular to the direction of span for continuity because the deck flutes will stretch out and flatten. Where the steel decking is spliced at the ends, a common structural member is needed to receive the attachment from both deck panels. In common steel joist systems with double-top chords, it is necessary that both deck panels be attached to the same individual top-chord half; otherwise, cross-tie loads will be inadvertently transferred through the steel joist top-chord separation plate or web welding, depending on the configuration. Another concern at the metal deck panel splice and direct ledger attachment is the weld tear-out through the metal deck edge. Proper deck gauge and puddle-weld edge distance must be maintained for adequate wall-anchorage strength.

If the metal decking is expected to carry wall-anchorage forces, it must be investigated for tension *and compression* axial loads in conjunction with acting gravity loads. The axial compression loads are associated with inward wall forces and require a special axial/bending analysis of the decking. The *North American Standard for Cold-Formed Steel Framing* (AISI, 2016) provides design criteria for the decking, and the Structural Steel Education Council (Mayo, 2001) illustrates one approach for this style of wall anchorage. A more robust approach to metal deck wall anchorage is to use small steel angles or tubes that provide tension and compression wall support and distribute the load into a metal deck subdiaphragm.

Another challenge with metal deck diaphragms is the need for thermal expansion joints. Metal deck roof diaphragms are much more vulnerable to temperature swings than wood diaphragm systems; and with the trend toward larger roof dimensions, thermal expansion joints become very important. However, these expansion joints interrupt the continuous cross-ties of the wall-anchorage system and thus create several independent buildings to be analyzed separately. The wall-anchorage forces must be fully developed into the main diaphragm and transferred to the applicable shear walls before reaching the expansion joint. This can result in larger diaphragm shears.

12.5 DESIGN GIRDER (CONTINUITY TIE) CONNECTION TO WALL PANEL

In this example, walls are bearing walls and pilasters are not used to support the joist girder vertically. Consequently, the kind of detail shown in Figure 5-25 must be used. This detail provides both vertical support for the girder and the necessary wall-anchorage capacity. The tie force is the same as that for the wall-roof tie of Part 10.2 ($F_p = 6788$ lb), but not less than 5 percent of the dead-load plus live-load reaction per ASCE 7 Section 12.1.4. The detail has the capacity to take both tension and shear forces. Details of the design are not given.

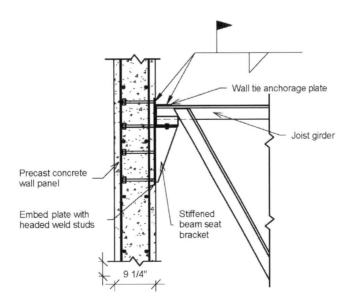

Figure 5-25 labels:
- Wall tie anchorage plate
- Joist girder
- Precast concrete wall panel
- Embed plate with headed weld studs
- Stiffened beam seat bracket
- 9 1/4"

Figure 5-25. Detail of girder to wall panel

13. Shear Wall Design Loads

After the wall-anchorage forces are distributed into the main diaphragm, the wall weight and diaphragm self-weight are then transferred to the concrete shear walls for a load path toward the ground. Tilt-up concrete buildings utilize their inherent concrete panels as a lateral-force-resisting system. In SDC C and higher, only intermediate precast shear walls and special reinforced concrete shear walls are permitted. While special reinforced concrete shear walls benefit from higher response modification coefficients, additional detailing and analysis provisions are applicable.

In one- and two-story tilt-up buildings, intermediate precast shear wall systems are more common. This lateral-force-resisting system has a height limitation of 40 feet, except in single-story storage warehouses where the limitation extends to 45 feet. These height limitations were selected to coordinate with similar height restrictions found in the fire-protection design normally found in these high-pile storage warehouses. The use of the intermediate precast shear wall system will be illustrated for this building example.

13.1 DESIGN SPECTRAL RESPONSE ACCELERATIONS S_{DS} AND S_{D1}

The site coefficients F_a and F_v are used to modify the mapped spectral accelerations S_S and S_1. Using the given spectral accelerations $S_S = 1.5$ and $S_1 = 0.6$ and Site Class D, the following site coefficients are determined accurately from the online ASCE 7-16 earthquake hazard maps based on information from the United States Geological Survey (www.usgs.gov); however, IBC Figure 1613.2.1 may also be consulted.

$F_a = 1$ (short period)

$F_v = 1.7$ (1-second period)

Using these site coefficients, the site-adjusted spectral accelerations are determined:

$$S_{MS} = F_a S_S = 1.0(1.5) = 1.5 \text{ (short period)} \qquad \text{IBC Eq 16-36}$$
$$S_{M1} = F_v S_1 = 1.7(0.6) = 1.02 \text{ (1-second period)} \qquad \text{IBC Eq 16-37}$$

The design spectral response accelerations are obtained as follows:

$$S_{DS} = 2/3 S_{MS} = 1.0 \text{ (short period)} \qquad \text{IBC Eq 16-38}$$
$$S_{D1} = 2/3 S_{M1} = 0.68 \text{ (1-second period)} \qquad \text{IBC Eq 16-39}$$

Using the design spectral response accelerations and the risk category from IBC Table 1604.5, the next step is to determine the appropriate seismic design category from IBC Tables 1613.2.5(1) and (2). With S_1 less than 0.75, both the short-period and 1-second-period design categories are level D; thus, SDC D governs.

Short-period category = D   IBC T 1613.2.5(1)

1-second-period category = D   IBC T 1613.2.5(2)

Governing SDC = D

Use ASCE 7 Section 12.6 in conjunction with Table 12.6-1 to obtain the appropriate analysis procedure. Use the equivalent lateral-force procedure of Section 12.8 to determine the seismic base shear coefficient. For a concrete shear wall building, the approximate fundamental period T is obtained using ASCE 7 Equation 12.8-7 (or 12.8-9) with a $C_T = 0.020$ and $x = 0.75$. For this building, use an average roof height $h_n = 28$ feet.

$$T_a = C_T h_n^{3/4} = (0.02)28^{0.75} = 0.24 \text{ sec} \qquad \text{ASCE 7 Eq 12.8-7}$$

If this example involved a regular structure five stories or fewer in height having a period T less than 0.5 seconds, the base shear coefficient C_s could have been based on an S_{DS} equal to 1.0 (Section 12.8.1.3). But in this example, the structure has a re-entrant corner irregularity per ASCE 7 Table 12.3-1, Type 2, and thus the design spectral response accelerations and SDC remain as originally calculated.

$$S_{DS\ design} = 1.0 \text{ (short period)}$$

$$S_{D1\ design} = 0.68 \text{ (1-second period)}$$

13.2 BASE SHEAR USING THE EQUIVALENT LATERAL-FORCE PROCEDURE   ASCE 7

ASCE 7 Section 12.8.1 defines the seismic base shear as

$$V = C_s W \qquad \text{Eq 12.8-1}$$

where

$$C_s = \frac{S_{DS}}{\dfrac{R}{I_e}} \qquad \text{Eq 12.8-2}$$

Because these tilt-up concrete walls will be considered load-bearing walls and intermediate precast shear walls, then

$$R = 4 \text{ (response modification factor)}$$

In addition, the importance factor described in ASCE 7 Section 11.5 is obtained from Table 1.5-2 based on the building's given Risk Category II:

$$I_e = 1.0 \qquad \text{T 1.5-2}$$

Therefore, per Equation 12.8-2:

$$C_s = \frac{S_{DS}}{\dfrac{R}{I_e}} = \frac{1.0}{\dfrac{4}{1.0}} = 0.25$$

Checking the maximum limit for C_s with Equation 12.8-3 where $T \le T_L$

$$C_{s\ max} = \frac{S_{D1}}{T\left(\dfrac{R}{I_e}\right)} = \frac{0.6}{0.24\left(\dfrac{4}{1.0}\right)} = 0.625 > 0.25 \ \dots \ \text{OK}$$

Checking the minimum allowed value for C_s, ASCE 7 Equations 12.8-5 and 12.8-6 are applicable. In this example, S_1 is equal to $0.6g$; therefore, Equation 12.8-6 is valid to check the minimum allowed C_s.

$$C_{s\,min} = 0.044 S_{DS} I_e = 0.044(1.0)(1.0) = 0.044 < 0.25 \ \ldots \ \text{OK} \qquad \text{Eq 12.8-5}$$

$$C_{s\,min} = 0.01 < 0.25 \ \ldots \ \text{OK} \qquad \text{Eq 12.8-5}$$

$$C_{s\,min} = \frac{0.5 S_1}{\dfrac{R}{I_e}} = \frac{0.5(0.6)}{\dfrac{4}{1.0}} = 0.075 < 0.25 \ \ldots \ \text{OK} \qquad \text{Eq 12.8-6}$$

The calculated value for $C_s = 0.25$ is between the maximum and minimum allowed values.

$$C_{s\,governs} = 0.25$$

Substituting into Equation 12.8-1:

$$V = C_s W = 0.25W$$

13.3 BASE SHEAR USING THE SIMPLIFIED ALTERNATIVE STRUCTURAL DESIGN CRITERIA

Instead of the lengthy seismic analysis shown above, simple buildings that meet the twelve limitations of ASCE 7 Section 12.14.1.1 may use the simplified analysis procedure in Section 12.14. Using Section 12.1.1, the simplified analysis procedure of Section 12.14 is allowed as an alternative method for determining this example's seismic forces.

13.4 SHEAR WALL DESIGN LOADS

With the base shear coefficient determined, the distribution of the lateral loads to the participating shear walls may be determined next. Because this is a flexible diaphragm, it is assumed the loads are distributed on a tributary basis with the diaphragm modeled as a series of simply supported beams with consideration for the relative distribution of mass. Example 2 in this volume provides an illustrative design example.

The seismic load into the walls includes the load from the diaphragm and from the walls' self-weights. In these heavy-walled buildings, the wall self-weight is a significant source of the walls' shear loads. Frequently, numerous wall penetrations complicate the shear wall design, resulting in some portions resembling frame-type column or pier elements. ACI Section 18.10.8 provides design provisions associated with walls containing wall-pier elements and frame-like column elements. The design of reinforced concrete shear walls in general is presented in the *2018 IBC Structural/Seismic Design Manual*, Volume 3.

14. References

See the reference listing at the front of this design volume.